WHEN ALL IS SAID AND DONE

Rose Franken

WHEN ALL IS SAID
AND DONE

W. H. ALLEN
LONDON
1962

Printed and bound in Great Britain by
The Camelot Press Ltd., Southampton, for the publishers,
W. H. Allen & Company, Essex Street, London, W.C.2.

CONTENTS

ILLUSTRATIONS

To my granddaughters,

JESSICA, BARBARA, and LYDIA

1

A LITTLE OF EVERYTHING AND NOT MUCH OF ANYTHING

I think that it's a mistake for me to write this book, and maybe I'm being a little clever in admitting it before anyone else has a chance to say it first. I've noticed recently that all kinds of people, for no very good reason, seem to have taken to recording their memoirs, and now I'm adding to the list. Of course if you're sufficiently prominent or famous, a publisher asks for your autobiography and pays a substantial advance into the bargain, but my publisher didn't even ask. Then, too, an author might be impelled to embark on the story of his life because he really feels that it's important for the world to hear what he has to say, although it often turns out to be more important to himself to tell the world what he has to say. Again, however, neither of these excuses applies to me, for I have never been blessed, or damned, by a great urge to write, nor do I have the slightest illusion that people are panting to hear about the not too eventful things that have happened to me in the past half-century. Nevertheless, for a peculiarly indirect reason yet to be divulged, I'll probably end up with a few hundred pages—but I'll still think that it's a mistake.

I recognize at the start the pitfall of equivocation, what with my glibly passing off sixty-three years as "half a century." Or will I be sixty-five on my next birthday? Being born at the tail-end of December affords a degree of latitude, one way or another. I regarded it as a shabby deal in childhood, because of Christmas presents doing double duty for birthday presents, but I discovered when I reached my teens that there was an advantage in claiming that I was a year older, in fact, than I actually was. Once I hit forty, though, I began to resent those twelve months being tacked on willy-nilly to my age, but now, having attained my sixties, I'm back to being pleased with the benefits of growing older. I find the state of maturity both agreeable and relaxing, with a few unexpected dividends thrown in on the side.

Hair, for example. My hair never did much for me, and I never did much for it, except to wash it with punctilious frequency. Even so, I was always what is commonly termed a "dirty blonde," until all at once—at least I thought it was all at once—splashes of white appeared, and took away that drab look. Naturally, I was delighted, since a number of my friends have to spend time and money to achieve exactly the same effect, albeit they perversely refuse to acknowledge any similarity in the finished product. On the contrary, they keep alluding to the ghastly way I've been turning grey in the last couple of years, and why in heaven's name don't I get smart and do something about it?

I intend to do nothing about it—in fact, I avoid beauty salons whenever possible. Being forced to confront my image while drying under a blower with my scalp sprouting metal clips beneath a sleazy mesh veil does something dreadful to my morale. It is only when I happen to run into myself in one of those nasty triple mirrors that I realize with a shock that I don't look as stylish as I imagined, nor—even more of a shock—anywhere near as young as I feel. Therefore, let me warn you not to be misled by the frontispiece photograph of me. It was taken by Arnold Genthe, who was well over eighty when he died, and he died in 1942. However, some residing shred of vanity compels me to add that mine was probably the last picture he took.

Actually, I didn't meet him until after he had retired, although I was familar with many of his photographs, including the enduring legacy of the Grecian isles in moonlight, and the seventy-two historic snapshots of the San Francisco fire, which latter accomplishment gave me the temerity to ask him for a sitting. I based my plea on the proven fact that I was a photogenic disaster second only to an earthquake, and that in the past decade

I had amassed batch after batch of elaborately mounted prints that had the sole virtue of causing me to be grateful that I was behind my face instead of in front of it.

He believed me. "If you will come back tomorrow morning at eleven o'clock," he granted after an inscrutable silence, "we will see what we can do."

I went; and at the first glimpse of his shabby studio I didn't think he could do much in so obvious a state of professional inactivity. The room was denuded of the usual batteries of intricate equipment and blinding lights, with only a single lamp teetering beside an ancient camera, hooded with a ragged black cloth. On a small shelf attached to the camera there was a sandwich and a roll of toilet paper, and this, I thought, was carrying the supreme art of simplification to extremes.

Mr. Genthe seemed in no hurry to begin. He gestured me towards a small Victorian sofa that was as hard as a board, and settled himself opposite me in a decrepit armchair that gave lumpily to his spare figure. He chatted leisurely until the stroke of noon, when he removed the sandwich from its envelope of waxed paper, and ate it. Then he unrolled a long stream of the toilet tissue, wet it with his tongue, and crumpled it carelessly against the lamp. After he had managed to get it anchored more or less around the bulb, he disappeared briefly beneath the black hood, and before I had time to powder my nose, tense, smirk, blink, lick at my wooden lips, or do any of the things I always do when I have my picture taken, I heard a small, familiar click.

"Good," he said. "Now turn your head just a trifle. And don't try to smile."

I will never understand how he performed that miracle of photography. All the proofs were so immensely flattering that I had the whole lot of them made up, and used them exclusively and repeatedly for more years than were decently legitimate. My conscience finally caught up with me, and with the greatest reluctance I laid them aside, resorting thereafter to candid shots in which I was partially hidden by a Great Dane, or a standard poodle, or a couple of cats.

I had far from exhausted my supply of livestock when I came

up against the problem of selecting a picture for my obituary, an occasion on which one feels obliged to stand on one's own feet, so to speak. I suppose the procedure is as macabre as picking out one's coffin, but it so happens that I had had a preview of the obituary that was all set to go into the morning papers a while back. And that close brush with death, I might add, remains a high point in my life, for I had never enjoyed anything but a chronic state of uninterestingly good health. Then one day, without so much as a stomach-ache to justify the indignity, I was unceremoniously shoved on to the operating table on the assumption that something or other was better out of me than in, and maybe it was, except for the one small drawback that removing it almost killed me.

Later, I learned that newspaper reporters always keep an alert eye on the critical lists of the various hospitals in order to be prepared for the worst, and apparently for twenty-four hours my name headed the current crop of candidates for eternity. Unhappily, it fell to my husband's lot to help bring my existing file up to date. The poor thing told me all about it once I was out of danger, but instead of sympathizing with him, I could only feel a gratified astonishment in having been given such a lovely write-up, lovely except that it had been clipped on to one of those discarded old photographs that I wouldn't be found dead with, and fortunately wasn't.

I'd like to fool myself into thinking that the brace of post-surgical embolisms was responsible for my growing interest in scanning the plump obituary columns in the morning *Times*, but I fear that the addiction is merely another symptom of advancing years. I used to read the headlines, the sales, the theatrical columns and snatches of the editorials in that precise order, but gradually I have developed the habit of glancing at the front page just long enough to deplore the grisly predominance of crime and catastrophe before I skip to see who has died a healthy, normal death during the night. All too frequently I am saddened by the alarming regularity with which my contemporaries are departing this earth; indeed, I am even saddened by the untimely demise of perfect strangers, until I discover that hardly any of them is ever within spitting distance of the youthfulness of their pictures. Which explains why I don't feel guilty about using my Genthe. It also explains, in a rather windy and roundabout way, how I just happened to have an extra print handy for this book.

An excessive use of the personal pronoun has always embarrassed me, but I seem to have overcome my reticence with such remarkable alacrity that I would appear to have no misgivings whatsoever in embarking upon the history of my life. None the less, my qualms persist, for I have little of significance to contribute to this already glutted market. I have gone through no more—though no less—than the average person. I cannot point to any basic problem that I have overcome, and furthermore, I lack the yeast of burning convictions. I regard mankind with pity, amusement and tolerance for its appalling lack of tolerance, and I carry neither torch nor chip towards anything at all. Therefore, in the absence of a message, spiritual or otherwise, I might as well confess that I am writing this book merely because—to put it into a nutshell of platitude—I am trying to kill two birds with one stone, an unworthy compulsion that assails me periodically, and goes hand in hand with a peculiar streak of stinginess that lards an otherwise improvident nature.

The specific urge to compile my memoirs came upon me when the University of Pittsburgh asked me to make a speech last winter, and liked it enough—after I'd made it—to ask for a copy of it. "Well," I thought, "if I have to go to all the work of typing it out, I might as well add a little to it, and send a carbon to my publisher."

Now I don't want to give the impression that I am a speechmaker, either by talent or by inclination; in fact it wouldn't have entered my mind to accept the invitation if the Head of the English Department hadn't happened to mention at the close of his letter, that in addition to what he called a "pitiful honorarium," my fare to, and expenses in Pittsburgh would of course be paid over a period of several days. This extra inducement immediately hit me in my stingy streak and started up the bird reflexes. The honorarium meant nothing to me, pitiful or munificent; it was the small item of the fare and expenses that I couldn't resist, because it meant that I could sneak in a visit to Peter while I was there, and wouldn't I be a fool not to?

Peter is the youngest of three sons. He had a new professorship in Physics at Ann Arbor along with a new baby, and my being asked to talk at the University couldn't have presented a more opportune excuse for me to see my grandchild. Of course if I had enlightened Bill (my husband) as to my ulterior motive, much would have been avoided, including this literary by-product. But I didn't have the courage to tell him. We've been married almost a quarter of a century, and the rationalization of my irrational economies still continues to baffle and infuriate him. I remember the first time he realized that he'd got himself tied up to a Jekyll and Hyde of finance. It was the afternoon we drove over to a cattle auction in Dutchess County. I've learned—I think—not to hanker after the past, but I do hanker after the farm at moments, for it holds many of our richest memories. The cattle auction might not be a rich memory in terms of a soul-shaking experience, but it's a vivid one, and I'm not apt to forget it in a hurry.

I'd never been to a cattle sale, and Bill did his share of rationalizing when he said that it was part of my agricultural education to see some of the outstanding blood-lines of the country. He didn't have to coax me, I love auctions—furniture, porcelain, books, it makes no difference as long as it's an auction. "Don't get that look on your face, we're going to watch, not buy," he stipulated firmly, and since we were already ankle-deep in a pedigreed herd of Jerseys, I agreed that we had enough cows for the present.

True to our resolve, we remained bystanders until the very end of the sale, when a certain stylish little heifer began to get under both our skins. Several other breeders apparently shared our enthusiasm, and after a cautious opening, the bidding sky-rocketed. Bill dropped out at a strong-minded seven-fifty, but I'm not strong-minded, and with a mere flick of my brows (a technique that I'd mastered only after years of feverish hand-waving), I made a bid for her behind his back at sixteen hundred. When he discovered that the mysterious buyer was none other than us, he gave me all sorts of hell for my extravagance, but he was also secretly and deeply pleased.

We drove back to the farm through the lovely, rolling countryside, and I recall enjoying the warm conspiracy of our indiscretion—there's nothing like a dash of recklessness to bring a married, or any other kind of couple, closer. We felt illicitly happy until, passing through one of those raggle-taggle little towns on the fringe of Connecticut, I spied a penny-sale in a drugstore. What luck! We were almost out of toothpaste.

He said, buy some the next day, he wanted to get home, but I said it was sheer lunacy to drive back fifty miles for a tube of dental cream. In stony silence, he drew to a very slow halt. "I won't be more than half a minute," I assured him blithely, and was off before he could stop me.

It stands to reason that nobody can be as little as half a minute in any shop, but he had to be literal about it, and no sooner was I back in the car than I saw by his set jaw that the penny-sale had completely cancelled out the harmonious aftermath of the auction sale. He began to rant. And why? Simply because I'd tried to save a little money by stocking in on a few items beside the toothpaste. Which started him off again. Dammit, what did I mean by a "few items," I'd damn near loaded the whole back of the station wagon with a lot of damn stuff we'd never use, while he sat parked in a hot car for an hour in the blazing heat!

In a voice I determined to keep level, I pointed out that he had waited scarcely half an hour, but that in any event, he should have had the intelligence to pull into the shade. This was catching him by the short hair of the head he hadn't used, and I remember being afraid he'd burst a blood vessel.

I'd like to report that the incident spelled my reformation, but it merely taught me cunning. I continued, over the years, to commit a minor economy here and there, but I was always wary of arousing my husband's contempt of the pusillanimous, and I suppose it was the lingering sting of that hornet's nest of damns that warned me that a free plane trip to see Peter might be hovering dangerously close to the penny-sale area. Therefore, I was relieved, and a little surprised, that he didn't get suspicious the minute he opened the letter from the university. It was addressed to me, but as it was one of those sexless looking communications in a long envelope, I didn't bother about it. Instead I tossed it on his desk with a bunch of bills and other unengaging mail. It was the season for donations, and the pile was already so big that he had to begin wading through it a few evenings later. "What's this doing here?" he said, halfway to the bottom.

"What's what doing where?" I asked from across the room.

"This. You shouldn't have put off answering it."

I recognized the envelope with indifference. "What's so important about it. Who's it from?"

"Can't you read?" he inquired testily. "It's from the University of Pittsburgh."

My heart jumped to my throat, and I jumped to my feet. "Let's see, is it something about Peter?"

"Peter? Why should it be anything about Peter?"

Nothing except a cliché is truer than an axiom. A leopard doesn't change his spots, and if he didn't immediately associate Peter with Pittsburgh I should have had the sense to investigate that woodpile on the instant. But no, I was too busy gobbling up the contents of the letter. "Why, I'm on their prescribed course of study!" I exclaimed.

"I thought you'd be pleased," he said, also seeming pleased, in his off-beat fashion.

"And they want me to make a speech!"

"I've seen the letter, dear." He split open another envelope. "Shall we contribute to arthritis, kidneys, or both?"

"Both," I said, being superstitious. "But I couldn't make a speech," I reverted, aghast at the very thought of it. "What do they want me to make a speech for?"

"I wouldn't know," he said. "Better write immediately so that they can get someone in your place."

His promptness in agreeing with me was uncalled for. "I've made speeches before," I bridled.

"Abroad," he reminded me succinctly. "You had interpreters."

"You sound as if I couldn't speak English. I see no reason why I shouldn't accept this invitation."

"I see no reason why you should." (And he didn't.) "I've taught in universities (and he did), and I advise you not to undertake the job of lecturing to an academic audience for an hour and a half. They won't like it, and you won't like it. You're not cut out for it."

He was absolutely right, but the extenuating circumstances appeared to have escaped him. I had flown out to Ann Arbor for a couple of days when the baby came, and I'd been waiting impatiently for a suitable interim to elapse before going again—a purely self-imposed discipline, for, like many women of my generation, I have become obsessed by an attritional sense of guilt for loving my children. My diffidence stems, of course, from the prejudice that has sprung up in the world towards parents in general, and mothers in particular, and I count myself fortunate that so far I haven't received a kick in the pants for my labour pains. I'm glad to say that none of the three boys has caused me to feel that I am responsible for everything bad, and nothing good that has happened to them in their lives, but nevertheless I've been careful not to press my luck, and that's why the invitation from the university seemed like some sort of special reward for my good conduct. It offered the dual benefit of a professional jaunt, with an emotional bonus thrown in for good measure. I'd be very silly, I told myself, to follow Bill's advice and turn it down cold, especially since there was no great rush about it. It was only the middle of December, and the speech wasn't scheduled until May, so I decided to compose a graceful little note of appreciation that would leave the matter up in the air for the time being.

Or rather, I thought it would, but as universities can't, or don't, function in that pleasantly haphazard manner, I had no way of knowing that Professor Laufe, the Head of the English Department, chose to interpret my gratitude as an acceptance, until somewhere about the middle of March, I received another communication from him, wanting to find out if I had a preference as to hotel accommodations, and would I be arriving by plane or train? He concluded his cordial letter by asking me to acquaint him with the general subject of my lecture, and assuring me that I would shortly receive a detailed schedule of the three-day conference, along with the names of my fellow-panellists, all of whom had achieved outstanding prominence in their elected fields.

I went into a panic as I envisioned myself in the middle of those distinguished personalities, all doubtless with erudite titles to their speeches. Having barely finished high school (I got married instead), I am possessed of less information and more mis-information than anyone suspects, for the simple reason that I know what I don't know, and therefore manage to maintain an enigmatic silence when in fast company. It would be no less than intellectual suicide for me to shed this protective cocoon of reticence, for how could I keep my mouth shut if I had to talk for an hour and a half on an island of platform completely surrounded by a university?

Luckily, it still wasn't too late to bow out of the commitment, and I was glad that, not having warned Peter of my intended visit, he wouldn't have to know about this embarrassing situation into which I had almost landed myself. In answering Professor Laufe's second letter I would not only be definite in my refusal, but I'd think up some excuse to make it sound legitimate. It took some considerable thought, but suddenly I hit on the perfect alibi—I'd tell him that I had tripped and broken my knee-cap. The explanation carried weight and finality, since it implied that I was on crutches in a plaster cast, and couldn't travel. But there might be just one small drawback: Bill knew exactly when I had tripped, and he would immediately jump to the conclusion that I was using last year's knee to hide a sudden pair of very cold feet, and I would never hear the end of it. However, you don't come by a broken knee-cap every day in the week (it had been pretty nearly thirty years since I'd broken the other one) so I decided to use it for the university, and concoct a fresh excuse for my husband's consumption.

It wasn't difficult. The mind is a devious instrument—mine

is, anyway—and it seemed very logical that if Peter was the reason for my making the speech, he could as readily be the reason for my not making it. In short, I would say that on mature reflection, I was reluctant to inject any part of my literary activity on to his professional horizon, preferring to be known as his mother rather than place him in the position of being known as my son. I was aware, of course, that I was betraying my sex in taking this oblique aim at "momism"—a cult-grown word that makes me see red, incidentally, because in my female opinion, the opprobrium tars the user as well as the recipient, or, to put it less elegantly, it takes a sick one to call a sick one. But this was hardly the moment to air my views. The important thing was to catch Bill in a receptive and trusting mood, and the sooner the better, because time was pressing. I set the stage for that same evening.

In a large family, where privacy is at a premium, bed is usually the most satisfactory place to discuss the problems that periodically bite into a marriage, but I had a feeling that bed wasn't going to be of much value to me in this instance. Among other contributing factors, we weren't a large family any longer, the boys were grown up, with homes of their own, and, frankly, we had more privacy than we knew what to do with. For all practical purposes, the library had gradually come to supersede the bedroom as our favoured retreat.

I began to condition my husband's frame of mind with dinner—kidneys and no fresh vegetables other than a salad of bib lettuce (I don't know what he sees in bib lettuce, except that it's hard to get, but I got it). "There's a fire in the library," I said, as I rose from the table, slightly hungry, as he's off desserts. "Let's have our coffee in there, shall we?"

He was all for it. And let me tell you that that coffee was out of the old world, strong and made from scratch in a pot for a change. He had two cups, and remarked that it was better than he ever got for breakfast—a spiked compliment, but flavoured with a mellowness that was slowly engulfing him. He filled a pipe, poured some cognac into a glass, and went through the customary rite of offering me a sip. I surprised him, and myself, by downing a generous swallow, after which I stealthily dug up a couple of stale bon-bons to take away the taste. It was a heathenish thing to do to Napoleon brandy, or whatever it was that made him look so crestfallen when I gulped half his glassful, but I only did it to be companionable, not because I liked the stuff. When I was a little girl, my mother used to give me castor oil sandwiched in whisky on the theory that it would burn my mouth and I wouldn't taste the oil. It worked in reverse. I still tasted the oil, but to this day I can't appreciate alcohol, which has made me into a teetotaler without benefit of scruples. I loved my mother deeply, but I hold a grievance against her for depriving me of one of the major social graces.

I waited for the cognac to weave its subtle spell upon my husband's palate before I suggested that another log on the fire might not be amiss. It was already blazing at a good rate, but it always coddles the male ego to reorganize a fire, and Bill was no exception. While he was poking and shoving, I removed from a lower cupboard, where I had strategically hidden it before dinner, a five pound sweet tin dating from that rosy past when I could afford to thumb my nose at calories. It was of a pretty lavender colour, painted with flowers, so I'd kept it in memoriam and used it as a sewing basket, as near to never as possible.

The room was full of peace, quiet, and a little smoke from one too many logs. I sat down in a comfortable chair, and tidied the muddled spools of thread, hoping to find one that was stabbed by a needle with a large eye. A new puppy cautiously gauged my intentions from beneath the sofa, and prepared to vanish utterly should a familiar curry-comb emerge from the mysterious inside of the box. We used to have, among other pets, twenty-six Great Danes (we also had skimmed milk, broken eggs, and an occasional casualty in the beef and hog department to contribute to their nourishment), but now one infinitesimal poodle was silent testimony of our diminshed responsibilities and the relative simplification of our lives. I suppose I was foolish—after we decided to simplify—not to head for the nearest hotel or live abroad, but I hate not being under my own roof with my own furniture, no matter what hurdles present-day housekeeping present. Bill insists that it's another of my rationalizations. He says I like the feeling of having a couple of spare rooms in case of emergency, and I don't like the feeling of putting a permanent ocean between myself and the family. Now, strictly for my own purposes, I was willing to admit this reprehensible weakness in my make-up. I was nothing but an overgrown mother hen for having tried to smuggle my apron strings into Pittsburgh under the pretence of making a speech.

I cleared my throat, preparatory to raising the curtain on my carefully set scene, and spoke my opening line: "Where's your fishing jacket with the button off, dear?"

I could feel "dear's" defences rise like a cat's fur in the presence of danger—he's learned from experience how I abhor mending, and how it abhors me. "What's up?" he asked in quick distrust.

"Why should anything be 'up'? The trout will be running soon, and surely you don't want to be caught with your buttons off," I retorted, with what I hoped was an engaging blend of charm and wit.

He rewarded me with a dubious grunt and departed for the sanctuary of his fishing cupboard, returning shortly with an unlovely garment which he grudgingly entrusted to my ministrations. "You must be sick," he commented shortly.

With effort I kept a puny smile plastered on my face. "Not at all. A crackling fire on a snowy night always brings out the woman in me.—You're not going to read, are you?" I broke off sharply.

He settled more firmly against the corner of the sofa. "I am reading," he modified with finality.

I hadn't expected to cater to his creature comforts only to lose him to a book. I peered over at a familiar binding. "This makes how many times?" I observed coldly.

"There are two kinds of people," he observed in return. "Those that read Thoreau, and those that don't." He raised his eyes briefly from the page. "That thread you're using won't hold."

He'd gone one step too far. "Look, Buster," I lashed out at him, "it's the strongest I've got, so leave it or take it!"

A faint grin twitched at his lips. Inexplicably, it fanned my irritation into a burning resentment that had been smouldering for some little time. "You don't bother to read anything that I write more than once," I accused him.—"Oh damn this thimble, it's no good!"

"Try wearing it on the finger you push the needle with," he advised mildly.

"Go fly a kite!" I muttered, resisting the impulse to tell him to go and do something else, which would only have elicited his usual lecture about not using words I don't know the significance of. Actually, I'm a purist in my speech. I rarely, if ever, take the Lord's name in vain, I don't care for slang or abbreviations like 'Frisco, or Hi, while expressions such as "stinker" and "louse" fill me with distaste. On the other hand, having spent my adult years in a family of men, a select assortment of crisp four and five letter words and phrases roll smoothly off my tongue without the least sense of blasphemy. I still say it's all in a person's mind. For example, I prick my finger every damn time I sew, and nobody bats an eyelash.

Anyway, rather than invite an argument on semantics, I recommended the kite, and harped back to my original grievance. "Thanks to your example, the boys don't take me seriously as a writer, either," I remarked tightly.

He said, "I wouldn't hold that against them, you don't take yourself seriously. Thank God."

Bitterness welled up in me. "For once you're right. I should have trained the whole lot of you to have a little respect towards my work, especially with my being on the reading list of one of the leading universities of the country—— Oh, stop making those silly faces!"

He made one last silly face, and put *Walden* aside with a resigned air. "All right. You want to talk. What's on your mind, if any?"

"That's a fine way to make me tongue-tied."

"Good. Now may I go back to my book?"

"You may not. I have something to discuss with you."

"Well?" He waited. "What is it?" He waited some more. "I'm listening."

His patience nettled me. The scene I had so carefully planned might have started him off in a receptive mood, but it wasn't keeping him there. I decided to switch the setting. "Never mind," I said. "Later. Let's go to bed."

"At nine o'clock?" he expostulated, without a vestige of co-operation or even interest. "We can't go to sleep at nine o'clock!"

"I didn't say we had to go to sleep."

"You haven't finished sewing the buttons on my fishing jacket," he demurred cagily.

"This thread won't hold."

"I don't know why I stay married to you." His voice was glum, but suddenly his mood was perfect, so I quickly changed my tactics again, on the theory of first things first. "It's Peter," I came out with it.

"Peter?" Clearly Peter was the farthest thing from his thoughts at that particular moment. "What's wrong with him?"

"Nothing's wrong with him. It's just that I've come to the conclusion that you were right about my not making the speech."

"What speech?"

I stiffened. "Are you being purposely obtuse, or have you forgotten that I happen to have been asked to address a literary conference?"

"Oh, that speech," he said expansively.

"Yes. That speech."

"But I don't see what Peter has to do with it."

"And I don't see why you don't. It's quite obvious." I ruled the annoyance from my voice. "The laboratory is his bailiwick, and it's not right for me to invade it." I was about to enlarge on the mother-son angle, but his look of utter blankness was disconcerting. I said, "Please don't place me in the position of making myself seem over-important. I'm trying not to."

"And I'm trying my damnedest," he said, "to understand what you're driving at. Where does Peter come into this?"

"Very well, since you force me to put it in words, I think it might be embarrassing to him if one of his students or associates were to come up to him and ask him if that was his mamma who was making a speech."

"A very laudable sentiment," Bill conceded, "but I don't see how this problematical student is going to get wind of the fact that his mamma's making a speech hundreds of miles away."

"What do you mean 'hundreds of miles away'?" I aped him waspishly.

"I mean that it is highly unlikely that your professional activities in Pittsburgh would have the slightest effect upon Peter in Ann Arbor."

"You're not making sense," I brazened it out against my slowly congealing bloodstream.

"I'm not?" His voice fairly oozed with blandness. "Then allow me to inform you, my love, that Pittsburgh is in Pennsylvania, and Ann Arbor just happens to be in Michigan."

"You're crazy," I denied flatly.

I don't recall that he said "Touché," exactly—a close relationship becomes closer with an avoidance of the predictable—but whatever he did say robbed me of what little bravado I could hang on to. Geography was never one of my strong points, but to mislay a university was going one step further than ignorance; indeed it was a mental lapse that could well portend an approaching senility. I covered my agitation with a shaky laugh. "Oh, stop it, you're just trying to upset me," I said. "I can prove I'm right."

"Go ahead," he returned unctuously. "I'm all ears."

"Very well, I distinctly remember that there were three Pittsburgh calls on last month's telephone bill. Pray, who would I be talking to if it wasn't Peter?"

"I distinctly remember that you were talking to Jonas, pray."

Relief cleared my confusion like sun dispelling mist. "Well, now, how stupid can I be!" I chided myself gaily. "I knew somebody I knew was at the University of Pittsburgh, only it happened to be my nephew instead of my son, so I'm not so crazy after all!"

My husband opened his mouth to speak, but no sound issued from his lips. "Besides"—I filled in the gap—"it settles the whole thing, because there's no point in having my fare and expenses paid to a place Peter isn't even at."

[24]

His eyes narrowed. "So that's it."

"And there's no need to look at me like that," I flared up. "I had a perfectly good reason for wanting to go to Pittsburgh, and now I haven't, so that's all there is to it. I don't even have to apologize or make any excuses in my letter tomorrow, I'll simply say that my acceptance was a misunderstanding, to get someone else instead."

"May I suggest," he said, with his lips getting as narrow as his eyes, "that you do not intimate that the university misrepresented itself by not being in Ann Arbor? And may I further suggest that you leave Jonas' name out of it? Unless, of course, you want them to think that you're more of a half-wit than you are."

"I have no intention of bringing Jonas into it," I assured him with hauteur. "I might be a half-wit, but I am not a name-dropper."

It is an entirely negative virtue, because I don't know too many important names intimately enough to drop. The only reason I'm mentioning Jonas Salk is because he's indirectly responsible for my making the speech in the first place, which in turn is responsible for my writing this book. And also because I regard him as a relative, rather than a name. Notwithstanding his infinite contribution to mankind, of which I am justifiably proud, he is to me the same modest, dedicated human being who spent his honeymoon with us at the farm, and that must be as far back as 1938. Normally, a bridegroom doesn't choose to spend his honeymoon with his wife's family, but with Jonas it was a matter of financial necessity. His marriage to my niece, Donna Lindsay, depended on the usual academic shoestring, and they'd both agreed that they preferred a gift of hospitality to a parental donation for a two-week wedding trip that they couldn't afford on their own.

Naturally, I applauded this praiseworthy spirit of independence, but I admit with a discomfiture that prevails to this day, that I was at a loss to understand why Donna had fallen so head over heels in love with this serious young medical student, beyond, of course, his basic attributes of integrity and decency

[25]

which were obvious and admirable. Nevertheless, I'd expected her to gravitate towards a more dominant and romantic type, being herself quite lovely, blonde and willowy, and blessed additionally with an excellent mind and a lively wit. Jonas, on the other hand, was extremely reticent, of no impressive height, dark, with a hairline conditioned to recede, and solemn brown eyes that hid behind oversized spectacles.

"Be glad," Bill advised elliptically.

"I am glad," I said, but I wasn't ecstatic about the marriage, because I thought I knew all the answers. Donna's mother—my only sister—had died a short while before, and it was my private opinion that Jonas had come along at a time when he filled a sudden emptiness in her life. Nor did that ten-day visit shake my opinion. You don't talk much to a man during the delicate and personal interlude of his honeymoon, but I doubt if Jonas would have talked very much under any circumstances.

In due course, Donna started having a baby, and although she bloomed richly into motherhood, it was difficult to think of Jonas as the head of a family. I have an aversion to using the word "boyish" to describe a grown man, but Jonas remained boyish, with a persistently immature complexion, and a voice that cracked a little with earnestness whenever he alluded to anything that had to do with his beloved research, which unfortunately didn't seem to be reaping any rewards, material or otherwise. Donna, a graduate of Smith, and raised in comparative luxury, cheerfully cooked and scrubbed, and never for a moment relinquished an abiding faith in her husband's genius. I respected her stamina, but I could only hope that she would, in time, gain the wisdom to accept him as one of a legion of budding but unremarkable young scientists, and settle for a life of contented mediocrity.

Not a bit of it. She had built herself a dream that Jonas was going to set the world on fire some day, and she stuck to it. Which brings me to one of their later visits to the farm. As they took their leave, refreshed and full of appreciation, Jonas presented me with a small oblong box, wrapped neatly in white paper. I have long deplored the passing of old-fashioned courtesies in

[26]

the young, and I received the gift with pleasure. By the look, shape and size of the package, it might have been anything from a porcelain figurine to a small bottle of perfume. "It feels exciting," I said, starting to untie the string.

"Oh, don't open it." Jonas stopped me quickly. "Keep it just as it is in the refrigerator until you're ready to use it."

No porcelain or perfume, this. "It sounds like champagne," I chirped with feeble humour.

"It's a lot better than champagne," Donna said. "Oh, come on, Jonas, you can brag a little," she mocked his modesty.

Jonas shook his head. "You don't brag about anything like this," he said. (He was right, even then.)

"Then I'll brag," said Donna. "Aunt Rose, Jonas has really done it. Isn't it thrilling?"

"It is, but done what?" I humoured her fatuousness.

"His inoculation against influenza! He told you he was working on it. Don't you remember?"

"Oh, yes. Yes, of course," I murmured politely.

"I think I've finally succeeded," Jonas offered, with his usual diffidence.

"No 'think' about it!" Donna interrupted. "Just have your local doctor inject the boys with it, Aunt Rose, and you won't have to worry about them the whole winter."

"But don't have it done until the weather gets cooler," Jonas cautioned. "And be sure to tell the doctor that each vial holds the correct dosage. Make that very clear to him, Aunt Rose."

Need I say that "Aunt Rose" tossed the unopened package into the garbage pail as soon as the car had driven out of the gate to take the budding young scientist and his adoring bride to the station? "And we always thought he was so quiet!" I exploded to Bill. "Why, the nerve of that precocious little snip, expecting me to endanger my children's lives with some poisonous stuff he's concocted in his so-called research, and Donna stands there and encourages him in these juvenile fantasies!"

Well, how wrong can you be? Donna's dream came true, she's still in love with her husband, they've raised a family, and the world that Jonas has set fire to hasn't destroyed the house they live in.—And that, too, is a kind of greatness.

I was sorry that in giving up my trip to Pittsburgh, I would be giving up a visit to them.

I was mistaken on both counts. Once you've said "yes" to a university, it's next to impossible to say "no." I thought surely my second letter would put an end to all further correspondence, especially having thrown my knee in at the last minute to make the cheese more binding, as it were. Which shows I didn't know my cheese, for the return mail brought a charming and solicitous reply from Professor Laufe, with a wheelchair in the last paragraph. It was a complication that I hadn't expected.

I caught Bill as he was leaving for a meeting with his publisher. He said, heartlessly, "Don't look to me for sympathy. I told you not to get mixed up with a university, and besides you ought to know by now that you're not a good enough liar to lie."

"You're right, I admit it, only just tell me what to do, and I'll do it." My surrender was abject and complete, but it did not appease his lust for retaliation.

"You can't do anything," he said. "You're in the works already."

I swallowed what was left of my pride and very nearly choked on it. "Then help me to get out of the works, because even if you wrote the speech for me, I'm no good at memorizing."

"If that's a hint, I'm not writing it for you," he said with finality. "Anyway, you're not supposed to memorize a speech, you make notes on little cards and refer to them occasionally.—I'm late for my meeting, good-bye."

"Wait a minute. Don't be silly, how could I 'refer' to notes on little cards without my glasses on!"

"Then wear them," he said, halfway out of the door.

"You know perfectly well I never wear them in public," I returned shortly. "I look like an old sheep in glasses."

"Well, now that you mention it," he grinned, "you sort of do." He came back to pat my shoulder. "But quite an intellectual old sheep. The very look you need on the platform."

"But not on my face, thank you." I held on to his sleeve.

"Also, I'm far-sighted, and if I wore my glasses, I couldn't see whether the audience was walking out on me."

He conceded, a little too readily, that I had a point there, and suggested the alternative of talking extemporaneously. "You were very good at it in Holland and Spain," he remembered to compliment me, after a number of years.

"I had interpreters," I reminded him acidly. "Never mind, I can see your heart isn't in this. I'll go ahead on my own and get an answer off to Professor Laufe in the next mail."

"You're wasting your time. You'll be writing letters backwards and forwards for the next month and you'll still end up in Pittsburgh."

"In that case I'll telephone and explain it personally."

He regarded me with all the dirty earmarks of another grin. "Come to think of it, a personal conversation might very well succeed where all else would fail," he said.

I don't think he thought I intended to telephone, and I don't think I thought so either, but no sooner was he out of the house than I decided to do it, and dialled Long Distance before I had a chance to change my mind.

"What's the number, Madam?"

I didn't know the number, but I proceeded on the vague premise that a Professor Laufe could probably be located, like a large stray package, somewhere in or around the University of Pittsburgh. "Pennsylvania," I added knowledgeably.

The operator appeared to accept the paucity of information as a challenge, and in her quiet, disembodied way, she reached into space, plucked Professor Laufe squarely between classes, and deposited him on the other end of the wire before I could properly organize my thoughts. I suppose this is the time to confess that I have never actually understood how a telephone works; indeed an ordinary electric light bulb floors me if I stop to think about it, and therefore the sound of a strange voice immediately booming in my ear out of nowhere, caused me to lose what little head I had, especially when he asked right off the bat how my knee was.

"Oh, fine," I said, leaving myself without a leg to stand on,

[29]

much less a wheelchair to meet me at the plane. The realization plunged me into a complete state of shock, and in the deadly silence that followed Professor Laufe's pleasure in my recovery, he assumed that we had been disconnected. He jiggled the receiver for the operator, who announced with such severity that the "party was still on the line," that I didn't have the courage to deny it even when my vocal chords began to function again. Instead, I tried to retract that gallant little monosyllable in order to get my knee back into the act, but it was too late. I had no choice but to blurt out the whole miserable story in a desperate attempt to convince him that it was a mistake for him to have asked me to the conference in the first place, and please, to let me out of it.

If there is any virtue in honesty besides not being caught in a lie, the truth should have made me free. I talked nine dollars worth of it, plus tax.

When Bill came home from his publisher's meeting, he found me on the verge of tears. It takes a lot to make me cry, but a twisted typewriter ribbon can do it every time. "Look what this blankety-blank thing does!" I greeted him, frothing with ink and frustration.

"How can anyone be such a mechanical moron?" he marvelled. With chagrin I watched the tangled ribbon turn to butter in his competent fingers, and as he typed out a trial sentence on the piece of manuscript paper already inserted, I prayed that he wouldn't notice the gibberish of crossed-out lines, all beginning with LADIES AND GENTLEMEN.

Fat chance of his not. "So?" he said merely, with his eyebrows climbing his forehead.

"Yes, so!" I raged back at him. "Thanks to your advice, I telephoned Professor Laufe and talked myself into it instead of out of it!"

"Impossible," he said. "How?"

"How?" My voice went hoarse. "I'll tell you how, because the more I talked, the more he said I sounded like Claudia, and it's just my bad luck that he happens to love her!"

"Well, bully for him——"

"Don't be so quick with your 'bullys'," I cut in tersely. "He also told me that Louis Kronenberger's going to be on the panel, he's making a speech on the Art of Dramatic Criticism."

Bill's face, eyebrows included, had the decency to drop a little, which should be sufficient to indicate that Mr. Kronenberger did not love *Claudia*. I could usually count on him for a bad review.

Outrageous Fortune, for example, was a good play, although a little ahead of its time. It was, and I say it dispassionately, good enough for Mr. George Jean Nathan, whose judgment I respected whether favourable or adverse, to have re-evaluated its merits in an article that he wrote shortly before his death, and long after the play had vanished from the Broadway scene. But Mr. Kronenberger thoroughly disapproved of everything about it, and ended his unflattering remarks by summarily dismissing me as a *hausfrau* excelling exclusively in scenes that had to do with food. I have never allowed myself the doubtful satisfaction of trying to combat a critic's opinion, and in particular, I have long since ceased to resent Mr Kronenberger's right to regard me as a dramatist of little or no consequence, but that barb must have really rankled, because it was the first thing that popped back into my mind when I discovered that I was finally to meet this least ardent of my admirers face to face at a literary conference of all places, and sounding like Claudia, of all things.

I am not apologising for her, nor for the thousands of pages I have written about her, to every one of which I have given, honestly and painstakingly, the best that was in me to give. Unhappily, for all my efforts, the impression prevails that she pyramided into one of the big financial gold mines of the decade, and her success, however felicitous, proved somewhat of a thorn in my literary side. I distrust alibis, and I have a deep-seated aversion to explaining my position, but this speech suddenly presented an opportunity I could not afford to ignore. I would write it in such terms as to dispel Professor Laufe's—and anybody else's—illusion that Claudia and I share anything in common beyond endorsing Great Danes, marriage and farming. And with

Mr. Kronenberger in the audience, it would be especially good insurance if, or when, I ever got around to writing another play.

I might just as well have written one, what with the time, effort and agony that went into trying to prove my point. I started off by saying that my career (like electricity or Gaul, I couldn't make up my mind which) was divided into two parts— B.C. and A.C., and incomprehensible as it might seem to certain of my critics, my first novel had blazed a fictional trail into the field of neuroses, with front-page reviews in the *New York Times* Book Section and newspapers all over the country, my second novel, dealing with the insecurity of the minorities, was suppressed in England, while my first play to reach Broadway had been likened to the best of the Russian writers. In short, I had been, in the years B.C., a fully accredited member of the Intelligentsia, with my advanced views on sex, race discrimination and mental illness commanding preferred space in magazines like the *New Masses, Crisis,* and one or two other slim but portentous publications of the period. . . .

I stopped to read over what I had written, and then gave it to Bill to read. "Does it sound a little conceited, do you think?" I asked him dubiously.

"Well," he finally said, "you don't sound like a shrinking violet, exactly."

"Everything I put down was the truth," I defended.

He didn't deny it. He said, "I know it, and you know it, but who's going to believe it?"

"That's exactly what I'm driving at. Nobody remembers the sort of writer I used to be——"

"Then be smart and skip to the Claudia period that everybody does remember."

"The whole purpose of this speech," I said testily, "is to forget Claudia."

"But why should you forget her? She's been damn good to you."

"And I've been damn good to her!" It had come to a pretty pass for him to stick up for Claudia against his wife, making it all too evident that I couldn't live her down. In which case, the next best thing was to live her up.

I slipped a piece of fresh paper into the machine. "I often wonder," I typed out brusquely, "why I undertook to write about the same character for some twenty-odd years without once deviating from her single point of view, but let me hasten to assure you that neither inertia nor laziness kept me at it, for the sheer technical task of remaining within her consciousness became increasingly onerous and demanding. The obvious question is, then, why did I go on writing about her? And I suppose the obvious answer is that I was making too much money to stop writing about her, but the money was a small part of the answer, and it got smaller as taxes got bigger. The real truth was that men and women alike identified themselves with this story of a marriage, and the letters that kept pouring in from all over the world urged me on to each succeeding novel. . . ."

I began bogging down again. "This is what you told me to do." I laid the page and the blame in Bill's lap.

"I didn't tell you to get so flowery," he demurred. "I'd take out the money part."

"But that takes out the taxes, and I need the humour. Or perhaps," I added bitingly, "you don't consider it funny."

"Not excruciatingly."

I locked my lips to keep my tongue in leash. "Funny or not, I can't afford to take the money out, I'm short as it is."

He looked crucified. "You asked for my opinion, but all right, leave it in, just finish the damn speech, you've been at it for ten bloody days."

He was wrong, I'd been at it for eleven bloody days, and all I had to show for hour after hour of laborious writing was eighteen minutes of talking. I felt like a woman who slaves over a hot stove all the afternoon cooking a dinner, only to have it gobbled up in half an hour—and according to Mr. Kronenberger, who should know that feeling better than I?

Nevertheless, I took out the money, and I also took out the letters from all over the world. Bill was right, it sounded flowery; and being flowery was coming close to being soap-opera, and I had no intention of making myself a sitting target for that darling weapon of the reviewer. I have yet to understand precisely what he means when he hurls the fatal opprobrium, but as nearly as I can analyse it, the word epitomizes all the things that happen to other people, but never to himself—may he continue to live his charmed existence. It's funny, though—I've noticed that if an author piles great orgies of sentimentality, catastrophe, sex, degradation, coincidence and suffering into a single novel or play, it transcends the category of cheap soap-opera, and soars into the realm of pure art.

Feeling as strongly as I do about the power and licence invested in our critics, I was cognizant of the danger of using the speech as a personal catharsis, and in order to avoid doing so I revised my approach, and disposed of Claudia in a single paragraph.

"I am not," I began over again, "fortunate, or perhaps unfortunate, in having had the advantages of learning how to write. I didn't take a short-story course, or attend a dramatic workshop, or study journalism. I grant, however, with a detachment in which conceit plays no part, that I was gratuitously endowed with a sense of composition, which is like a traveller's cheque that can be applied to any form of writing, from a television script to a novel. But apart from that, I began by relying, as many young authors do, upon a kind of benign inspiration which is often the front for nothing more than a heady rush of new ideas and a replenishment of enthusiasms or indignations, as the case may be. Except in the rare instances of genius, this facility is a snare that not only substitutes for technique but provides an easy short-cut that by-passes the solid foundation of hard work. I got away with quite a lot of by-passing until, in the self-inflicted ordeal of getting involved with Claudia, I was constrained, with each new facet of her development, to achieve emotional content without subjective stimulation. It was a long and tedious indoctrination, but I emerged from it a more competent craftsman equipped to use at will the reliable tools of a profession.

"I do not contend that all writing, competent or otherwise, is not more or less subjective, since it represents the reservoir of experience from which one draws, but I do maintain that the mature author does not tap that reservoir until the discipline of objectivity cleanses and crystallizes his flow of words to paper.

[34]

The angry, brooding young writers of today seem to me either to lack that objectivity, or to submerge it in the passionate and frequently garbled voltage of their verbal outpourings. Some of them will, no doubt, make an ultimate contribution to posterity, but I venture the belief that it will not be until such time as they have worked through their problems instead of foisting upon a vulnerable public the unfinished analyses of their confusions and resentments. "I am aware," I finally ended, "that my opinions are vestigial, and place me in the position of being antagonistic to any injection of fresh concepts and new ideas in our literary progress. It is partially, but not entirely the fact, for while I heartily endorse the abandon and vitality of a younger generation, I refuse to accept genius as a synonym for sickness, and I reserve the right to revere form as a symptom of clarity. In short, I am old-fashioned to the point of expecting, whether implied or stated, middles, beginnings and endings to what I read as well as to what I write, and I shall continue to believe that the world is not completely infested with a realism that exceeds reality, nor overshadowed by a state of perpetual frustration that assumes the guise of art."

I knew that I had reached my closing sentence by the way it sat stubbornly on its haunches, and balked at being subtracted from or added to. Tingling with a belated sense of accomplishment I read the entire speech aloud to Bill in a burst of oratorical eloquence. Then I laid the final page down on top of the other pages and squared the whole into a neat rectangle.

"Is that the end?" Bill queried mildly.

I nodded. "With some water-drinking, throat-clearing and thanking the audience for listening, it'll be just about the right length."

"I wasn't worried about it being long enough," he said.

I was quick to take offence. "What then?"

"It sounds as if you have a little chip on your shoulder."

"A chip," I interrupted firmly, "is the one thing I do not have."

"Don't misunderstand me," he said. "I don't blame you if you do have a small one."

[35]

"Well, I haven't. Is there any other criticism?"

"Nope."

"Then it's all right?"

"Yep."

I wasn't convinced of his sincerity. "It certainly doesn't sound like Claudia, does it?"

"Nope."

"And you can't say that it hasn't got an intellectual quality, can you?" I pursued a little desperately.

"Yep. I mean nope."

I could scarcely speak for disappointment. "You don't like it."

"I didn't say that."

"You didn't have to."

He put his arm around me. "Oh, come now, it's no worse than most speeches. It's full of nice big words and double talk, and it's bound to show Louis Kronenberger that you're a highbrow and not a *hausfrau*."

I couldn't rise to his levity. I felt shrivelled with misery. "I don't care about Mr. Kronenberger, I care about what you think. What can I do to make it good enough for you to like it?"

"Nothing. That is," he corrected himself hastily, "unless you try to create the impression that you're the kind of person who'd make that kind of a speech."

"How?" I broke in, and eagerly, like a fool.

"I told you before. Wear your glasses."

I gathered up the pages in silence and started for the door. He stopped me, a trifle anxious, as well he should have been. "What's your hurry? Where are you going?"

"To find a train I can walk in front of."

"Try a window," he grinned. "It's no messier, and much handier."

He did not remotely suspect how sorely I was tempted.

At last the day came when I was to leave for Pittsburgh. Heavy of limb and heart, I trudged up to the cedar cupboard in the attic to get my grey suit to travel in. Before storing it for the winter I had had it cleaned, and the skirt shortened as a tardy concession to style. I knew I didn't have to slip it on ahead of time, as it was one of those well-tailored garments that keeps its shape for ever, even if you don't. I was comfortable in it, I'd been comfortable in it for years, and the same went for my black chiffon, which I intended to use for the speech itself. It was off the shoulders, with a good bust line, and although I've been depreciating my assets up to this point, I'll concede that I'm still quite passable in the shoulders, too. Bill said it was high time I went on a buying spree, but I don't feel at home in new clothes until they get used to me and I get used to them, and then they're not new any longer.

I was about to close the door of the cedar cupboard when I suddenly remembered something that I should never have forgotten. My chinchilla coat! Why hadn't I thought of it before and saved myself all the worrying? I stepped back into the darkness of the spicy interior, and dragged forth a large, oblong box where it lay embalmed beneath layers of tissue paper, sprinkled with camphor flakes. I knelt down, carefully lifted it out, blowing gently on the soft fur, which stirred to life at my breath and showed the skin beneath, delicate and pink as an old lady's scalp, with little bald spots here and there.

I bumped into Bill in the hall below. He saw the coat over my arm. "You're not!" he expostulated. "You wouldn't have the nerve——"

"I must, it's my only hope. These chinchillas have brought me luck for as long as we've been married," I added sentimentally.

"Look. Even rabbits get tired and wear out," he tried to argue with me, but I shook my head. "They may be worn out, but they can't, they won't fail me now, in my hour of direst need."

"You really believe it, you cluck."

"I really believe it," I said. Indeed, my trepidation had all but vanished as we drove to the airport. The coat rested across my knees, its mellowed silk lining uppermost. "Try to get material like this today," I challenged my silent husband.

He didn't rise to the challenge. "You're going to look like decayed gentry," he warned me dourly.

"That's the way chinchillas ought to look," I said.

I won't stop now to go into the story of how I originally happened to buy the coat at a sale for something like twenty dollars; it is sufficient to say, for the present, that the guard at the airport allowed Bill to go past the gates with me, and the stewardess smiled her permission for him to see me settled in my seat.

"Don't try to be smart, fasten your safety-belt," he gave me parting instructions. "And telephone me when you get there, don't forget to call me right after the speech, I'll be waiting to hear how it went."

I nodded, rather than try to talk over the sudden lump in my throat. I've always hated good-byes, for short or for long.

He bent to kiss me. "Good luck, darling." He patted the coat. "And see that she gets it, you poor, hard-working little bunnies." He kissed me again, and was gone.

The plane wasn't crowded. The stewardess hovered beside me with a collection of wraps she had gathered up. She said, "I could let yours stay in the empty seat across the aisle instead of crushing it in with all the others at the back."

"I wish you would," I thanked her. "I have to handle it with kid gloves, or it'll fall apart."

"That's what I thought," she said, which left me thinking.

She returned a few minutes later, her arms empty. I gave her the coat. She held it for a moment with her cheek against it. "It feels so soft, so delicate," she murmured. "I've never really touched a chinchilla coat before."

I didn't have the heart to tell her that she wasn't touching one now.

The plane was late, and I was glad I had begged Professor Laufe not to trouble to meet me at the airport. I took a taxi to the hotel, and found a note for me at the desk, saying that he would ring me at six-thirty, and would I dine with him? Louis Kronenberger and Joseph Verner Reed had arrived on an earlier flight, and would join us.

"My luck's beginning already, I don't have to accept," I told

Bill over the phone. "Donna just called to ask me for supper."

"Good. Have a nice time."

"I will, and I hope you're going down to the 'Players' for a game of poker," I urged him generously.

"That I am," he said, but amended like a gentleman that he missed me anyway.

The one who stays at home usually does do the missing; I miss him terribly when he's in Canada fishing. I always went with him until I got smart enough to stop pretending to enjoy it. It undoubtedly gave him a great something to sit for hours in a smelly boat, preferably in vile weather, waiting for a trout to make up its mind, but all I got out of it was bites from insects and a stiff behind. Few women are great fishermen, and if they are, they're competition, and if they're not, they're a nuisance. The same goes for poker. I was glad he was going to have a good time without me.

I'd have had a good time too, if the conference the next day hadn't been hanging over my head all the evening. The Salks aren't a strain to be with. The boys do not dominate the conversation, Jonas could be anyone, and Donna is an excellent cook, unchatty, and not obsessed with cramming sour cream and herbs into everything. She was unobtrusively efficient, and didn't want me to help her with the dishes after supper, but I said, "Don't be an ass," and she said, "As you wish. Do you want to wash or dry?" I told her I loathed drying, and she said she did too, so we compromised by scraping and stacking, and went outdoors to walk around the grounds while it was still light. "What a wonderful lawn you have," I said enviously. For all our pampering, ours was still a brownish stubble while theirs was already as green as grass and as smooth as suède. "Lawns just seem to grow that way in Pittsburgh," Jonas said.

"There must be a moral to everything that happens and doesn't happen," I remarked, with decent obliqueness, as he drove me back to the hotel. "I haven't discovered yet what it is, though."

"I haven't either," he said.

We stood for a moment at the door of the lobby. "You

wouldn't happen to have a sleeping pill on you, would you?"

He withdrew a yellow capsule from his pocket. "I thought you might need one. I always get nervous before a speech, too."

I couldn't believe it. "What have you of all people got to be nervous about? You don't make speeches. You speak, and give something of vast importance to humanity."

"That's why," he answered.

I wondered how two small words could say so much, and yet leave so much unsaid. In the hazy glow of a street lamp, he appeared scarcely older than the unsure, dedicated boy who had spent his honeymoon on the farm with us, but sitting opposite him at dinner, I had sensed a deep tiredness from within. Later, as I fell asleep, I saw behind my closed lids, a picture of Madame Curie, autographed to Bill, that hangs in our library. He knew her well—it was his mother who had first brought Madame Curie to this country—and he had told me so many little stories about her that I felt as though I too had known her. Fragile and monastic in her one everlasting plain black dress, the quiet face held a look as ancient as the saints', and suddenly I realized that there is crucifixion in being chosen as an instrument of greatness. I felt ashamed for having wasted so many hours fretting over a speech that was no more than a puny performance of my ego.

When I wakened it was morning, I felt curiously relaxed, and the foolishness was out of me.

It could have been the effects of the pill that continued to induce such a pleasant suspension of feeling. Nothing bothered me, and everybody was pleasant, particularly Mr. Kronenberger. Indeed, none of the members of the panel turned out to be in the least formidable, and Professor Laufe reciprocated the compliment he had paid me, by being just like his voice—enthusiastic but comfortable.

The panel itself couldn't have been easier. It was even a little silly, it was so easy. We sat in a row in front of a large assemblage of students who asked us dutiful questions about writing, which we dutifully answered. A few of them scribbled notes (or something), others yawned politely at the back of their throats, and sharp at noon all of them leaped to their feet with alacrity and dashed noisily out to lunch.

At half-past one they straggled back to listen to Mr. Kronenberger's dissertation on being a dramatic critic, coupled with Mr. Reed's history of the Shakespeare Theatre. Although they both blatantly read from a sheaf of papers in front of them (I could have killed Bill for his fancy advice), they sounded nervous, anyway. But with their speeches behind them, they were positively gay, and I wished that mine was behind me, too. Mr. Reed said he was looking forward to the evening, which didn't make me feel any happier, but when Mr. Kronenberger added that he was sorry that he couldn't stay over to hear me because he had to catch a six o'clock plane back to New York, it was like the old joke of taking a boarder and letting him go. Indeed, I suddenly felt so gay myself that I agreed to join the remaining members of the conference in the hotel bar before dinner for a drink.

In the meantime, I had a couple of hours that Professor Laufe assumed I would lie-down-and-take-a-nap in. Doctors say that it's a good thing to do after a certain age, but I haven't got into the habit of it as yet, so instead I accepted Jonas' offer to show me through his laboratory.

In those long corridors of white tiled rooms, I saw medical history in the making, but I was depressed by the hundreds of crates of squalling ducks and chickens, and the cages of monkeys. In my youth I had been a rabid anti-vivisectionist. Now I wasn't sure what I was.

The telephone was ringing in my room as I fitted the clumsy hotel key into the latch. It was Professor Laufe, hoping he hadn't wakened me; he supposed his news could have waited until dinner, but he thought I'd like to know that my speech had been changed over from the lecture hall to the main auditorium. "It looks as if half the town and all the faculty are turning out to hear you," he said.

I knew he thought he was giving my morale a great boost, but instead he gave me a palpitation, and once more I became the swollen centre of my universe. I begged off dinner, and spent the next hour alternately mumbling my speech from memory, and practising with the stack of white cards in case my memory failed me. Towards eight o'clock, an all-gone feeling in my middle reminded me that I had skipped supper. I ordered a sandwich and some consommé, which I at once recognized to be a bouillon cube sporting a shredded carrot, and throwing its weight around in a silver tureen. I managed to swallow most of it, but the sandwich wouldn't go down. Nothing has ever been known to spoil my appetite—except worrying about the family—but if I had the slightest inkling of what the evening held in store for me, I wouldn't have ordered a sandwich, I'd have ordered a lobster.

Poor Professor Laufe. He thought he was cheering me up again when he hurried over to me as I was about to walk on to the platform, and whispered in my ear that the Dean had just said to him, "Well, we finally managed to get her here, chinchillas and all."

It was the last thing I wanted to hear; I don't intentionally fool anyone about the coat, unless it happens to be some nice person like the stewardess, who wanted to be fooled, or some not-so-nice person, who deserved to be fooled. Professor Laufe did not fall into either category, but there wasn't time to explain that I wasn't wearing a symbol of prosperity, I was wearing a superstition, a faithful little band of rabbits who had adopted me almost a quarter of a century ago, and proceeded to inflate my importance and promote my career like some unscrupulous press agent. "It's just an old thing," I stammered, salving part of my conscience. "I only brought it along for luck."

His beaming smile told me that I had accomplished little more than to strengthen his conviction that I was exactly like Claudia, and I wished I could die then and there, but again there wasn't time. I walked on to the platform with my knees shaking, especially the patched-up one, but my fur-draped shoulders emanating, as always, that air of assurance that goes with success. I bowed my head stiffly in acknowledgment of the perfunctory hand-clapping that greeted my appearance, noting blindly that there seemed to be people's heads in all the seats of the vast hall.

I had intended to keep the coat on during my speech so that I wouldn't have to hold my stomach in. I am not overweight and I don't bulge noticeably, but I'm bound to admit that I'm not as flat as I used to be, unless I struggle somewhat. However, I was afraid that if I didn't remove my wrap, it would look as if I were purposely flaunting a fifty thousand dollar chinchilla—or whatever it is that chinchillas are supposed to cost. Hastily, I slipped it off, scrunched it into an inconspicuous ball, and thrust it behind me on a chair. Too late I realized that this was the most ostentatious of gestures, since only those who can afford to own chinchilla coats can afford to scrunch them. Having done it, though, I should have let well enough alone. But no. I had to make it worse by unscrunching it and smoothing it out, thereby calling attention to its delicateness, and adding to its value. My little rabbits had certainly screwed me up by stealing the act. I didn't know what to do next, so I told the truth.

I said, "It's not real chinchilla, it's only imitation."

A noisy silence greeted this simple statement of fact, and then a ripple of laughter swept over the big hall. The blood froze in my veins, my face burned with the hotness of a flame held against my cheeks. Did they think that I was trying to be a pixie? How long I stood there, drenched in mortification, I will never know, but suddenly, someone in the audience started to applaud and others followed, and all at once I knew that this was friendly laughter, and they were waiting for me to go on. In the theatre, the magic of rapport is as tenuous as a cobweb, but the sense of its being there is as warm and powerful as the sun coming from behind a cloud. It was like that now. The chill went out of my bones. As I placed my notes on the dais, a quietness settled over the hall.

Ladies and gentlemen: It is a great honour for me to be here with you this evening—

Although the words were in my brain, my lips refused to shape them. Instinct told me that these warmly attentive people had carried me beyond the pontifical introduction I had gone to such pains to prepare, and I would be wiser to skip the opening lines and jump right into the speech. But instinct is one thing, and memory another. I couldn't jump, because I couldn't remember what came after the first paragraph; leaving it out had the same effect as losing a cue in a play. I snaked off the top card from the dais, and peered down at my notes, only to realize that the worst that could happen had happened—what with all the coat business, I hadn't thought to take my glasses out of my handbag. The figurative sun that had peeped from behind a cloud, vanished, plunging me into the blackness of a nightmare. My mind was a blank, my eyes were sightless, and my throat felt as if I had swallowed sawdust. I could do one of two things. I could walk off the platform and keep walking and never be heard of again, or I could try to jabber on about the coat until somehow I could manage to fish out my glasses and find my way back into the speech.

I did neither. I stuck it out, but that didn't mean that I was able to remember a single word I had written (which Bill was frank enough to tell me afterwards, was a great break for everyone, including myself). Inconsistently, however, he pooh-poohed the theory that if one rabbit's paw can bring a person luck, there's no limit to what a whole slew of them sewn together can do. And I'm here to tell you that they worked their little tails off for me that night, because no sooner did I start to go on with the saga of "my chinchillas," than my knees stopped shaking, I didn't need my glasses on account of not needing my notes, and as one anecdote led to another, I could feel myself not only falling in love with the sound of my own voice, but beginning to understand why authors like to talk about themselves as well as write about themselves.

Not the least of my luck was the fact that I felt utterly relaxed in the comforting thought that Mr. Kronenberger was not amongst my listeners. Nor did I have the slightest premonition that he was not in fact winging his way back to New York, until he came up to me at the Dean's reception later that evening. My spirit swooned. Again, I'd laid myself wide open to his criticism.

"You told me you'd left," I got in first, thereby putting him in the wrong at once.

"I intended to," he said, "but I'm glad I stayed. I can't tell you how much I enjoyed your talk."

I could see that he really meant it, and I was profoundly disappointed in him. It was sad, in a way, that he should have changed so much since the days of *Outrageous Fortune*.

"So few people," I told him regretfully, "have the courage not to mince words but to say exactly what they think and feel."

He agreed with me, seemingly unaware that it was he himself who had compromised with the cardinal principle of honesty. Indeed, he was genuinely surprised to learn that he hadn't always quite heartily approved of me.

Perhaps we had both mellowed a little through the years.

The next day Professor Laufe, and the Dean too, insisted on escorting me to the airport. I welcomed the gesture as an indication that on sober reflection they hadn't changed their opinions, and decided that the speech might not have measured up to the dignity of a university conference. On the contrary, Professor Laufe asked me to be sure to send on a copy of it so that he could use it in class, which flattered rather than pleased me, since it involved my having to type out the whole thing from memory. Nevertheless, I promised that I would do it, and in case you've forgotten, that's how, and why, I happened to begin writing this book.

The return flight was crowded, there wasn't an empty seat, and this time I had to keep my chinchillas on my lap, along with a bulky cornucopia of flowers. As I was leaving the hotel, a nice, middle-aged lady, unmistakably green of thumb, had rushed up to present them to me, explaining breathlessly that she had picked them from her own garden and put wet newspaper and cotton round the stems so that they would be sure to stay fresh on my journey. I thanked her profusely and gathered the moist bundle into my arms, knowing that they'd have wilted long before the plane reached New York. I, too, used to be an impulsive thruster of flowers-from-my-own-garden, until I lost enough friends to make me realize that there is nothing, but nothing, more two-faced and spineless than a delicate, fragrant bouquet of spring blooms.

The ravishing assortment that presently occupied the better part of my anatomy proved no exception, in spite of the voluminous padding of watered cotton that leaked from the vicinity of my bosom into a large damp area on my skirt. With the mounting heat of the plane, the longer stemmed blossoms began to droop languidly against the neck of the taciturn gentleman who had the misfortune to have chosen the space beside me, and the lilacs took to daintily vomiting their sticky, tiny petals over his dark blue suit. I guess he was as glad as I was to see the lights of Manhattan winking up at us through the dusk.

As I squirmed around to undig my safety-strap, a precocious red tulip beheaded itself completely, and plopped on to his trousers. "It couldn't have been worse for you if I'd been travelling with an armful of babies," I apologized, and I remember well how his sour face did not break suddenly into sweetness.

Bill was waiting for me at the gate. We managed a kiss above a barrier of sodden newspaper. "Everything all right at home?"

"You've only been gone two days," he reminded me.

"It seems like months."

"Me too," he admitted sheepishly.

That's why, when an offer to go on a lecture tour arrived a week or so later, nothing could have induced me to accept it. That is, until Bill said, "Forget it, it's not your cup of tea," which started the same business of the speech all over again. "And why isn't it?" I took umbrage at once. "I can name any number of women who lecture all over the country all the time and find it extremely stimulating and broadening."

"Good-bye, have a nice trip," he gave in with a sunny smile. "Drop me a postcard now and again to tell me how you're enjoying yourself."

It was one of his more infuriating tactics. What would it avail me to rail against something he didn't give me a chance to back down from? It's a grave mistake for a wife to allow her husband to know her inside out, and specifically Bill is smugly confident that I am not given to attacks of wanderlust unless transportation is made completely painless by his expert chauffeuring; the luxury of flinging last-minute stuff into a car doesn't narrow packing down to a fine art, which I haven't got. We have driven from one end of the United States to the other, and across the continents of Europe, Africa, Asia and the British Isles, yet I never fail to marvel at his ability to fold and tuck everything into a suitcase with such calculated precision that he always comes out with the top closing, and space to spare. He also has the ability to get a car started that's stopped, is acutely map-minded, and has an infallible sense of direction. Of course I, too, have a number of motoring virtues that he wouldn't be apt to find in another woman. I have no nerves in a car, I travel light on transient stops, being physically and mentally equipped to fit into one small overnight bag, including a change of drip-dry clothing (and I don't catch cold if I'm more dripping than dry), I wake early and instantly, dress fast, exhibit great flexibility in any sudden switch of itinerary, am not susceptible to food poisoning, and can outlast any petrol tank, foreign or domestic.

There remains, however, one major psychological hurdle for me to meet whenever we embark on a trip. I have an aversion to sleeping in strange rooms, although primarily it isn't the rooms I mind, it's the sheets and blankets, for I am obsessed by the fear that they might not be as clean as they're cracked up to be, and how do I know what kind of person, or persons, slept under them before me? No one need remind me of the well-known fact that extreme fastidiousness is highly suspect. But not in my case. My trouble is not Freudian; it springs from personal experience plus a guilty conscience that keeps badgering me no matter if I'm in a hotel in England, a villa in France, a paradore in Spain, or a motel in America. Getting back to the lecture tour, I knew that visiting celebrities frequently enjoyed the hospitality of private homes, which was even worse, because it was in a private home that I was first conditioned to this chronic state of bed-linen phobia—my own private home, to be frank.

It's not a story to be proud of, and I don't go around advertising it, but this is what happened. One summer day on the farm, I ran out of rags, and the next thing I knew, I'd run out of sheets. Any housewife, good, bad or indifferent, has at one time or another experienced that delicious sensation of tearing one's way from hem to hem through a long expanse of linen that's outlived its day. It acts as a sort of catharsis to the average woman, and once started, a worn spot in this sheet, a small hole in that one, a tiny rent in another, builds up to a compulsion to become the proud possessor of the grandest, snowiest collection of dusting cloths in the whole countryside.

Unfortunately, I had revelled in just such a debauch at a moment when we were unexpectedly saddled with a lot of week-end company. We ourselves are not professional guests. We do not enjoy waking up in other people's houses, and therefore we cannot comprehend why other people should enjoy waking up in ours—provided that they have homes of their own to wake up in. If they haven't, our hospitality knows no bounds, but the agile week-ender who nurtures a chronic tan from Memorial Day to Labor Day, is apt to receive scant encouragement to soak up sun and liquor at the expense of our decently occupied lives.

For some reason, though (I don't recall just why), we seemed to have been running a rural boarding house over that particular Friday-through-Sunday, with both Bill and me catering to wet bathing suits and dry throats until we could hardly wait for the last car to drive away so that we could take off our wooden smiles, move back into our faces, and restore our home to its usual peace and order. (I think it was Benjamin Franklin who said that house guests are like fish out of water because after two days they both begin to smell.)

Anyway, alone once more, we went out to lie on the terrace, feeling nothing but bliss until we heard the front doorbell ring. "It can't be anybody," I said. "Who is it?"

"Nobody," said Bill.

It was wishful thinking, and Bill's publisher, who was on his way down from Rhode Island. He said the roads were jammed, and could I put him up overnight so that he could get an early start the next morning and escape the traffic? But please not to bother about giving him supper, and as for breakfast, not to bother with that either, he could get it on the road.

He was most considerate, but he was making the wrong thing easy for me. Food was no problem whatsoever, as the refrigerator was stacked with enough left-overs to deprive us of the novelty of eating for days ahead. It was the linen cupboard that presented the real snag. Stripping the beds after everyone was out of them, I had congratulated myself that nobody had spilled coffee or orange juice off a tray, or otherwise necessitated a change of bedding that I didn't have. But the last minute appearance of an additional and unexpected guest was a problem I hadn't reckoned with.

Well, I decided philosophically if not accurately, you can't get blood out of a stone. I went down to the laundry where a white mountain of rumpled linen awaited the next day's loading into the washing machine. I knew exactly the two sheets I was after, and they weren't hard to spot—they stood out like Abou Ben Adhem above all the rest. Most week-enders are sloppy sleepers, especially when they come in pairs, but one little bachelor had conducted his slumbers with impeccable propriety —no tossing or turning or anything. What was to prevent? Who would be the wiser? A few swishes of a hot iron, and *voila!*

I'm sure I couldn't possibly have cornered the market on that ingenious but simple little trick, and the conviction not only haunts me, but is the crux of my whole trouble. Every time I climb into a strange bed, I automatically start to pull the sheet up over the blanket only to remember how a hot iron can press out the last person's wrinkles. And how can I tell that it hasn't? I can't. So there I lie, doomed for ever, when away from home, to sleep in a quandary, which is not restful.

Being one of, if not the severest of, my critics, I am loath to read over what I have written so far. If I did, I would say to myself, "These pages have exceeded the bounds of reticence, you have accomplished nothing but an indulgent orgy of personal trivia."

"Oh come now, it's not that bad," I'd answer myself back. "Everyone can't reek of importance. And anyway, what are you supposed to do in your memoirs, hang your clothes on yonder tree and not go near the water?"

Thus am I rationalizing this book at the end of a first rambling chapter, in which I have covered a tendency to digress by titling it "A Little of Everything and not Much of Anything." But before I go on to the second chapter, I want again to emphasize the fact that I am not neurotic, even though I confess to being squeamish about other things than sheets. For instance, I wince at tasting from anybody else's fork, spoon or glass; I don't like people to use my comb; and I can't bear sitting down in a chair, or anywhere else, that has recently been vacated and left warm. Happily, however, two very suspect symptoms are absent from my pattern of functioning: I do not indulge in frequent hand-washing (unless weeding or changing typewriter ribbons), and my daily bath bores me immeasurably. Indeed I am not upset, or the worse for it, should untoward conditions force me to skip a day. Or two. Or even three. Nor does a bath induce in me a sublimating desire to linger, dream or luxuriate in lotions that exude exotic fragrances. I'm in and out before the water has a chance to run in and out.

And I want to reiterate, too, that the character of Claudia is completely alien to my own. This in-and-out-of-the-bath business just happens to be one of the few traits I share with her.

As for the lecture tour, Bill was right when he said that it wasn't my cup of tea. I've never hankered for freedom, and it's too late for me to try to learn new habits. I've lived long enough to know that the years grow shorter every day, and unless you're truly young, or circumstances make it necessary, it's silly to go away from the people you love, and who love you.

Sometimes I wonder how free, really, is a free soul.

2

THE YEARS B.C.

Any life is a story. The dullest existence attains a kind of stylish significance by virtue of its very dullness, and pinpointed at its highlights, an average life could be, and has been, translated into fiction—and sometimes stranger than. Autobiography, on the other hand, falls into the category of a special kind of writing, and I dare say should not be guilty of reading like a novel, spattered with dialogue. Furthermore, such important memoirs as come to my mind, have observed the orderly technique of beginning at the beginning, and proceeding to the end in sustained sequence and mood, but it is already evident that mine will not lend themselves to that discipline. What I have to say is hardly of sufficient moment in our life and times to justify an objective recording of events and dates, neither of which would be accurate or even pertinent to the unpretentious chronicle of a single individual who, when all is said and done, has finally come to realize that there is a certain importance in not being too earnest. It's taken me a lot of ordinary day-to-day living to have distilled that highly debatable philosophy, albeit I am not unaware of the vast problems that beset and threaten the very core of civilization. Still, I sometimes wonder whether the human race is so much better off, or worse off, than it used to be. For all the immensity of our progress in space, and on land, and under the sea, people seem to end up being pretty nearly the same as always, good or bad, heroes or cowards, and history balances off one way or another, without too heavy a tipping of the scales in either direction. It is only recently that I have attained this stage of emotional sedation. The miracles that modern man has wrought continue to awe and confound me, but the future no longer shadows the present with its stupendous potential of annihilation. Doom has existed since the inception of life, and I have reached the comparatively comfortable conclusion that I am as secure in my insecurity as the day I was born—which wasn't, I might add, under the most auspicious circumstances.

Everyone likes to think that he has gone through just a little more than the next person, and I'd like to think so too, but I have only to look around me to realize that by and large, I've probably gone through less. However, I can boast of one thing—I was off to a running start with as sorrowful a childhood as a child ever had, barring illness or deformity. Of course a child suffers even when he has nothing to suffer about. Idyllic as it is apt to seem in retrospect, the happiest childhood is a period of only intermittent happiness, chiefly, I suppose, because of being dependent upon, and subservient to, an adult world. There is, at the very outset, the rather dirty deal of having had to be brought into that world in the first place. Birth is no picnic at best. Youngest child, oldest child, middle child or only child—a child's in trouble no matter what. I, being the youngest of four, could have really been up against it. I could have suffered a generic trauma enough to knock the pins out of my whole future life, but nobody in my family (or any family in those days), knew enough to recognize the danger signals that may well have pointed towards any number of later emotional difficulties. Whatever ailed me was promptly attended to, and frequently rectified, by a hefty dose of castor oil supplemented with a tonic called "Iron Tropon."

Mindful of the many problems that beset our young today, I am amazed to reflect how inexpensively I survived my adolescence, escaping even the elementary pitfalls of nail-biting, stuttering, wetting, wheezing and tooth-straightening. Ruling out the latter (although it might not be long before orthodontia will also be suspect as a psychosomatic symptom), these seemingly innocuous childhood afflictions have come to assume deep significance in our present state of enlightenment, and in privileged instances, warrant prolonged and costly sessions of mental therapy. In my case, however, I was seventeen and married before castor oil went out and the psychiatrist's couch came in.

I am not implying that I grew up to be a model of stability. It is reasonable to suppose that I would have benefited by a thorough ploughing-up of my subconscious, but in the early years of my marriage, I didn't have the time, and when I got the time I didn't have the money, and when finally I had a little of both, I didn't feel the need. Which, again, is not the same as saying that I didn't need it, for nobody could have been a more likely candidate for mid-channel disaster than I was. It's just as well that I wasn't aware of it, though. Occasionally, of course, I felt "disturbed," like everyone else does at times, but I always had so many other people to worry about that my own problems had to take a back seat, and mighty lucky I was that they didn't explode and upset the apple cart. Knowing what I now know I realize that it would have been quite a wreck, because I was dragging along a lot of apples.

I still carry a goodly amount of psychic luggage, but it's a mere fraction of what I started off with, including a hazardous load of love—that protective loving love that is presumably responsible for a large percentage of the dis-orientations we encounter as we advance towards middle-age. In fact, I shudder to think that I was raised on enough of the wrong kind of love to backfire on me for the remainder of my days. For one thing, an unusually close bond existed between my mother, my sister and myself, and I am almost ashamed to add that I was deeply attached to my aunts, uncles and brothers. To make the picture even darker, the entire lot of us lived together quite abnormally but very happily, in one of those five-story private houses in Harlem. My grandfather had bought it as a refuge for his children to turn to in the event of catastrophe or need, and those who didn't return to it, never went out of it, which alone is sufficient evidence that I was brought up in a veritable nest of psychoses. I marvel now that nobody went off the deep end, but nobody did. In the due course of time, the family just died off, inconspicuously, of natural causes.

Once in a great while, I yield to an impulse to return to the old neighbourhood, so changed in character, so sordid, that each time the ghosts walk more remotely, stirring nostalgia without pain. The new developments of modern brick have not yet invaded our street—the drug store on the corner and the Catholic Church opposite are still there. I linger a little always to look up at the pitted grey façade of the House, its dignity besmirched by the slovenly windows staring out like clouded, senile eyes. If I allow myself to linger too long, I lose step with time, and I climb the high stone steps, and open the heavily carved door and walk into the front parlour, dim, and mostly saved for company and funerals, with its satin wallpaper and cupids on the ceiling. From there, the back parlour beckons me, cheerful and usable because of the dumb-waiter concealed in its rich mahogany panelling. And now I'm truly slave to the past, I can't turn back before I wander up the heavy Victorian stairs to the large, sunny bedroom above, that I shared with my mother.

I don't recall ever seeing my father in my mother's bedroom, or hearing her speak of him with naturalness and ease. At the mere whisper of a marriage that existed in name alone, she would seem, to my frightened eyes, to dwindle into a small, pale shadow of herself. How much healthier a solution it would have been had she asked for a divorce or a formal separation, but that sort of thing didn't happen in our family. We kept our heads proudly aloft by saying that while my father's affairs kept him in Texas, my mother stayed in New York, in Grandpa's house.

I still have a faded photograph of our home in a little town near Fort Worth where I was born. It was all white, and very large, with wide verandahs, and columns and cupolas, and I think I have a hazy recollection of a cyclone cellar. But I know I remember a pet goose that didn't mind being dressed in doll's clothes, only one day it smothered in its frilly cap, and my sister cried. And I also remember all the dark, smiling faces around us. My mother talked of them so often and so lovingly that my imagination built them into guardian angels of the frail young bride from "up north," who grew more frail after presenting the community with three new citizens in as many years. A long while passed before I came, and I gathered, as soon as I was old enough to know the way things were, that I shouldn't have happened.

Being an accident and unwanted, left no buried resentment, but being named "Rosebud" with "Dougherty" tacked on after my father's best friend, caused me deep bitterness. Even after I nipped the "bud," and changed my middle name to Dorothy, I wished that I'd had the sense to use it as my first name as long as I was at it. "Rose" fits a flower, but on me I don't care for it. And as for "Rosie"—John Golden was the only person who dared.

My mother couldn't seem to regain her strength after I was born, and eventually she returned to New York to undergo surgery. For long weeks she was in the hospital, and even after she was carried home on a stretcher, the house was muted with the presence of a trained nurse, and no one questioned the unspoken edict that she wasn't strong enough to go back to Texas.

It wasn't said in so many words, but I sensed from the way my aunts and uncles talked to each other in undertones that my father "drank."

Disgrace. Verb and noun hovered like a cloud over my childhood. As I grew up, though, I began to wonder whether an empty whisky bottle here and there might not have loomed over horrific to my artless mother, who was Keokuk born and bred. And would she have overlooked an occasional insobriety in a man who fitted into the conventional pattern of husband and father? How ironic that he should have played benefactor to everyone else in that small Texas town, where he was known, adoringly, as "Uncle Mike" for miles around. He befriended the sick and needy, put other people's sons through college, and I recall some big to-do about his giving the gardener's little boy an expensive black velvet Lord Fauntleroy suit that my grandmother had sent to my younger brother for his birthday—it was gone before my brother had a chance to wear it. Disgrace? We were hiding nothing more than a harmless little family skeleton with a God complex.

I wish I could have known my father as others knew him. To those who were not of his flesh and blood, he must have been a rare spirit, generous and engaging, with a besetting flair for the dramatic. That much I do remember of him, believing as I did, that he carried a gun to shoot himself—and us. It wasn't true, of course. It was only the way he held his hand in his pocket. . . .

Will I ever forget the recurrent, waking nightmare of his unexpected trips to New York. He'd always seem to be waiting for me to come home from school, and with the first glimpse of that thin, familiar figure walking down the street, my heart would plummet with a thud that made me sick to my stomach, and an ocean would roar up into my ears. Unless someone of the family happened to be looking out of the window—unlikely at that hour—his presence was invariably left for me to discover, and I think perhaps he timed his being there to three o'clock. And I think, too, that he always saw me as I'd streak down into the areaway, and scramble up the iron gate to stick my hand through the grating to open the door, too frantic to wait for someone to answer the bell. "Papa's here!" I'd gasp out, and soon my aunts would have scurried to an upper floor like leaves before a storm, to sit with my mother and buffer the shock of her husband's return. I will never lose the memory of the abiding strength that lay beneath her fragile prettiness—she had the bluest eyes and the most truly flaxen hair I have ever known—but at those moments when a broken marriage impinged upon her life, she became my child, rather than my mother. It was that strange sense of protection that gave me the courage to go through with the pathetic little farce that was always a sequel to my father's arrival. Once more I would be sent forth to re-enact my coming home from school, carefully coached, now, in the flimsy deceit of greeting him and asking him into the house.

With what consummate art did he play upon my sympathy when he would sadly shake his head and tell me that he was fearful of his welcome. "Oh, please, Papa," I would beseech him, moved to tears, "we want you to come in!" And still he would demur that he didn't want to upset anyone, he didn't want to be any trouble to anyone, he just wanted to see his children for the last time. . . . My heart would lurch with fear. Did he

[56]

mean that this time he was really going to kill himself . . . ?

I remember once, as we sat in the back parlour, how he tried, clumsy with apprehension, to brush up with his hand some ashes from his cigarette that had spilled to the floor. He even begged to go down to the kitchen for a broom and dustpan. *"I don't want to be any trouble to anyone."* My soul grew old with pity and grief, and the pull of divided loyalties destroyed my world.

He seldom remained long in New York, and on the day of his departure, no matter what day it was, it was like a Sunday, stilled. I'd stay home from school, and all four of us children would go downtown to the old McAlpin Hotel. We never went up to his room, he would meet us in the lobby, and he would buy candy, and books for us at the news stand. Then we would have a fine lunch in the main dining-room, but we had no appetite for the delicacies that he had ordered ahead of time.

In the lobby once more, he would shake hands with my brothers, and kiss my sister and me good-bye. Until the next time. It was part of the nightmare that we never knew when "the next time" would be. There was no telling whether he'd come back in a week, a month, a year.

A disrupted family is hard on children.

Strange that I remember vividly so much of the past—open trolley-cars; and high peaks of grimy snow that lined the gutters until spring; and lamp-posts lit at dusk by shadowy figures reaching up long tapers; and driving up and down Seventh Avenue in a carriage behind two beautiful horses with proud, gleaming rumps and no inhibitions. All of those things I remember and yet I cannot recall a single incident that might have pointed the way to my being an author of sorts. People often ask me how, not having an urge and certainly no training, I managed to end up with a fair list of novels and plays, but I have no explanation other than that I got married; and after that I began to write.

We met at my sister's wedding. I was almost seventeen, neat but not glamorous, in a white lingerie dress that my favourite Aunt Jane had embroidered "by hand." We were all still living in the House, except of course, for Grandpa and Grandma who had died long since. Inevitably, big families begin to crumble, like an old wagon with its wheels falling off one by one, but it didn't happen to us until much later, and then, suddenly, and fast. Three deaths in a row? It was nearer twice that.

But there we were, together, all of us at my sister's wedding. It was June, and the simple ceremony took place in the backyard. It wasn't an ordinary city yard. It was a garden, a real garden, behind a high green woven fence in place of the usual mud-brown pickets. There were climbing roses on the fence, and lilacs and magnolias and hydrangeas, along with every variety of annual that could be bought from the wagons that would pass through the streets at the first hint of spring. "Flooooweres—freeeesh flowers——" At seventeen, I wasn't too old to listen for the call, and to rush, with my mother, to select the best flats of pansies and candy-tuft and nasturtiums, and the most gorgeous of the pots of geraniums and begonias. One thing we didn't agree on. She favoured bleeding heart, and I didn't.

The garden had never been more beautiful than the day my sister was married. I was maid of honour, and my brother-in-law's closest friend was the best man, and at the moment, he didn't exist for me. I was enjoying a normal quota of boys and parties, where we danced the Maxixe and the Hesitation, and had refreshments of chicken salad and ice-cream, and held hands, which I didn't care for, because boys' hands were usually clammy. I think, looking back on it, that the first thing about my husband that I became conscious of was his hands. They were big, and warm, and clean, with the strong, gentle cleanliness of a surgeon's hands, and something stirred within me and came alive at his touch, and I saw all at once that his eyes were blue, and straight, and grave and smiling, at one and the same time, and I heard his voice with a new awareness, and it was deep and tender, and gruff to hide the tenderness. I was too young to realize that this, which had suddenly happened to me, was the full awakening of sex. I only knew that I was miserably, ecstatically in love, and I wanted to be close to him, and a part of him for as long as I lived.

It is hard to believe that he could have fallen in love with me at my sister's wedding, for I was as skinny as a blue-fish and as flat as a pancake and with a broken nose that I haven't had fixed to this day. But he did, and it gave me a lasting sense that God was looking after me with a very special interest.

We didn't become engaged, because my mother said I was to put such nonsense out of my mind, enter Barnard in September, and after I was out of college, it would be time enough to talk about getting married. I didn't argue. The postponement made sense to me, since my ignorance was surpassed only by my innocence. What did it matter whether we were engaged, or married, as long as we loved each other? I suppose I would have felt differently if I had had to go away to college, but Barnard was in the middle of New York, and we could either talk or see one another every day. I doubt, however, that proximity would have compensated for the privileges implicit in a formal betrothal, but I never found out, because I only got as far as the motions of registering on the proper day. And then, early the next morning, I opened my eyes, jumped out of bed, flung on my clothes, and said to my mother, "I'm getting married this afternoon."

"That's nice," my mother said.

There wasn't time to convince her that I meant it. The important thing was to telephone the news to my future husband before he left for his office. He lived with his parents in a brownstone house much like ours, except that it was in the sixties, on Lexington Avenue. I had a feeling, as I lifted the receiver, that his mother, in particular, wasn't going to be very pleased at the immediate prospect of having me for a daughter-in-law. I didn't blame her. If I had a wonderful son, I wouldn't have wanted him to marry me either. The least he was entitled to was a college graduate, instead of somebody who hadn't even got a proper diploma from the Ethical Culture High School because of flunking a sewing course.

I caught him just in time, and I cannot hope to explain the miracle of his understanding, except that he possessed the gift of healing, and sentience and healing are akin. He could so easily have dismissed my impetuous impulse as a childish whim, but instead he heard me out in silence, and then very quietly, he told me to meet him for lunch, and we would talk it over.

We were married at four o'clock in City Hall.

We didn't spend the evening or the night together. We went to our separate brownstone houses to break the news to our separate families. It is another small miracle that my mother was not angry. She did not attempt to uncover any rational impulse that might have compelled me to the urgency of marriage, nor could I have given her an explanation had she asked. I am not psychic, nor prone to seek the help of cults or isms. Simply, I am, and always have been, obedient to a kind of inaudible and invisible dictation. I suppose I could say that I act on hunches, like everyone else, but I would like to think that it was more than a hunch that directed the course of my life when I wakened that morning to the certain knowledge that before the day was over I must marry the man I loved.

There is nothing unnatural or supernatural in this extension of conscious reasoning, and yet, even today, I experience a wonderment of gratitude for our fortnight of complete and utter oneness before it happened. Had he known that he was ill, he would not have married me, not then, not ever, perhaps. Neither of us knew it, and at first we could not believe that it could be anything more serious than a bleeding tooth, or the left overs of a summer cold. And then we had another ten days of tests and X-rays with anguish replacing ecstasy, and Dr. James Alexander Miller replacing God. He sat behind his large desk, and told us we were fortunate. Fortunate. It was an old word with a new meaning, and in time I learned the meaning. I even tried to be grateful because the involvement had not gone beyond a small lesion in the apex of the left lung, the sputum was negative, and the prognosis favourable.

I wish that this were my husband's story, instead of mine. In the many but all too short years of our marriage, I had often to reach high, as at that moment in Dr. Miller's office, to meet his courage and his greatness, and to realize that a dream can change, but it need not die.

A plaque to his memory hangs in the Lenox Hill Hospital.

We spent our first ten months in the Trudeau Sanitarium at

Saranac Lake. Nearly thirty years later, I began diffidently, in one of the last Claudia books, to write about the small, separate world of the invalid, but I was vigilant of any subjective parallel beyond a hard-won philosophy towards illness and death. Yet we had fun in that year, too, although our laughter was for ever tempered by the shadow of tragedy all around us. I wrote endless letters to relieve the anxiety of those at home, and quite often they were amusing. At least my family thought they were funny, but my mother-in-law, who had finally become used to the idea of me, couldn't get used to my handwriting much less my wit. For weeks, indeed, she brooded secretly upon the stranger Sam, who appeared so persistently to invade the privacy of a newly married couple. "Sam spending the night at the Sanitarium on account of the blizzard." (I slept at a farmhouse without conveniences two miles away and walked the distance night and morning.) "Sam feeling fine." "Sam terribly happy about the last fluroscope, as I know you must be." "Sam spending the night again at the Sanitarium, which is a blessing because the roads are waist-deep in snow."

At last my poor little mother-in-law could keep the worrying question to herself no longer. She wrote: "I am very confused about this Sam, please tell me who he is."

We put her mind at ease, and thereafter I tried exclusively for legibility, but without notable success, short of printing. One day, on a trip to the village for a haircut, my husband bought me a second-hand Oliver typewriter for twelve dollars. I doubt if anyone remembers that there was such a typewriter as an Oliver, but there was. It belonged to the vintage of the Auburn car we had.

At first my typing wasn't much easier to read than my writing, aiming as I did towards speed rather than accuracy. I took keen pleasure in the noise of the keys clacking up and down, and the faster they clacked, the more noise they made. Good old Oliver! Month after month, it stood up manfully under my one-finger pecking, and then got eraser-poisoning and collapsed a few weeks before we were ready to return to New York. The keys, once so loose and lively, stuck and groaned in their whiskers, but it

[61]

didn't matter any longer. My letter-writing was at an end. We were going home.

Illness creates a minature universe unto itself, in which trifles assume magnitude, and matters of moment fade into unimportance. The inhabitants speak a special language, and their customs and rituals have no parallel in the outside world. At Trudeau, the applause accorded a departing patient is one of those rituals, and we had experienced it on the first day we arrived. We had almost finished our lunch—what little we felt like eating—when everyone in the big dining-room stood up and clapped their hands. "The man walking towards the door," someone at the table explained to us, "is going home this afternoon."

I thought, with the sharpest jealousy I have ever known, "Will it ever happen to us?"

And now it was happening. Everyone was "clapping us out." New patients were envying us, old patients were resigned. We had made many friends. We were sorry to say good-bye to them. My heart was very full.

"What was that all about?" a voice said.

We turned quickly. It was Dr. Heise, who had followed us from the room. He was Head Physician.

We were surprised that he had forgotten that we were leaving. When we told him, he frowned. He said, "There's some mistake."

I couldn't speak. My husband said, "What kind of a mistake, Dr. Heise?"

"You're not ready to go home, yet. Your last X-rays showed activity around the area of the cavity."

My husband said, smilingly, "Doctor, I think you have your X-rays mixed. I've never had a cavity."

Dr. Heise looked at him for a long, long moment. Then he said, shortly, "Come to my office in half an hour."

We didn't want to talk to anyone. We walked the short distance to my husband's cottage, and sat like visitors, in his room. It looked empty with his trunk and belongings already gone. The metal rolling bed on the sleeping porch, smoothly blanketed, was waiting for the next occupant. Who would it be? I prayed. "Please God. Let Dr. Heise be wrong. Please."

"Stop worrying. It's a mistake," my husband said, as if he'd heard me.

"Of course," I agreed. "He must be ready for us now, it's almost time."

"Almost. Not quite. But let's get started."

As we stepped out of the door, a nurse turned in at the path and hurried towards the cottage. When she saw us, she waved us back. "You needn't come to the office!" she called out. "Dr. Heise says you can go home, but to be careful and not overdo it. Good luck!" Her hurrying meant that someone was having a haemorrhage.

"I wonder what poor devil Heise got my X-rays mixed up with," my husband said.

I was afraid to wonder.

My sister had lined up some small apartments for us to look at, and the four-room one on Morningside Drive was the best of them. It was on the wide tree-lined street that faced Columbia College, it had a doorman and a lift-man, it was sunny with cross-ventilation in the bedroom, and all for fifty dollars a month.

We lived at the House until the place was ready, and clear of the smell of fresh paint. Harlem was on its way to meeting its ultimate fate, but along with a few other intrepid property owners, the family continued to hold out against the invasion of parlour-floor millinery establishments, and worse. But it was a losing battle. A proud era had come to a shabby end, and the House was sold—practically given away—a few months after we were settled in our new home. My aunts moved to a hotel with my uncle, and my mother took an apartment with my unmarried brother, not very far from where we lived. Being close to her gave me a sense of safety. It was not easy to forget that year in the sanitarium. I had seen and heard too much about the "flare-ups" that lay in wait for patients who considered themselves well. "No one is ever cured of tuberculosis," Dr. Heise had once impressed upon my husband in my presence. "When the time

comes for you to leave here, you may consider yourself 'arrested'
—but never 'cured'. Remember it."

Small chance that I could forget it. *"There's some mistake. You're
not ready to go home."* I would never forget that, either. Was it
really a mix-up, or could there be different interpretations of
an X-ray? One doctor might read a lesion, another a cavity. . . .

"You worry too much," my mother reproved me.

I tried not to. I worked hard at furnishing the apartment, and
discovered the excitement of auction sales versus department
stores. I cleaned and cooked, and loved going to bed early every
night, pretending to be exhausted.

"Who do you think you're fooling?" my husband asked me.

One day I came home from marketing and found a big, black
square typewriter sitting outside the door. I didn't question its
being there. Simply, my husband had replaced the Oliver, and I
accepted the implication, realizing humbly that I was in need
of help. If I kept my mind busy I might be able to fight off the
shadow of apprehension that stalked me through every hour of the
day. I couldn't escape from it. I lived for his telephone call at
noon, alert to the faintest trace of tiredness in his voice; I hung
out of the window towards evening, watching for him to turn the
corner so that I could spy on the spring in his walk. But always, he
was wonderfully gay, and quick to clown away my worry. He had
surmounted fear. He was well. It was I who was ill. Maybe this
big black typewriter would be a kind of medicine to quiet my
uneasy soul. I'd buy a book of instructions and teach myself the
touch system, and then I'd be able to type his medical papers and
lectures for him. I'd at least be doing something more constructive
than going into a cold sweat of panic every time he cleared his
throat.

I picked up the machine from the outside hall, put it on a
small table in the living-room, and placed a chair in front of it. I
tried out the action of the keys, and was pleased to find that they
responded with the same loose noisiness of the Oliver. I was all
set to go except that I had no letters to write, and no lectures to
copy, so just for the fun of it I slipped a fresh piece of paper into
the platen and began to write about the two old ladies who had

My mother

My sister and
DONNA

The youngest of four

The first of the livestock photographs w
the parrot

Myself at two

Myself in the slinky days

come up beside me that morning as I'd stood peering into the window of one of those after-Christmas toy shops that used to spring up like seasonal weeds in every empty store.

I had no idea how late it was until I heard the scrape of a key in the latch. I felt as though my heart was clapping its hand over its mouth—I had not only forgotten to watch out of the window, I had forgotten to put the roast in the oven. "I'm sorry, it's your own fault," I greeted my husband happily. "You shouldn't have sent me the typewriter!" He looked blank, and I could see he wasn't putting it on. He didn't know what I was talking about, because he hadn't sent it.

Eventually, a tab on the bottom of the machine disclosed the name of a second-hand dealer, and a telephone call solved the mystery. The typewriter was supposed to have been delivered to "The party opposite in 6D," but a heavily rhythmic voice on the other end of the wire assured me that for thirty dollars I could keep it, and he would send "the party opposite" another one. It was hard to tell who was the most gratified at the trans-action—the dealer, me or my husband.

The story was finished before he came home the next evening. He hurried through supper to read it. I held my breath, watching his face. As he turned the last untidy page, he looked so proud he looked silly.

I remember vividly that the day after that was Thursday, because I always had two dollars' worth of Bessie, the cleaning woman, on Thursdays, which was how I happened to take the story to *Good Housekeeping*. On her way to work, Bessie made a practice of scavenging left-behind newspapers in the subway, but on this particular morning she'd turned up with an old magazine instead. Several pages were torn out of the middle, but the front was what I was after. I made a note of the name of the Editor-in-Chief and the address of the publication offices, and then I went out and bought a ream of white paper and a dozen sheets of carbon.

For once I refrained from supervising the cataclysmic ritual of thorough-cleaning, barely managing to keep me and my cumbersome typewriter one room ahead of the clumsy vacuum cleaner. By six o'clock I had completed a fairly readable copy of the story, dropped the black oilcloth cover over the machine, and started to prepare supper. I wasn't going to tell my husband what I intended to do until I had sold the story to the Editor of Bessie's tattered magazine. Then, indeed, he'd be proud enough to burst.

How I gained entrance to Mr. Bigelow's private sanctum I will never know. Weighing only eighty-eight pounds, I might have slipped through a crack in the wall, or the mysterious importance of myself might have mesmerized the befogged secretary in the outer office into announcing my arrival. "I'm Rose Franken," I told her, as if surely she must recognize the name of the wife of the most wonderful man in the world. In any event, I found nothing untoward in cordially extending my hand to the esteemed head of one of the leading publications in the country, who looked as if he wanted to grab back his handshake when he discovered that Rose Franken was a nineteen-year-old nobody with an incredible nerve and a badly typed manuscript. "I hope," I braved his fishy stare, "that you will read my story as soon as possible. You'll find my telephone number at the bottom of the last page."

Although I don't think he could have actually hissed at me, he made some sort of a sound that warned me to back out fast. "Good-bye," I tossed over my shoulder by the skin of my teeth, "and thank you very much, Mr. Bigelow!"

I didn't mention the interview to my husband, since I wanted to astound him with the news that I had definitely sold my first creative effort. He could tell I was keeping something from him, though. "Now look," he said sternly, "no monkey shines, we're not having a baby until I can put in a full day at the office."

"All right," I said, meekly, glad that he was barking down the wrong alley. I hadn't even thought about having a baby, I guess he was all the baby I wanted.

I waited out the week to hear from *Good Housekeeping* and then went down to see what the delay was all about. This time the secretary did recognize me, and by the set of her jaw, it was only too evident that she didn't intend to make the same mistake twice. She said that Mr. Bigelow was unavailable. She said he couldn't be disturbed. She said he was very busy.

It could have all been true, one way or another. The door to the corridor was ajar, and at that very instant I could see him come out of the wash-room near the lift. What luck! I planted myself squarely in his path. "Oh, hello, Mr. Bigelow, you remember me, don't you?"

As he focused his attention, the agitated secretary began disclaiming any part of this unfortuitous meeting. Mr. Bigelow raised his hand—I hope, to silence her—for I'm almost certain he didn't intend to hit me any more than he had hissed at me on my first visit. If he did, however, he suddenly thought better of it. "Come into my office," he said, instead.

"Come." What a mundane word. I floated behind him on a rosy cloud. Surely his invitation to follow him could only mean that he had bought my story.

Falling off a rosy cloud hurts more than falling off anything else. When I finally came to, I realized numbly that Mr. Bigelow was telling me, with stinging directness, precisely what he thought of me, my story, and my unmitigated impertinence in presuming on more of his valuable time. "You have talent," he summed up with the precision of a knife cutting each word from his lips, "but not for writing."

Then he stood awaiting my departure with a terrible patience. I hung back, clinging to the last shreds of that lovely cloud. "But you don't understand," I implored him, and I think I must have also clung to his coat tails in order to explain to him that I merely wanted to sell the story to surprise my husband, and it really didn't matter how much I got paid for it.

Mr. Bigelow replied that quite obviously he had failed to make himself clear, whereupon he repeated, with a combination of zest and finality that he had no interest in purchasing my story at any price whatsoever.

Still I hung on, clutching at a straw and his arm at one and the same moment. "Then you don't have to pay me anything." I pleaded. "All you have to do is publish it!"

[67]

It was certainly the best proposition that Mr. Bigelow had received that day, but he turned it down flat. He widened the angle of the door of his office, and I'm positive he shoved me.

The incident loses its ironic overtones if I don't add here and now that, twenty years later, *Good Housekeeping* bought the same story, without a word of it re-written, for five thousand dollars.

Since I didn't aspire to be a writer anyway, the dismal fiasco of my initial excursion into the literary field disturbed me very little, and if my husband hadn't shamed me into it, I would never have bothered to lift the oilcloth cover off that big black typewriter again. Success doesn't always follow failure, however, and my second, third and fourth attempts were equally discouraging, but he kept spurring me on.

"You don't honestly think my stories are as good as you say they are," I accused him. "You just think they take my mind off worrying about the way you're overworking again."

"I'm not overworking, I feel great, and your stories are better than good."

"Then how is it that nobody else thinks so? All I have to show for the boxes of paper and carbon I've bought is a pile of printed rejection slips."

I had a lot more to show than that. Each time I wrote a new story, it was worth everything, even disappointment, just to watch his face as he read it. I remember that he especially liked "Little Cakes," the story about the coloured laundress, and he said that any editor who didn't grab it was a horse's ass.

All I can say is, that the world must have been full of horses' asses. But long, long afterwards when "Little Cakes" was published in *Harper's Bazaar*, I wished he could have known about it.

In the meantime, nothing really mattered except that Dr. Miller's bi-annual report on his condition was all that even I could ask for, and fear moved finally from my shoulder. I had no need to write. I hoisted the typewriter off the living-room table and stuck it in the back of the hall cupboard. I had more important things to do than make up stories. It was high time I started getting pregnant.

With beginner's luck, it was no sooner said than done, and each day of those early months was like the shimmering delicate perfection of a bubble suspended in space. Once more I had a sense that there was a special little desk in Heaven where God personally supervised everything that happened to me, and saw to it that all worked out for the best. How could I help but feel that way with a war raging somewhere in Europe? It was as remote as the pages of a history book. The small island of my happiness was safe.

"A fine time for a man to have a spot on his lung," my husband brooded.

"A fine time," I exulted secretly, and rolled bandages and helped at the clinic, and baked butterless-eggless-sugarless cakes in return for this strange beneficence.

I have small excuse to offer that the war touched me so little, except that there were no radios or television sets to bring it close. My brothers were in khaki, but I could not believe that they would ever be a part of the horror and the bloodshed. It was all happening so far away.

A day came, though, when my unmarried brother boarded a troopship, and my heart broke, but only because of the look in my mother's eyes.

We were moving anyway to a larger apartment, and I didn't have to say, "Let's get one with an extra room." My husband said it for me. He loved my mother very much, and she loved him.

"Just until after the baby is born," she finally gave in.

Having a first baby should be one of the most wonderful experiences in a woman's life, and it started out to be that way for me, until, first of all, my brother's plane crashed, and I lived vicariously my mother's torment until word finally reached us that he was alive. And then the epidemic of Spanish Influenza took its ruthless toll of civilian lives, and suddenly my chest hurt and my head felt queer. I was like an ostrich, staying on my feet so that I wouldn't go down with it. Still as skinny as a blue-fish, I must have been as strong as an ox to have kept on walking around with pneumonia. I think it was fear that pulled me through it—fear that if I went to bed and stayed there, both my husband

and my mother would be more apt to catch it, because they would have to take care of me. Doctors were working round the clock, and private nurses were unavailable.

Few pregnant women survived that epidemic. I was lucky to have kept the baby, although he came earlier than he should have, I had a long, hard labour, and for forty-eight hours my mother never left my side. Hospitals were crowded and understaffed, with one probationer for an entire floor.

"The baby's not little, he weighs six pounds," my mother lied, and knew enough to keep him wrapped in cotton in a basket beside my bed. The strain was heavy on her, and she looked so tired and pale. And the baby was so tiny and weak, and my husband's face showed signs of fatigue from his long vigil. I didn't know which of the three to worry about first.

"Go home now and take Mamma with you. You both have to have some rest."

"I'll see that Mother gets to bed and then I'll come back and sleep in the big chair by the window."

"It isn't necessary, I can watch the baby."

"No, you mustn't be alone," my mother said. "Let him stay, and I'll be here first thing in the morning."

I didn't have the strength to argue. She kissed me good-bye, and I thought, how strange, for much as we loved each other, we kissed so rarely.

She didn't come back the next morning, nor did my husband return to sleep that night in the big chair as he had promised. I lay for hours, waiting for his step outside my door. Something must have happened to have kept him from me. My imaginings were torture.

Finally, I couldn't stand the agony of not knowing. Bedside telephones were an unheard of luxury, so I inched myself down out of the high hospital cot, and managed to reach the booth at the end of the long deserted corridor, perversely thankful for the conspicuous absence of nurses. Not even a probationer would have countenanced my foolhardiness, for maternity cases in those days were two-week affairs, no matter how easy the confinement, and mine had been far from easy.

It was only when I heard my sister's voice over the wire that I knew that my fear had not been a fantasy of weakness. What had brought her to our apartment in the middle of the night? What dreadful thing had happened to one or the other of the two people I loved most on earth? My bones dissolved with the terror that invaded me, but she kept assuring me that nothing was wrong, she had simply come over to hear all about the baby.

How I wished I could have made myself believe her. I was certain that she wasn't telling me the truth, but my teeth began chattering so hard that I could not push another word past my lips. I don't remember getting back to my room, but I remember the baby screaming thinly, and my trying in vain to nurse him. I pressed the call-bell again and again, sobbing with helplessness, and at last I gave up, sick with the knowledge that the baby was too little and too weak to nurse. He whimpered off into a frightening stillness, and I put him back in his basket, and climbed into bed, leaning dizzily on my elbow to keep watch on the faint rise and fall of his breathing. I lost track of the hours. I lost track of God. Or was it He who had lost track of me? Would nobody come to tell me whether it was my husband or my mother that something had happened to? If one of them would only walk into the room, then I would know. . . .

Dawn was fingering its way around the dark curtain on the window when the door cautiously opened, and my husband came towards me. He knelt beside me and took me in his arms. "I wanted to come sooner, darling. It's been a tough night for you."

One look at his face and I knew that it had been a tough night for him, too. My mother had had a stroke.

When I returned home from the hospital, I saw her. Her face looked strange and empty. She seemed to be asleep. When she opened her eyes, she seemed still to be asleep, for she did not know me.

After her death, which was mercifully soon, my sister and I grew even closer. As well as being sisters, we were friends, we liked each other, we enjoyed being together. My mother had shared our closeness, and we missed her as we would have missed a beloved companion, but my missing went deeper than that, it was edged with rebellion; she was too young to die. Her room was so full of her, and yet so unfilled. "I'd like to have another baby as soon as Paul is old enough," I told my husband.

"I'd like to read another story," he replied.

"No thanks," I said. "I've had enough rejection slips." But I knew he was right. Again I needed to write, but now it was for myself, and not for him. I ordered a metal table and a proper chair, and put them in the empty room. A new contraption was on the market. It was called a "Boggins," an oblong steel cage that fastened on to the outside of the window-sill. I'd never seen one before, and I've never seen one since, but it was an answer to a prayer from an unnatural young mother who didn't like to wheel a perambulator in the park for six hours a day. At least my mother-in-law thought I was unnatural.

I tested the safety element of the "Boggins" by climbing into the cage myself every morning before I put the baby out into it. Still, I didn't dare leave him unwatched for more than a few minutes at a stretch, so I put the typewriter close up against the window so that I could quickly snatch him out of it at the faintest creak of danger.

I made up my mind to take one more try at a short story, but this time I'd pattern my writing on the sort of thing that the editors seemed to want—romantic fairy-tales about beautiful girls with eyes like dewy pansies, and bronzed young men with flashing smiles.

I worked all the morning. My idyllic young couple landed in the scrapbasket. In the afternoon, I put the baby in his perambulator for a change. Although my sister shared my antipathy to the national pastime of sitting on a park bench, she obligingly wheeled Donna over in her go-cart to keep me company.

The next morning I couldn't face another day of fresh air and maternal inactivity. I plopped the baby back in his cage, and inserted a blank sheet of paper in the typewriter. My mind was a blank, too, but soon the keys began to move up and down, making words and sentences as if they had a separate brain and I was little more than an extension of the machine. I peered over the bar with a kind of detached interest:

"One afternoon there was a mothers' meeting in school. Each girl was supposed to have only her mother come, but Uncle Al, Aunt Lucy, and Aunt Martha came too, taking up most of the seats in the side row. They came because Virginia was going to recite a piece:

'Come, little leaves,' said the wind, one day.
'Come over the meadows with me, and play!'

"Virginia was mortified when she saw them file in, one after another. . . ."

The baby cried. He was wet. I changed him, re-rolled him in his blanket, and shoved him back into the Boggins like a loaf of bread. In spite of the interruption, "Virginia" kept on saying what she had to say. The dumb-waiter buzzed hoarsely. It was an order from the grocery store. I returned to the typewriter, curious to find out whether Virginia did, or did not, approve of being brought up in a large family.

The baby let out another kind of a yell. I looked at my watch. It was past noon, no wonder he was hungry.

Where did the day go to? All at once, it was time for his supper. Our own supper was no problem. I had concocted a Beef Bourguignonne the night before, trying out the theory that anything with wine in it is always better for the marinating, and with a salad to be tossed at the last minute, dinner was as good as on. If it seems unlikely that I should remember the smallest details of a day that happened so many many years ago, it is because it stands out in my memory for so many, many reasons. I remember the sense of peace that I felt in a sunny room that suddenly was no longer grey and empty. I remember starting my first novel, and the long, strange friendship with Maxwell Perkins that emerged from it. But I remember, above all, that when my husband came home that evening, he sensed at once that I was more friendly with myself than I had been since my mother's death. "You look nice tonight," he said. "Nice outside and inside."

"It's about time," I apologized obliquely.

"Don't be so hard on yourself.—Would you like to go to a movie? Or theatre?"

"I've made other plans. You have a batch of pages to read after supper. I think it's going to turn into a novel. Not that I know how to write one."

"You'll know," he said.

"I'd hate to go on with it, just out of therapeutic reasons, so tell me if it isn't any good. Don't fool me."

"I'll try not to. I'd be fooling myself, too, and that wouldn't do much of a job for either of us."

"Not much of a one," I agreed soberly, and I wondered if all marriages could say so many things without saying them.

After he read the opening chapter, which I had managed to finish after I put the baby to bed, he squared the pages into a neat oblong and gave them back to me.

"It's good," he said.

I wrote quickly in those days. As I had no regular schedule of work, I never felt under pressure, for the simple reason that my mind seemed to function more efficiently without my interfering with it. It had to, I didn't have the time to coax it along and wait for it to hatch out ideas.

I look back and wonder at the casualness with which I tackled that first novel, and the effortless speed with which I finished it. My husband was impressed enough for both of us, though. I forget just what he said when he manfully re-read the entire thing in one fell swoop, but it was everything I wanted to hear him say. He took the disreputable bundle of manuscript to his office the next morning, and sent it off to a typist.

Only when I got it back was I properly awed by the sight of all those magnificently neat and professional looking pages encased in a shiny cardboard binding importantly entitled "PATTERN," with my name underneath. It was so freshly beautiful, that I hated to send it out to be tossed around with all the thousands of other packages in the post office, but Mr. Bigelow had taught me a lesson about popping in an editor's office with a story under my arm.

It hadn't occurred to me that there were literary agents whose sole function it was to painlessly execute the popping or the posting—not that it would have been easy to find one who would have gambled time and the effort on a complete unknown. Although I didn't know how to go about the job myself, I nevertheless decided that if I worked out an efficient system of approach, I'd be bound to hit on the right publisher sooner or later. I made a list of all the names I could think of, and with the aid of the *Classified Directory*, the names I couldn't think of. I wrote them down in big print and in alphabetical order, on one of those pieces of laundry cardboard from a shirt of my husband. Then I started my campaign by beginning in the middle of the list, and putting a cross through H because there were more publishers beginning with H than any other letter. Harpers, Holt, Harcourt Brace, Houghton-Mifflin . . . I tried them all, one after another, but to my chagrin, the Hs wanted no part of my novel.

There was no I, and no J, so I moved on to K, and felt a glimmer of hope when Knopf's favoured me with a brief note saying that they liked the last half of the book but not the first half. If I would care to rewrite, they would be glad to consider the manuscript.

"I happen to like the first half," my husband put his foot down.

His highhandedness was vindicated, because Morrow & Co. liked the first half, too. But unfortunately Mr. Morrow did not see eye to eye with the second half. If I would rewrite . . .

It was confusing, but encouraging. With renewed confidence, I sent it forth to Macmillan, who didn't like either half, and Putnam was equally indifferent. Undaunted, I decided that if I moved in the opposite direction from H, it might change my luck. It didn't. Farrar and Rinehart kept the manuscript just long enough to be polite about it and returned it with a printed slip. Doubleday-Doran wasn't enthusiastic either, and so fast did that package come winging back from Bobbs-Merrill, and Boni-Liveright that they couldn't have read beyond the first page.

It wasn't worth while trying the other end of the list again. Random House and Viking couldn't have been in existence then, or I'm sure that they would have joined the rejection parade, and I honestly didn't care any longer. Either I was getting accustomed to being disappointed or the certainty that I was going to have another baby seemed more important than having a book.

"You're not going to turn tail and quit, are you?" my husband challenged what I smugly felt was an evidence of maturity.

He couldn't have phrased it more aptly, but I knew how deeply and foolishly he believed in me so I assured him that I had no intention of quitting while there was still an A left in the alphabet. My mind was made up, however. After the manuscript came back from Appleton's, I'd add to it all the short-story manuscripts that nobody wanted, and burn up the whole kit and kaboodle in the temperamental marble fireplace in the living-room. Then it would have something to splutter and smoulder about in earnest.

Pat though it might sound, six weeks passed, and there was no sign of that big, bulging envelope. Gone was my apathy about not caring whether it was accepted or not. I felt, inappropriately, as if I were floating on air every time a plop of mail against the front door sent my hopes a little higher. "No publisher would have the nerve to keep a novel that long if he didn't intend to publish it," I finally gave voice to my secret conviction.

My husband, who was living on as many pins and needles as I was, admitted cautiously that he didn't want me to count on it, but it looked as if something might happen this time.

As more days went by, and still the manuscript did not come back, I tried to live a good life to show how grateful I was. I took Paul to visit my mother-in-law without seeming to "rush off" as soon as I arrived, and brought her a cactus plant to boot. At home, I tidied up cupboards and drawers like mad, and one rainy afternoon I gilded the lily by polishing the silver. I was wrist-deep in the messy job when the dumb-waiter gave out its unpleasant buzz. I ignored it under the assumption that some delivery boy must have pressed the wrong bell, since I hadn't done any shopping that day, and the rubbish was always collected in the morning.

When it buzzed for the third time, I wiped my hands in exasperation and peered into the black cavern, closing my nostrils against the acrid smell of dankness, and other things. "It's not for us!" I called down. "I didn't order anything!"

"You Franken?" a disembodied voice yelled back at me.

"Me Franken!" I retorted smartly. "But there's a Franklin in the building, so if you don't mind, ring their bell instead!"

He ignored my ill-temper. "Apples coming up," he informed me laconically but firmly, and immediately the ropes began to twitch and groan, and I could hear the wooden cage knock its way drunkenly skyward from the cellar. I awaited its appearance in pleasant anticipation. It was not impossible that some patient of my husband could be sending me a premature basket of fruit for my confinement.

"A little higher, please!"

"Okay, lady, tell me when you get it!"

"Not yet, still higher!"

Whoops—the cage whizzed past me. "A little lower, please!" (An affluent service-entrance was never as stimulating as a dumb-waiter.) "I'm sorry—*too* low! That's all right, it's all right now, thank you," I carolled to the echo of departing footsteps. It wasn't that I couldn't have pulled a little on the ropes myself, but I invariably got a splinter for my trouble. Now, apparently, I was getting nothing at all for my trouble, for at first sight the cage looked empty. Certainly no fruit, basketed or otherwise, met my probing gaze. And then, on the top shelf towards the back, I spied something. It was white, and oblong. There was no mistaking it, and it wasn't apples—my manuscript had finally been returned from Appleton's.

"And sending it back as if it were garbage!" I sputtered in fury to my husband that evening. "With just a printed rejection slip slapped on it, and not so much as a note of apology for keeping it so long, and the binding torn off besides——"

"The bastards," he sympathized. "Never mind, we'll try again. Let's see your list."

"Don't waste your time," I rejoined bitterly. "I've used up all the letters."

"Let's see it anyway."

He surveyed the criss-crossed cardboard. "You may have gone through the front end, but you've still got a couple of letters at the back end."

"Yes. A publisher that publishes dictionaries, with a Funk before him, which puts him on the other side anyway. So why not just call it a day. I'm not a writer."

"The hell you're not," he said. "And don't be so quick to call it a day, you skipped the S by mistake."

"I skipped it on purpose."

"Why? What's wrong with Scribner's?"

My voice dripped irony. "Not a thing, except that Scribner's happens to be about the best and oldest firm in the country. Can't you just see them falling over themselves to get me as their author?"

"There's nothing to be lost by trying," he insisted stubbornly.

"There's nothing to be gained, either. Besides, the manuscript's so worn out it won't last another trip through the mail."

"Then don't mail it," he said. "Take it yourself."

Somehow the idea appealed to me. It was time the shoe was on the other foot. "I'd like just once to give a publisher a piece of my mind, straight to his face," I said.

My husband grinned. "Do that," he said.

I must confess that I didn't intend to give quite such a large piece of my mind, but a final flare of indignation swept over me as I stepped out of the small, old-fashioned lift that opened on to the traditional, but not too overwhelming, reception room of Charles A. Scribner and Son. I stalked over to the receptionist's desk, and without preamble, requested an immediate audience with Mr. Charles A. Scribner. Himself. And personally.

I have a faint recollection that my imperious voice might have echoed quite loudly through the quiet hall, for several people turned to stare at me—though of course, it could have been my appearance that attracted attention. Because it was a hot day in late June, I wore a sheer, flowery dress and a large picture hat. The baby was due early in October, and although I was sure nobody could possibly tell, I must have given the impression of having swallowed either a small water-melon or a huge cantaloupe.

The nice person behind the desk glanced fleetingly at my middle, and then at the bulky sheaf of pages under my arm. "I'm sorry, he isn't in, but if you'd care to leave your manuscript——"

"That is exactly what I do not care to do," I interrupted with hauteur. "I wish to see Mr. Scribner. Himself," I again emphasized pointedly, in a tone which implied that I wished to see him whether he was in or not, because I had already been pushed around enough, and had no intention of putting up with any more of it.

I suppose it is not unheard of for young women in delicate conditions to go suddenly berserk, and for all the poor receptionist knew, I might have been carrying a concealed weapon along with the baby. "Just a moment," she placated me, and vanished speedily. She returned almost as speedily, and led me past a labyrinth of small inner offices until we reached a cubicle that was equally unimposing, except for a grudging view of Fifth Avenue. A tallish, sandy-haired man of no determinate age stood before a square, high desk with his hat on. He was busy making notes on a calendar, but he turned as I entered, carefully placed his hat on a wooden side chair, and said, in a slow, and rather shy voice, "How do you do. I can close the window if it's open too far for you."

I waved the window away. I merely wanted to see Mr. Charles Scribner, and I was willing to bet that this blandly blue-eyed, timid sounding individual was not the guiding power of one of the most distinguished publishing firms in the country. "Are you"—I coldly gave him the benefit of the doubt "—Mr. Charles Scribner?"

He shook his head. "No," he admitted ruefully. "I'm Maxwell Perkins."

I regarded him with mounting hostility. Maxwell Perkins, forsooth. An improbable combination of names if ever I heard one, yet peculiarly fitting to this mild-mannered underling. "I wish to see someone in authority," I informed him, and started towards the door.

"I'm in authority," he mentioned, quite humbly.

"Not enough. Good-bye."

The diffident touch of his hand on my shoulder caught me half-way out. He reached for the manuscript and removed it gently from my protesting grasp. He glanced at the page that bore my name, address and telephone number. "I take it," he offered with a hesitant smile trembling over his lips, "that this is a novel, Mrs. Franken?"

"Naturally it's a novel." I was disgruntled because he hadn't given *me* the benefit of the doubt by at least calling me "Miss" Franken. What made him so quick to assume I was married? I was accustomed to being mistaken for my husband's younger sister, but never his wife, even though he was only eight years older than I was. "However," I added, "I do not care to leave it, so please give it back to me."

His greyish-blue eyes probed quietly. "Why?"

"Because I have no intention of waiting weeks and weeks until Mr. Scribner finally decides not to publish it," I retorted with asperity.

Once more a smile moved hesitantly across his lips. "But I am the one who usually makes those decisions," he said, "and I will be very happy to read your novel if you will allow me to."

I snorted silently. The publishing business was in a sorry state if this ineffectual young man (or was he so young?) was vested with the authority to accept or reject a manuscript. However, I had nothing to lose at this final stage of a career that was non-existent. "Very well," I acceded, tersely. "But I want it to be read immediately. This is Tuesday. I expect an answer by Friday. Friday noon."

"Friday noon?" he echoed, as if he might not have heard correctly. "Of this week?"

"Of this week," I stipulated with finality. "I'm going to the country on Saturday for the summer."

There was little connection between the two statements, but Mr. Perkins accorded me a slow nod of comprehension. "I see," he said. "Friday noon, then."

His acquiescence was disconcerting. I took my departure with a belated sense that I had been brutally shouting him down. Poor thing, he didn't mean any harm, it was simply that his timid voice brought out the beast in me. He was doubtless doing the best he could within his limited capacity.

I did not know, at that first meeting, that Max was slightly

DR. FRANKEN

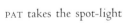

PAT takes the spot-light

"MISSY" (on the right) and HELEN REID

"Mr. Mitchell"

PAUL, PETER and JOHN at the Military
Academy in Hollywood

deaf; that he always worked standing up, with his hat on; and that he was one of the great and revered editors of all time, responsible for shepherding Thomas Wolfe, Scott Fitzgerald and innumerable others into the ranks of literary prominence, if not posterity. I often felt afterwards, that it was a sad waste of our close association that I lacked the passionate drive to become a writer. My dedication went no deeper than a desire to fulfil my husband's belief in me, and when I walked into Scribner's that first time, I was chiefly intent upon getting back at all the publishers who did not share his opinion of my ability and talent. Unhappily—or perhaps happily—Maxwell Perkins happened to be the innocent victim of my irascibility.

I counted the hours until Friday. It was true that we were packed and ready to leave town the following day. We had rented, for the summer months, a roomy, turn-of-the-century monstrosity in Chappaqua, pooling our expenses with my sister and her husband. We also shared the services of a now extinct breed of eager-to-please couple, blessed with a teen-age daughter who was overjoyed at the thought of being nursemaid to Donna and Paul. The prospect of such an ideal vacation dulled the edge of the imminent blow that was about to sever my alliance with the world of writing, but my outraged spirit still clamoured for its last measure of revenge. An agreement was an agreement, and I intended to teach one Mr. Maxwell Perkins not to make glib promises that he had no intention of fulfilling.

"Don't be unreasonable," my husband had cautioned me before leaving for the office on Friday morning. "You can't expect a decision in three days, and whoever told you you could, didn't know what he was talking about."

"And that's precisely the reason I'm going to call Scribner's on the stroke of twelve, and demand my manuscript back."

"But what will that get you?"

"Satisfaction," I returned, and the word tasted sweet upon my lips.

The stroke of twelve—we didn't have a clock that struck, but my watch told me that it was exactly noon—found me at the telephone, literally frothing at the mouth. There was no delay whatsoever in reaching Mr. Maxwell Perkins—personally—which was sufficient evidence that he must be a very inconsequential wheel indeed in the firm of Charles A. Scribner and Son. It also showed up his guilty conscience, because he began to make excuses before I had a chance to open my mouth. "It isn't quite twelve o'clock, Mrs. Franken," he anticipated me in that soft, unhurried voice of his. "At least, I don't think it is. Or perhaps I'm a little slow."

"You're a little slow, Mr. Perkins," I returned elliptically.

Far from seeming offended, he was quick to apologize. "I'm sorry," he said. "I probably am a minute or two behind." He sounded so abject about it, that I melted a little. "That's all right," I said more kindly. "I'll give you my address in Chappaqua, you might as well mail the manuscript there as to New York. It'll save forwarding."

"Oh," he said, "I was thinking it might be better to keep it here until you come to town again."

So. Something new had been added—my manuscript didn't merit even the expense of return postage.

"I have a few suggestions—very minor ones—that I would like to discuss with you," he went on, oblivious that I had stopped melting and was freezing up. I had had enough suggestions. Change the beginning. Change the end. He probably wanted the middle changed. "Under the circumstances, I think that any suggestions that you have to make would be a waste of time," I replied, rigid with control.

"Oh," he said, for the second time. And then he didn't say anything else for so long that I was afraid I had really hurt his feelings.

"What I mean is," I explained, "I think it's better just to mail the manuscript to me. I'm not really upset about it, I expected to get it back."

"But I don't want to send it back," he insisted earnestly. "I'm afraid I haven't made myself clear. You see, when you called I was just about to pick up the telephone to let you know that I like your novel tremendously, and we will be very happy to publish it."

My senses reeled with the shock of it. When a room went around in circles, I'd always thought it was just a figure of speech, but it wasn't. "It's awfully nice of you, Mr. Perkins," I finally managed to stammer out. "Thank you very much for accepting my book."

"Thank you very much for writing it," he returned. "When do you think we could arrange to meet?"

"Would this afternoon be too soon?"

"It would be splendid," he said, "especially since we want to schedule publication as soon as possible."

Now I knew I was dreaming. I hoped I wouldn't wake up until after I'd telephoned my husband.

By October, I had incorporated into the manuscript Max's truly minor suggestions, and performed, in addition, a major surgery of my own election. He riffled through the pile of freshly typed pages, and said, in a troubled voice, "I hope you haven't done too much revision." He doubtless detected symptoms of acute perfectionism, and guessed that I was also going to want to keep on rewriting each of the three succeeding galley proofs.

I had arrived at his office around noon, and he invited me to lunch. I felt funny about it because I wasn't used to going out with anyone but my husband. I think Max felt slightly unaccustomed, too, but maybe it was only because, when we reached the restaurant at the Ritz, it didn't occur to me to order a cocktail, and after a moment of deadly conflict, he didn't order one either. Instead, we buried ourselves in the extravagant bill of fare, and I blindly settled on a Waldorf Salad. I don't know what possessed me to order a concoction for which I had no liking or respect, except that I was afraid of taking, as always, too long to make up my mind, and even when I made it up, I could never resist changing it a couple of times. But a Waldorf Salad promptly and neatly cut the umbilical cord between me and the menu, and I put it down on the table, threw back my coat, and dropped my gloves. Max leaped to pick them up. "I'll have the same," he told the waiter from the floor, very likely in an effort to further simplify matters. I wanted to warn him that he was in for a mess of chopped-up apples and nuts congealed in mayonnaise, but it was too late, the waiter had already curled his lip and shrugged off.

The salad had the single virtue of doing double duty as a main course and a sort of half-assed dessert, so all we had to do was finish up with coffee, after which Max saw me safely on the bus, assuring me that he would read the corrected manuscript over the week-end and telephone me on Monday.

I thanked him for his many kindnesses, including the lunch, and swung gracefully up the awkward steps. I felt as light as a feather, and as slim as a lily.

Some twenty years later, Max talked about that lunch. We were both living in New Canaan at the time and I was happy that he had overcome his shyness enough to ask if he could come for dinner that evening. We were sitting on the lawn, when all at once he said, without continuity or reason, "You wore a big hat and a flowered dress the first time you walked into my office, and you wore the same dress under a coat the day we had that dreadful salad together."

I tried not to show my surprise at his remembering. I said, "I'm sorry about the salad, and the dress was probably the only thing that still fitted me, although it hurts my vanity even now to admit it."

He smiled. "You were very young. You were afraid the baby might come early, or wouldn't weigh enough."

It was true. Paul had been so tiny—he hadn't stayed tiny long—yet the anguish of uncertainty had left its mark, as everything leaves a mark. . . . But how had Max known my fear? And what strange sentience possessed his being on this quiet summer evening?

Two short days afterwards the telephone rang at dawn. It was Bertha, his oldest daughter. I think I must have known, before she told me, that Max was dead.

I needn't have worried about John coming early. He was on the dot, a hefty seven pounds, and as I recall, he gave me a bad Sunday, which was more my fault than his. Now that I had become a writer, about to have a novel published by Scribner's, I thought that I should know what all the shouting was about. "No matter if I want it, don't let them give me an anaesthetic," I had impressed on my husband weeks before. He'd promised, and when, after I'd torn my handkerchief to bits, I begged for a whiff of ether, he whispered, "Hold on just a little longer. . . ."

The next morning I told him I was glad he hadn't weakened, and he said he thought I would be. "Shall I let Max Perkins know where you are in case he wants to reach you about the corrections, or do you want to wait and do it yourself?"

"Myself."

As soon as the nurse's back was turned, I reached for the telephone by my bed. "I just thought I'd better tell you not to call me at home," I began nonchalantly, and weighed out a moment of silence before disclosing the fact that I was in the hospital—surely he would think I'd met with an accident or suffered an acute attack of appendicitis over the week-end, but he didn't wait for me to finish my silence. He said, in his nice, bashful way, "Is it a boy or a girl?"

"Now who told you!" I demanded, much deflated.

He evaded the question. "If it's a boy, I envy you. I have five girls."

"We're calling him John," I acknowledged tersely.

"I read your changes," he went on, after one of his hesitant pauses. "It's unusual for an author to be able to use a red pencil on his own work to such advantage."

I was not sufficiently entrenched in literary circles to accept this as high praise from an editor who had frequently to reduce by dozens, and occasionally hundreds of pages, some of the outstanding manuscripts of our time. It wasn't until after his death that I learned, in a roundabout way, that Max thought it was a great pity that I had not stayed with the novel as my sole form of expression. Even then, I was deeply moved to think that he had shared my husband's faith in me.

I recently unearthed an old copy of *Pattern* and skimmed through it with the detachment that comes with time. I was puzzled. Why hadn't Max told me to go easy on the exclamation marks? Or why hadn't I had the perspicacity to take out a couple of gross of them myself while I was making such profuse and costly corrections on the galleys? Apart from the wretched punctuation—I was almost as heavy on dashes—I couldn't understand, either, why the critics should have given an untried novelist so much space. There was scarcely a review less than several columns in length, usually accompanied by a photograph, or rather a photograph of an oil painting of me. This isn't as imposing as it sounds, since I had merely consented to be guinea-pig for an old school friend, who wanted to see if she could "catch" me. Secretly, I considered the result inept and needlessly unattractive (although her work, signed "Bry" now hangs in every important museum in America), but the fact remains that she must have caught something other than my pointed chin and a blob of hair across my forehead, because of an incident that happened shortly after *Pattern* was published. I haven't managed to make the front page of the Sunday *Times* since, with or without my picture, and I regret that such enviable recognition had to be wasted when I didn't have enough sense to appreciate it. My main objective was to find out whether anyone outside the family had any intention of buying my novel, and to gain this devious purpose I took a subway all the way down to Wall Street and walked and walked until I came to a bookshop.

When finally I got up the courage to enter the shop, I was seized by a sudden attack of amnesia. I couldn't for the life of me remember the name of the book I wanted to purchase, except that it had a one-word title, beginning with a "P", and was written by some woman or other. Had the salesman ever heard of it? I asked faintly.

The salesman was a gentlemen. With impeccable courtesy, he said, "I believe I know the novel you have in mind, I read several excellent reviews of it. Unfortunately, I have only a display copy at the moment, but I'll be glad to order it for you, Mrs. Franken."

It was the last time I ever played detective to one of my own books. At that, I was lucky that the salesman knew who I was from the guinea-pig painting, and didn't offer to sell me his display copy. I'd have squirmed out of it, anyway, rather than pay two dollars for a novel that I could get direct from Scribner's at author's discount. My husband, however, proved to be the worst kind of a spendthrift. He came home that same evening with an armful of identically shaped packages. "Each one," he announced proudly, "is from a different shop."

I was aghast at his extravagance. "You bought all those with good money?"

"You don't think they were giving them away, do you?"

"But you're crazy, you spent fourteen dollars!"

"I had fourteen dollars' worth of fun," he said.

"I hope you didn't tell anybody who you were, for God's sake."

"They guessed," he admitted sheepishly.

The success of my first novel meant a great deal more to him than to me. Except for the bookshop episode, I felt oddly divorced from any sense of personal accomplishment. It wasn't an exaggerated case of modesty, it was simply that I had the wits to realize that it was none of my doing to have been born with a facility to put words down on paper, and whatever knowledge and sagacity lay behind those words, I owed to my husband. Even a bus ride together had taught me more about people than I could have absorbed from books or college courses, for I learned to read the little ways in which the human animal telegraphs its trouble-signals—the uneasy yawn, the neurotic blue eye, the unhappy massage of a neck imperceptibly shrunk from the contour of a collar, the tight, papery look of an ear, the reddened cushion of a hand, the maladjustment of a gesture—those were the lessons learned hand in hand with the joyous camaraderie of two people deeply in love. Ours was a marriage of many moods, many facets. Our ages blended, and my mind stretched to meet the level of his wisdom, his contempts, and his compassions. I remember that when Maxwell Perkins read my second novel, he was startled by the stuff and context of it, but I knew I wasn't as knowledgeable as I appeared to be, notwithstanding that the book was suppressed in England. And I believe that it was somewhere around that time that I decided to add three years to my age. I felt entitled to some small prestige due to a sophisticated writer, and as two children had done nothing whatsoever for my figure—I still tipped the scales at ninety pounds—the additional years afforded me the mental weight of saying that I was hitting thirty. I forgot all about the deception until, about a decade later, my Aunt Jane happened to hear me mention that I was forty. "Nonsense," she corrected me rather tartly, "If you're forty it would make me seventy-one, and I'm only sixty-eight."

"So you are," I agreed with alacrity, quite pleased to reclaim my little nest egg of youth. Unfortunately, however, I soon found that the reverse process of subtraction was not so easily achieved. Firstly, it looked a little fishy to insist that I was younger than I was, and secondly, the change back entailed a lot of complicated paper work that wasn't worth the trouble. So now I have different birth dates on different documents, including my New York and Connecticut driver's licences.

I'm not sure which date is on my obituary, but I think it's the one I'd now prefer not to have on it.

It could be that these memoirs are turning out to be more interesting to me than to the reader, for I've never taken time off to contemplate the person that I was, or to examine the events that have contributed to making me, for better or for worse, the person that I am. Therefore much of what I'm remembering seems as new to me, as if it were someone else that I were writing about.

For one thing, I am mildly astonished to reflect on the number and variety of fairly important people who gathered gladly and frequently around our slightly warped eighteenth-century dining-table. My husband and I made no pretence towards any sort of social activity other than these small dinner parties, for which I suppose I had a flair, because I managed to carry them off without the usual bungling of the novice, and our home, even the little flat in Morningside Drive, escaped the newly married look. My cooking was pretty good from the start, too, with some guiding spirit staying my hand from mushy concoctions embellished with cream sauces or marshmallows.

I don't want to snowball my opinions into a treatise, but a percentage of women never seem to graduate from that arrested state of culinary development, nor do their homes emerge from an immature clutter of knick-knacks into a clear background to adult living. It is one of the cardinal mistakes in marriage to minimize the importance of good food and the maintenance of a fastidious and well-run household, no matter how limited the budget. In the lean years that followed our return from Saranac I learned, the hard way, that shoddiness is the most expensive of all commodities. One fine chair is cheaper than two second-rate reproductions, a good goulash pays handsomer dividends than cold meat from the delicatessen store, and a firm apple with a piece of bona-fide cheese is more apt to cement a man's love than a soggy pudding.

Of course even in the periods of trial and error my husband thought I was wonderful and never said "No" to anything I did, or wanted to buy. Once I said "No" to him, though. He was much attracted to a painting in the window of a small art gallery, but I told him he had lost his senses. "A hundred dollars for that atrocity?" I disapproved. "Her neck is too long!"

I saw the picture recently in one of the world's great modern art collections, and it is to my credit that I still wouldn't care to live with it, and to my husband's credit that he'd wanted to own it without knowing who Modigliani was; and I doubt whether Modigliani himself knew, in those days, who he was.

By and large, though, our tastes and ideas were in full accord, especially when it came to really important things. For example, we shared a theory that it was foolish to have one dog if you could have two, and little dogs, if you could have big ones, but we tacitly settled for one cat, which got big enough for two, anyway, after certain necessary deletions. Once we even tried having a monkey, but a monkey probably needs an organ grinder, a red cap, and pennies to bring out his full complement of charm, because all he brought out with us was a horrid habit. Up to that point I had managed, I don't know how, to keep the apartment from looking and smelling like a zoo, but with a monkey swinging his weight around, it was a losing battle, so we took him back to the shop where we'd bought him, and where we then flirted, I remember, with a gorgeous macaw. We were about to fall for him when my husband noticed that he had unobtrusively ripped off an important button from his trousers and we figured that if

[89]

he could nip off buttons so expertly, we'd better not risk the boys' fingers, and so forth. I think we settled on a mynah bird with a brilliant but aborted vocabulary and a soft bill.

I could let it appear that we kept a menagerie in a seven room apartment for the benefit of the children, but it wouldn't hold water later on. The truth is, that if they had been afraid of animals, we'd have got rid of them. The children, I mean, not the animals. Fortunately, though, Paul was a nice, normal boy, and we liked him very much. John, at two, wasn't old enough for us to know whether we liked him or not, but as he was no trouble and beautiful, with my husband's blue eyes and my mother's golden hair, we loved him. It goes without saying that we gave both children the best of physical care, but that was as far as it went. We didn't bring them up by a book, so we didn't feel constrained to read aloud to them or to get chummy with them beyond the call of ordinary intercourse, but for all practical and spiritual purposes, they didn't come off too badly with us as parents, and vice versa. No longer a baby, Paul and his father developed a solid respect for each other, and I recall the specific occasion when that very valuable ingredient was added to their filial relationship. Once a week Paul was allowed to have dinner with us, and I always planned a menu that catered exclusively to his six-year-old palate. This particular dinner was in celebration of his lately departed tonsils, and featured softish hamburgers with catsup, tinned corn, and a dessert of sponge-cake-chocolate-pudding-whipped-cream-and-maraschino-cherries. We restrained a shudder at the mere sight of the obscene confection but, to Paul, it was a veritable preview of Heaven.

"Which would you rather," his father queried curiously, "put that mess in your face or let me have it in mine?"

It was no more than a rhetorical question, but within a split second, Paul had made his decision. "I'll get towels," I murmured faintly, and fled from the room, hoping, ignominiously, that the fireworks would be over by the time I got back.

There weren't any fireworks. When I returned with a heap of damp cloths, father and son were shaking hands. "Nice work," my husband was saying through a mask of dribbling chocolate pudding, "but don't think you're going to get another helping, you can't throw your cake and eat it, too."

"Hot dog," said Paul. Or maybe it was some other expression that little boys used in the middle-twenties to show that they were supremely content with the way things were.

That once-a-week supper was our only concession to gearing our lives to the children, until it came to an issue of letting them stay with my sister for a month. My husband had been asked to read a paper in Prague and to attend a series of meetings in Munich and Heidelberg, and it was a wrench for me to leave the boys to go with him. It was just as much of a wrench for me not to go with him, though, and I was miserable with conflict while I was making up my mind that I'd been a wife before I'd been a mother. And we had a wonderful long-delayed honeymoon. The *Paris* on which we went over, and the *Ile de France* on which we came back, remain in my memory as the happiest ships that ever sailed the ocean. There are bigger and faster ones now, but none as lovely.

A few days after our return to America, each of us skipped off to a different doctor, and each of us reported back with good news. My husband was in good shape, for which I was profoundly thankful, and I was once more on the way to being in bad shape, which meant that we had outgrown our present apartment. Housing shortages didn't exist then, but we narrowed our choice down to a toss-up between The Dakota and The Kenilworth, both within the seventies on Central Park West, and both offering an established dignity and éclat against the conveniences and innovations of the new buildings that were beginning to go up.

We chose the Kenilworth, because it wasn't over-weighted by its own architectural importance, and was therefore a lot more sunny and cheerful than the Dakota. Large corner windows overlooked the city and the park, and the halls were wide and gracious. By tearing down one wall and putting up another, I made a separate wing and dining-room for the children, and developed an incipient mania for "doing over" houses that devils me to this day.

The big old-fashioned rooms ate up furniture. Treading clouds of bliss, I haunted the Anderson Galleries—now the Parke-Bernet

—and searched tirelessly for fabrics and carpeting. We weren't rich by any means, but our bank account had ceased to be the measuring stick of our way of life. Money had never been an issue between us, no matter how low our finances, and it was even less an issue in the windfall years that preceded 1929. My liberal household allowance was sufficient to replace the makeshift services of a "mother's help" with a competent Fraulein (engaged in the hope that the children would learn German, which they didn't), and an elderly houseman who had all the better qualities of the opposite sex and none of the more difficult ones. Week in, week out serenity reigned in the sun-filled apartment, until one morning I discovered that we didn't need a new nursery, because there wasn't going to be a new baby.

A miscarriage, particularly after the stirring of life, parallels no other emotional crisis in a woman's experience. For me, at least, frustration, inadequacy, and bereavement combined into one single overwhelming sense of desolation, I tried to scold myself back into a grateful acknowledgement of my abundant blessings, and went to work on my second novel. Lassitude blanketed me with stupidity. I couldn't write. "Don't force it," my husband told me.

We began to brush up on our social life. One party seemed to breed another in endless procession, and we met a lot of people who weren't famous then, but are now—those of them that are still alive. They relished scintillating talk, and it was at those earnestly vivacious gatherings that I learned to practise the sneaky art of silence. When they ran out of conversation, they played games, inflicting upon me a permanent aversion to anything even remotely resembling a charade. Then there was another type of party where extra-marital flirtations were the order of the evening, but I was a total loss at those, too. On the whole, I preferred the theatre, not because I was stage struck, but because some of our old friends were playwrights and always sent us tickets for their first nights.

We were especially fond of Sydney Howard, and it was he who unwittingly inspired me to write for the theatre. I remember that we had gone to his second première of the season—*The Silver Cord* and *Ned McCobb's Daughter* had opened within a few months of each other—and I said to my husband as the curtain fell on a burst of tumultuous applause, "It must be a great satisfaction to write a good play."

"Why don't you try one?" he suggested with an air of inviting me to try a sandwich.

"Don't be silly," I said, "I don't know anything about writing a play."

"You didn't know anything about writing a novel."

"That was different."

"Why was it different?"

"Don't be silly," I said again.

Nevertheless, the idea stuck in my mind, and I was right back to the old *Good Housekeeping* days. I thought how wonderful it would be if I could surprise him with a finished product, no matter how inept. I had bogged down in the middle of my book, and I hadn't given him anything new to read for a long time. Where to begin, though and, once begun, how to go on? I decided to telephone Sydney and ask him to lend me the manuscript of *The Silver Cord* so that I could study the form and get an idea of the number of typed pages to each act.

The maid who answered the telephone said that Mr. Howard had left for London the previous day. I called Vincent Lawrence instead. He was a patient of my husband's and I knew him quite well, but apparently not well enough to ask a favour of him so early in the morning. It was only ten o'clock, and he made small pretence of disguising the horror in his voice when I told him that I wanted to come up and see him right away. He lived in Washington Heights, and it took me the better part of an hour to get there, but even so, he hadn't had his breakfast. He wore a heavy maroon sweater over his pyjama trousers, and I distinctly recall that the sweater had a big hole in the sleeve.

I stated my mission as quickly as I could. "Any old manuscript you happen to have will do," I explained.

He glowered at me. "Just like that"—he finally managed an ironical response—"you want to write a play."

[93]

"Not an important one," I placated him hastily. "I only want to try my hand at it, but I need a little help."

Well, sir, I got my first lesson in playwriting on the spot, and if I had had any whimsical idea that it was as easy as Mr. Howard's recent brace of successes had made it appear to be, Mr. Lawrence took pains to set me straight, and in no uncertain terms. "Do you realize"—he shook a figurative if not a literal fist in my face—"that I spent months thinking out a single line of dialogue to hang a scene on?"

I said meekly that I didn't, but I was consumed with curiosity to hear what the line was.

He stared at me, sunk in gloom. "I'll give you the manuscript of *Sour Grapes* and then get the hell out of here. You'll find it in the first act where Richard Halliday says to Alice Brady, 'I'd like to buy you for a million dollars. . . .' "

I happened to remember the line, but I didn't realize that it represented all that arduous effort. I got-the-hell-out as fast as I could, with the uncomfortable feeling that I had demeaned the ancient and honourable medium of the theatre by my impudent assumption that I could sit down and turn out a play "just like that." It was a good thing that I hadn't made a fool of myself in Sydney's eyes, especially since he had written me a long and enthusiastic letter after he'd read *Pattern*, telling me how much he'd enjoyed it, and what high regard he had for my ability. (I wish now that I'd kept a lot of letters from people like Sydney and Floyd Dell and Arthur Machen, but I didn't.)

It was raining hard when I emerged from the Seventy-Second Street subway station. "Oh dear," I thought, "no park for the children in this weather."

I found the apartment in its usual noon uproar, with Paul sneaking bits of calves' liver under the table to the cat, John banging the tray of his high chair with spinach holed up in his cheeks, and Fraulein looking very natty in the long blue nurse's cape that she hadn't taken time to remove before ministering to a stew of lights for the dogs, with an eye to snitching some for her own lunch. The lights smelled heavenly, while cooking, but I refused to be cajoled into "a taste only," and gulped down a hard-boiled egg and a tomato, standing up. Then I sat down at my typewriter, moodily re-reading a half-finished page of my half-finished novel in which I detected the word "eventually" used twice in succession. I changed one of them to "finally," crossed out a "retorted," and substituted another "said." Said—said—said. So what? Why get fancy with verbs that meant the same thing? I took out the third "said," which took out a "He" that I needed, because the "said" before it was "She." "*I'm not certain,*' *she said slowly.*" Maybe that was the "said" that could come out. "*'I'm not certain.'*" No, dammit, it wasn't clear, I couldn't lose any of the "saids." I crossed out the "slowly." Too naked, I had to have an adverb in that spot for rhythm.—"Gently." I had a "gently" already. I tore up the page. The whole damn thing was no good, anyway, and novels were a damn tedious medium.

All at once it was half-past three and John woke up from his nap and Paul came home from school. "Are you writing again?" he asked in disgust from the doorway.

"Yes. I'm writing a play. Any objections?"

He smirked self-consciously. "It's raining, can I go to the movies?"

"You may not. But it was a good try!" I threw after him. I put a clean sheet of paper in the typewriter. "Come back."

He reappeared, hopeful.

"Don't tell your father about the play."

It hadn't occurred to him to do so, but it was like telling him not to put beans up his nose. "Why not?" he objected. "Why can't I tell him?"

"Because I want it to be a surprise."

"Then can I go to the movies if I don't tell him?"

"Another word out of you and I'll wallop you."

It turned out to be the sort of an afternoon I thought it would, but the noise and the interruptions rolled off the top of my mind, and I kept on writing. With my humblest apologies to playwrights the world over, and Mr. Lawrence in particular, I had finished the first act a few minutes before my husband's key sounded in the door. Maybe I did it all wrong, but it certainly seemed to me that a play was a hundred times easier and quicker than a novel; no *he-saids*, or *she-saids*, and not a single description except for describing the stage-setting. And as for dialogue, I didn't have trouble thinking up a single line of it, it just kept running on and on until finally, at curtain time, it shut itself off, and I couldn't have gone past it, or stopped short of it.

Two evenings later, I presented my husband with a hundred and twenty-four not too badly crossed-out pages of manuscript. "Make yourself comfortable. Here's your pipe," I said. "Read."

"Well," he said, very pleased, "maybe Max can schedule that fall publication after all."

"You told me to write a play," I reminded him.

He grinned, like Paul. "So I did." He riffled through the pile. "Hey," he said. "I don't believe it."

"Neither do I."

"What's it about?"

"Do you remember *Holiday*?"

"Wasn't that the short story about the young boy and the older woman?"

"That no one would buy," I confirmed grimly. "And so that it shouldn't be a complete loss, this is it. Only Philip Barry used the title already, which is why I changed to *Fortnight*."

"It's a dramatic theme for a play."

"It fell into three acts as if it was made for it," I admitted. "But it can't be any good. A play is supposed to be the most difficult of all techniques to master."

"Shut up," he said. "Let me read it."

I sat myself in another chair and watched his face from behind a magazine. When he turned the last page he said, "I guess I don't know anything about playwriting either, because I happen to think it's pretty goddam good."

"Is it worth while having it typed, do you think?"

"What do you mean, 'do I think.' Of course 'I think.'—And don't meddle with it, leave it as it is."

I clipped the raggle-taggle bunch of pages together and took them to a typing bureau, the name of which was on the cover of Vincent Lawrence's manuscript. The place was like a factory, with a number of girls working on the separate acts of a single script. I didn't expect six beautiful copies all within a week, but that's what I got, each one tidily bound into a cardboard folder.

"I don't know whether I should slip in one of the carbons when I mail back *Sour Grapes*," I deferred to my husband's sense of fitness, of which he had none, because he said, with zest, "You certainly should, and I'd like to be there when Vin reads it."

"Not me. He's going to sound off in all directions—*if* he reads it," I amended.

I underestimated Vincent Lawrence's generosity. His voice, when he telephoned me a few days later, sounded as if he were still scratching his puzzled head. He didn't say much, but he offered to send the play to his producer—I think it was Sam Harris, or Somebody Harris. I thanked him profusely, and said it was wonderful of him to want to take the trouble, but I had an agent, and had already sent her the remaining five copies. It was true, for with the publication of *Pattern*, I had, amazingly, received innumerable letters from literary representatives who professed themselves competent and eager to protect my interests in the writing field.

I really didn't feel that I needed any protection with Scribner's, but Max said that he'd feel happier, personally, if an agent handled the contract of my next book.

"Which one shall I take?" I gave in reluctantly.

"You make your choice, and then let me approve it. There are a number of good ones, and an equal number that I wouldn't like to see you get mixed up with."

I chose Ann Watkins for two reasons. Her name was not only the prettiest of the lot, but her address was very convenient— Thirty-sixth Street and Madison Avenue, half a block from my husband's office. And with more luck than brains, I had, according to Max, picked myself one of the best negotiators in the business. Honest, too. Having taken me on as a novelist and short-story writer, she hadn't expected me to come along with a play. "It's too good for me to fool around with," she said, "so I gave it to Adrienne Morrison to see if she'd act as co-agent, and she's crazy about it. She handles plays exclusively, and she can do a better

G

job for you than I can with my limited theatrical contacts. How about it?"

"Whatever you say," I complied.

"Good. You'll like her."

On our first meeting, I didn't. I had already become accustomed to Ann Watkins' crisp business-like approach, and Miss Morrison was effusively of the stage. She enfolded me in a scented embrace, and told me I looked much, much too young to have written so wise and beautiful a play, and that Brock was already reading it, and was wildly excited about Toni for the lead, and Toni adored the part just from hearing about it. I hadn't the faintest idea who Brock and Toni were, but I didn't care. Their enthusiasms were too akin to Miss Morrison's.

Evidently Ann sensed a reservation towards my new agent. "Make no mistake," she adjured me, as we went down in the lift together, "Adrienne's a hard worker, and she has access to every producer in town."

"But she gushes, and I don't trust gushiness."

"That's the actress in her," Ann explained. "I'll lay a bet she sells the play."

Ann won her bet. Within the week, Brock Pemberton bought it on the usual option fee of five hundred dollars, and as soon as Antoinette Perry was free of her present commitment to *The Ladder*—a horrendous fiasco that was playing to empty houses—he planned to put *Fortnight* into immediate production.

"He's already talked to Lee Shubert about bookings on the road and in New York," Adrienne exulted when she told me the astonishing news. "Isn't it exciting? Aren't you thrilled?" She gave me a great hug, and although I am not a hugger-back by nature, I felt constrained to reciprocate. Then she put her arm around me and led me to an adjoining office and introduced me to the head of the agency, who also happened to be her recently acquired husband. I remember thinking that it was a strange set-up, but everything about this world of the theatre seemed strange to me, including the people who inhabited it. I could hardly make myself believe that last month at this time I hadn't even thought of writing a play, and now it was almost ready to open on Broadway.

"Almost"—the biggest little word in front of, or behind, the footlights.

Fortnight may have started off like one of those improbable success stories, but that was as far as it went. Casting trouble is often a feeble excuse for plays that never reach Broadway, but we really had it. It began with losing our leading lady. Although *The Ladder* soon petered out into oblivion, ill health put an end to Antoinette Perry's stage career. I was sorry chiefly because she was more truly a lovely woman than an actress, and we had become friends at once.

Adrienne, undaunted at this first disappointment, suggested Alice Brady instead. I had liked Alice Brady in *Sour Grapes* (my having chanced to see a performance was my sole measure of an actor's art), but I was inclined to agree with Miss Brady's own opinion that she was too young to play a mother part. Doggedly, Adrienne came up with one star after another, but they were all too young, or considered themselves to be, whether they were or not. Finally, I hit on the idea of Marjorie Rambeau, whom I remembered from Zoe Akin's *Daddy-Goes-a-Hunting*, and even Mr. Pemberton perked up at the possibility. She happened to be in Hollywood, but Adrienne assured him that Marjorie wanted desperately to get back to the legitimate theatre, and negotiations promptly commenced and then dragged along for an interminable period. I have a vague recollection that Miss Rambeau may have got as far as the Los Angeles Railroad Station, but if she ever boarded the train, she never got off it. More weeks passed, and by that time the theatre was no longer available, Adrienne's daughter, "Joanie," who was slated for the part of the daughter in the play, started having a baby, and Mr. Pemberton threw up his hands and dropped the option.

And still Adrienne wasn't discouraged. "Al Lewis has been dying to get the play," she said, and sure enough I immediately received another five hundred dollars, which, much against my will, went into a special bank account to join the first option cheque, the royalties from *Pattern*, and the negligible proceeds of two articles (I forget on what) that I had been asked to write for some highbrow magazine. "You're not playing fair," I reproached my husband. "When we got married we decided that we'd never argue about finances, what was mine was yours."

"That's right, what's mine is yours," he agreed amiably. "Anyway, this isn't income, it's pin-money, which is not to be spent on the house or the children."

"Only on pins, I suppose."

"Only on pins," he stipulated.

As I had little need for pins, and less for money, the account remained intact until a third option fee swelled the balance. In short, *Fortnight* flourished biannually for a number of years, and became one of the most optioned plays in theatrical history without benefit of production, until Adrienne's tireless perseverance showed signs of wilting a little. She said, "Surely you're not a one-play author. The theatre's full of broken hearts, but you have to rise above the disappointments."

I tactfully refrained from telling her that my heart wasn't broken, and I wasn't disappointed. I had been callously working on my novel, but now I put it aside, curious to find out if, indeed, *Fortnight* had been an accident of ignorance, and whether I could apply to a second try whatever I had learned from my first endeavour. For one thing, I knew enough to steer clear of building this play around a single personality; and for another, I'd study every textbook on drama that I could lay my hands on.

"Why?" my husband inquired flatly.

"Because," I said.

"When do I see the first act?"

"I'll be lucky if you see it in three months."

"Better let me see it when I come home tonight."

It was ready for him. The dogs barked, the children ran in and out, the groceries for lunch didn't come, but my characters kept on talking and my typewriter kept on going. Again, I felt quite guilty about it, but time has proved that an act a day for three days in succession seems to be the only way that I can write a play, and with no rewriting on the road.

I'm not bragging about it, it just happens to be the truth.

I called my second attempt *Another Language*, for want of a better title. I liked the play fairly well, and of course, my husband thought it was wonderful. Unhappily, we were in the minority. I experienced my first real professional disappointment when Ann Watkins hedged from her usual directness, and Adrienne, admittedly dubious of the speed with which I had written it, said that if I wanted her straight-from-the-shoulder opinion, she didn't care for it as much as *Fortnight*. "It lacks the humour and the action," she said.

"I don't agree with you," I protested. "The love story has more weight, and lots of little things like the grapes and umbrella-stand can be quite funny—I think."

"I might be wrong about it," she conceded without conviction.

But apparently she wasn't wrong. Gilbert Miller turned the play down at once, and three or four other top producers felt, as she did, that the story lacked force and comedy. No one took an option on it.

" They're very wrong," my husband said. "How would you like to go to Bermuda for a couple of weeks?"

"With the children?"

"Without the children. You can trust Fraulein with them."

It was a lovely holiday, being, for me, one of the few completely unapprehensive and carefree intervals of my marriage. We took long bicycle rides in the sun (frequently bumping into Eugene O'Neill, with whom we became very friendly), danced in the moonlight, and ate huge breakfasts in bed, and when we got back, Peter was on the way.

So, of all unlikely things, was *Another Language*. During our absence Adrienne had succeeded in finding a producer for it. "His name is Philip Goodman," she said.

"I never heard of him."

"Well, he's not very well known," she admitted, "but he thinks you've written a great play, and frankly, we can't afford to be choosy at this point, can we?"

Far from being "choosy," I felt that I was very fortunate in having won Mr. Goodman's interest. White haired, portly, exuding a vibrant physical cleanliness, I thoroughly enjoyed and benefited from our sessions together, until one day I realized that we hadn't progressed very far beyond the talking stage, and I'd better tell him to get moving on production because I was going to have a baby in the autumn.

For a long moment, Mr. Goodman said nothing at all. Then he said, eyeing me up and down, "I have found you full of surprises, my dear, but this is the biggest surprise of all."

The next morning, there was a letter from him in the mail—it was his habit to augment our meetings with literate and witty notes, therefore I opened the familiar envelope with no foreboding of its contents. Unlike the others, it was quite formal in its salutation, and very short and to the point. He wrote that he had decided to buy Vin Lawrence's new play, which would necessarily postpone his plans for *Another Language*.

There was a kind of justice that it should have been Vin who supplanted me, and I was genuinely sorry when *Washington Heights* opened to a devastating press. Its failure marked the end of Philip Goodman's career as a producer, which was a pity, because he was a man of great brilliance and impeccable taste. He went to Europe shortly after the play closed, and I never saw or heard from him again. I had a let-down feeling for a while, but it didn't last long. It was nice to be back in my own world. I worked on my novel off and on, cleaned out cupboards, tidied drawers and medicine chests, and waited for Peter.

He was born in November, and a very successful production he was. My stage was complete with cast—three children and a husband. What more could a woman ask of life? I had a feeling that the days were going too fast, that I would never again savour the perfection of this moment in time. Thanksgiving, Christmas, Decoration Day. Heat blistered the pavements in a vicious onslaught of summer. I rented a house in Rye for July and August, which was near enough to New York for my husband to commute, and far enough away to give the children a change of air.

I had no sooner unpacked, than Adrienne telephoned to thank me for an eighteenth-century bowl that I had sent her before

leaving town, in grateful recognition of all her hopes and efforts
that had come to nothing. She said she adored Meissen, but not
for one minute to think she had given up on either of the plays.
"To be absolutely frank, I have a brand new young producer," she
said, "who's just taken on the summer theatre at Greenwich. His
name's Arthur Beckhard. He's absolutely mad about *Fortnight*,
and wants to try it out with Blanche Yurka."

Apart from the fact that I'd always associated Miss Yurka with
Ibsen, the idea failed to spark any fire in me, the last embers
having sputtered out with Mr. Goodman's exit. But Adrienne was
richly persuasive. "There's everything to gain and nothing to
lose," she said. "Besides, Greenwich is only a few miles from
Rye, you might even enjoy watching your play finally come to life."

I didn't enjoy it. "I'm glad now that *Fortnight* never got as far
as Broadway," I told my husband, as we drove home after the
opening night performance. "I suppose you can't really judge a
play until it's on the stage, where it belongs."

"It was a bad performance," he insisted.

"Well, anyway, it's a good thing it's only going to run a week.
And maybe it won't even last the full week," I added hopefully.

My words came back to confound me. Audiences liked
Fortnight, the box-office did a brisk business, Adrienne's faith in
the play was bolstered rather than shaken, and when her enter-
prising young producer talked of bringing it to New York, she was
in two minds about it. I was in one mind, though. "No," I said.

"But it might not be so simple to say 'No.' He has a contractual
interest, you know, and he might not be willing to relinquish it."

"You never told me that part of it."

"But, lambie, I didn't think I had to, it's the usual clause in any
summer try-out."

"If I'd realized it, I'd never have agreed to let him do it," I
said miserably.

"Now aren't you being a little unreasonable?" she suggested
gently. "After all, you're going to have plenty of time to work on
the play with him."

I was probably being more than a little unreasonable, for the
truth of the matter was that I had taken such an instant dislike to

this summer-time producer with his flamboyant black moustache, that even at the end of the try-out, I could not bring myself to address him by his first name, whereas I was calling Mr. Goodman "Phil" halfway through our first session together. Little things make a difference to a woman, but I doubted that Adrienne would have considered my prejudices a sound basis for rejecting a professional contact that she had gone to considerable pains to bring about. "No amount of work is going to make *Fortnight* into a play that I'll ever be proud of," I excused my lack of co-operation.

"I couldn't disagree with you more," she said. "However, since you feel so strongly about it, I'll see what I can do to shelve it."

It was to Adrienne's credit that she was able to effect any sort of compromise with Mr. Beckhard. Unhappily, however, she succeeded only at a price. "He's willing to forgo his hold on *Fortnight*," she reported a few days later, "provided he can close his season in Greenwich with *Another Language*. Incidentally"—she quickly forestalled my negative reaction—"he shares your opinion that it has a great comedy potential. And, personally, I think we're very fortunate in being given an opportunity to see what values we have, or haven't got, in the play. But this time, young lady, you're going to take a little interest and go to rehearsals instead of just showing up on opening night."

"He asked me to stay away," I explained without umbrage.

"I'll see to that," she promised grimly. She was assuming that we had already arrived at an amicable swap of the two plays, but I decided not to argue the matter further until I'd discussed it with my husband.

Although he didn't like the bartering aspect any more than I did, he felt that there wasn't very much we could do about it. "Except that I'm going to make damned sure," he said, "that any and all rights in *Another Language* are limited to the try-out, otherwise there's no deal."

"We're laying down some pretty stiff terms, but under the circumstances you're perfectly right," Adrienne told him, and proceeded to draw up what she assured him was a very tough contract, producer-wise.

My husband read it, approved it, and I signed it. But from the events that followed, there might just as well have been no contract at all.

It isn't necessary to give a detailed account of the disillusionments that preceded that second opening night in Greenwich. Suffice it to say that the play had been cast by my soft-voiced producer before he had, according to our firm agreement, notified me of the first reading. I was furious, but it didn't seem worth making an issue that would only have resulted in discomfiting innocent actors, most of whom were competent enough performers, with Marie Ouspenskaya head and shoulders above all of them. When, many years later, I directed her in *Outrageous Fortune,* I found her a joy to work with, but nevertheless she was embarrassingly miscast as the matriarch in *Another Language.* Eventually, Margaret Wycherly played the part in New York, and Dame May Whitty played it in London, and although they were no more expert than Ouspenskaya they were of an English-speaking tradition that enabled them to portray the character that I had conceived and written.

On Adrienne's advice, and fortified by her instructions as to my rights as author, I went back to the rehearsal the day after the reading, to discover that the chess-game, which was to have been quietly played in the background according to my stage directions, had been rewritten into a prolonged and ribald round of pinochle —a game I didn't know anything about and disliked from the very sound of the word. "Please do not change my script," I told Mr. Beckhard, standing pat on the first of my rights.

"But I did it for a purpose," he explained in his smoothest voice. "Believe me, it's much better this way, I can get a lot of laughs out of a pinochle game."

"I don't want a lot of laughs in that particular scene. You're keying the whole play to the wrong kind of comedy."

"Aren't you being a little quick to judge?" he returned with unruffled suavity. "You're not giving me a fair chance to show you what I can do. If you stay away until the actors know their lines and I've blocked in the staging, you can make all the notes you want, and I'll be glad to read them."

"But he won't follow them, so you might as well spare your energies," my husband advised me. "You'll only upset yourself by going to rehearsals."

"I'm more afraid of upsetting the actors," I said, glumly. "Once the direction is set there isn't enough time to be able to make any changes or suggestions."

It is one of the abiding miracles of summer try-outs that, good or bad, the curtain always manages to go up on opening nights. *Another Language* was no exception. I thought it was "bad," but the evening had all the buzz and fanfare of a gala occasion. People who had liked *Fortnight* returned to see a new play by the same author, and Ouspenskaya was an additional draw. Her entrance elicited a burst of applause, and the lines, spoken in her deep Russian accent, set the note for entertainment of a piece with the noisy game of pinochle and the padded busts and behinds on daughters-in-law.

"Cheer up," my husband whispered, as the final curtain fell to wild hand-clapping and foot-stomping. "It's a fine play, and no amount of hoking it up could ruin it."

"It ruined it for me," I said.

Once more, we drove home in the black night, kicking ourselves for not having learned a lesson from our first experience.

It should have been the end of it, but it wasn't. My beaming producer appeared on the doorstep early the following morning, and with him was my beaming agent. She kissed me warmly, and said that she had stayed in Greenwich overnight so that we could all sit down together and thrash things out. "If you're talking about the pinochle game, it doesn't matter," I said, "I'm not going to be petty."

"Petty!" Mr. Beckhard expostulated. "Why that scene went over bigger than anything else in the show except the cockroaches!"

"I must admit that the audience really loved it," Adrienne injected with a deprecatory smile. "But that's a minor point. The important thing is that now we know without a doubt that the play has tremendous possibilities, and we ought to iron out here and now any little sticky problems we might have about bringing it into New York."

I edged away from her encircling arm. Whose side was she on, or had I heard her incorrectly? "It was clearly understood that there was no hold on the play beyond this try-out," I said coldly, "so I don't see what there is to iron out."

"There's this to iron out!" Mr. Beckhard protested. "You double-crossed me with *Fortnight*, and now you want to do the same thing again!"

"Arthur didn't mean that." Adrienne continued her peace-making mission. "Of course you didn't double-cross him, and yet I can understand how he feels. He has a financial investment at stake with both plays, and I want us all to be reasonable and fair about his not having to lose the chance of doing *Another Language*."

I felt sick. I told myself that Adrienne was only trying to do her job as an agent, and Mr. Beckhard was only trying to become a producer, but I felt sick just the same. Double-crossed was an ugly word, no matter who did it to whom, and the best play in the world wasn't worth that ugliness. I wanted no part of it, so I gave in, and Adrienne drew up another contract, and again my husband went over it carefully before I signed it. To the best of his, and my, limited experience, it seemed to have really "ironed out" all the difficulties of the try-out. We couldn't ask for anything fairer than for the New York production to be subject to my complete supervision of casting, staging and direction.

I had no intention of misusing my power of veto, and I was glad to suggest that we keep two of the actors from the original cast. One was an unknown girl, a schoolteacher, whose name was Margaret Hamilton; and the other, a young boy, equally unknown, whose name was John Beal. "You're showing a very nice spirit," Adrienne commended me, "only our producer would be happier if you chose the two leads instead of a couple of amateurs."

"But the leads aren't right for the parts, and the amateurs can be, if they're directed properly. Besides, how can they ever get to be leads if nobody gives them the chance not to be amateurs?"

"Frankly, I couldn't agree with you more," she said. "In fact, I'm going to do my level best to get an experienced director for the play."

"Frankly, I couldn't agree with you more," I gave her back her favourite phrase. She laughed and hugged me, and I was happy that once again I could like her without the reservations that continued, occasionally, to disturb me.

Months passed and nothing crystallized in the way of production, because Mr. Beckhard was having difficulty raising money, and secretly, I hoped he would keep on having it. My husband came down with an attack of pleurisy, and the children all came down with measles, so I was relieved to scrap *Another Language* along with *Fortnight*. My home was my kingdom, but less poetically I suppose I should say that I was completely lacking in ambition.

In either case, I was anything but happy, when, at the very expiration of his option, Mr. Beckhard announced to the newspapers that he was ready to embark on the production and direction of his first play, and only in retrospect did I realize how little my name appeared in the numerous press releases. "I'm sorry I couldn't get him to consider an outside director," Adrienne reported to me. "I really tried. Actually, he hasn't sufficient backing yet to start production, and he's gearing his costs to the proverbial shoestring. We'll have to watch that we don't stint on assembling a good cast."

It took some very close watching, for Mr. Beckhard's preferences were not mine. Unfortunately, my counter-suggestions were again limited to the actors whose performances I had seen and remembered, and rather diffidently I offered the names of Glenn Anders, whom I had liked in Sydney Howard's *They knew what they wanted*, and Dorothy Stickney, who had done a fine job in one of George Kelley's plays. And quite a way back, Margaret Wycherly had impressed me greatly in *The Verge*.

To my surprise, all three names met with Adrienne's seasoned approval. She promptly went to bat for them, and they were signed for the leading roles, along with John Beal and Margaret Hamilton. We met with greater resistance, however, when it came to the smaller parts. Evidently word had been sent out favouring wide rumps, big busts and ludicrous hair-dos for the sisters-in-law, and broad pranksters for the sons. Even with Adrienne as my ally, I had finally to stand firmly on my contractual right to insist on two pleasantly middle-aged women with normally inconspicuous anatomies, and three quietly mannered middle-aged men, who didn't look like comedians. It was not an agreeable victory, for I detested disharmony, and Beckhard was openly antagonistic to my interference. Under the circumstances, I thought it only fair to accede to his request that, having enjoyed my triumph, I now allow him three days, free of my presence, in which to establish his authority as director, and win the confidence of his actors.

In token of my own confidence, I voluntarily absented myself for an additional day, and dropped into the rehearsal hall on the following afternoon, just in time to catch the pinochle game, in all its ribaldry. I restrained my impulse to blow up on the spot, and waited until the session was over and the last member of the cast had departed before I told my producer exactly what I thought. He heard me out with a smile, and then apologized.

"I knew you'd be annoyed, but I wasn't expecting a dragout fight over it. I can't help it if I never learned how to play chess, I wouldn't know how to get any comedy out of a chess game."

"But I've already explained to you that the scene shouldn't be played for comedy," I reiterated hoarsely. "Don't you see that I wrote it in a low key, purposely, in order not to overshadow the action on the other side of the room."

"I'll keep it in a low key," he gave me his word. "I admit they might have punched their lines a little too hard, but that was because your watching made them nervous."

"They'll have to get used to my watching," I informed him tersely. "You might warn them that I intend to be at every rehearsal from now on."

His smile never wavered. "Certainly. It's in your contract. Two o'clock tomorrow. Same place."

Trusting novice that I was, it didn't occur to me that by two o'clock a whole day's damage would have been accomplished. On the contrary, I was glad to have the morning free because I had made an appointment for the dachshunds to be bathed and groomed.

Which brings me to the shamed admission that we had recently degenerated to the lap-dog status after having had a run of bad luck with our Dane and Newfoundland—Juno developed killer tendencies, and Rogo developed a bad heart. The veterinary surgeon was pessimistic and rightly so, in both instances, and after a suitable period of mourning had elapsed, we reached the reluctant conclusion that perhaps some smaller breed might present less problems in a city apartment. But what? Scottie? No. Irish terrier? Sealyham or Bedlington? Airedale? Might as well go a size larger into a Wolfhound. Pekingese? God, no. (Forgive me, Pekes, it's taken me thirty years to admit that you're wonderful pups.)

We had been miserably dogless for over a month when the breeder who had sold us Juno, telephoned one snowy night to say that he had just returned from a kennel in Vermont with an outstanding pair of dachshunds. My husband looked at me, and I looked at him. Dachshunds? Well, maybe . . .

"Still snowing," he remarked as he peered out of the window. I glanced at my watch. "And it's late. Almost nine o'clock."

It wasn't easy to find a taxi driver willing to go all the way to the outskirts of Yonkers at that hour, and in one of the near blizzards that can make a fool out of April 1st, but we managed to sell one of them a bill of goods, and after we finally reached our destination, we sold ourselves a bill of goods on dachshunds.

We bought them with the kennel smells of two states thrown in with no extra charge. "They're not going to be bathed in my bathtub, nor in the children's, nor yet in the laundry sink," I gave an ultimatum, and called up a canine beauty parlour to do the job.

The shop was on Thirty-seventh Street and Second Avenue, which was near enough my husband's office to fit in agreeably with the afternoon rehearsal. I planned to have lunch with him after leaving the dogs to be bathed, and he could pick them up on his way home, and up to a point it worked out like that, but with some slight modifications. I emerged from the taxi, holding Hansel and Gretel each on a separate chain leash—they wouldn't answer to any other names, and I soon discovered that they wouldn't answer to those, either. They scrambled like deaf maniacs towards a nearby fire hydrant, tangling the three of us up in a swirl of leashes that made an effective lassoo round my ankles. The remains of the snow had melted into a slippery mush, and I'd have had to be an acrobat not to lose my balance along with most of my change from a five-dollar bill. A passer-by helped me to get up. I hobbled into the shop, gritting my teeth against the ghastly pain that shot through my knees. I didn't have the presence of mind to keep the taxi, and when I hobbled out of the shop, the few that whizzed past had heads in them. There was nothing to do but to start walking.

The long, crosstown blocks were interminable. People turned to stare at me, because I wasn't really walking, I was doing a grotesque sort of schottische to keep from bending my knees. I had vowed to be at my husband's office on time for once, but I was lucky that I was able to get there at all. The first thing he said was, "Why are you limping?" and added suspiciously, knowing that if it were at all possible not to look where I was going, I didn't, "You fell down again."

"This wasn't my fault, it was those damn dachshunds."

"Sit," he ordered briefly.

Inch by inch, I sat. He eyed the bloody patches through my torn stockings. "They're only scraped," I apologized. "Ouch! Don't touch."

He frowned. "Does that hurt when I press?"

"No," I lied, not wanting to worry him.

"We'll see how you feel after lunch." He told his nurse to bring some iodine, and I was glad to screech, which he didn't take seriously, as I always screeched when he smeared iodine on my various wounds.

We went to a nearby restaurant. I ordered a lobster thermidor, and put on an act of polishing it off with gusto. "You come back to the office anyway," he said. "I'd better take a quick X-ray."

"You will not, I'm perfectly all right. Besides, I'll never be at the rehearsal before they begin if I don't hurry."

"Are you sure you feel up to going with those knees?"

"I can't very well go without them, and I'd have to be dead not to go."

"It's only a play," he reminded me.

"But it's *my* play, and I'm not going to stand by and see it murdered."

Against his better judgment, he put me into a taxi, and gave the driver the address. I winced at taking the high step. "It's

[111]

your fault," I railed at him. "That iodine still stings like blazes!"

As soon as the taxi turned the corner, I changed the instructions. "Go straight up to Seventy-sixth and Park Avenue, please." That raw flesh certainly bothered me every time I bent my knees, so maybe I'd better ask De Witt to put some sort of a soft bandage under my stockings, or I wouldn't be able to keep my mind on rehearsals.

Dr. De Witt Stetten was not only one of our close friends, but he'd attended to me enough times for me to know that if he wasn't in his office I'd probably find him doing his rounds at the Lenox Hill Hospital across the street. I called at his office first, and met him just as he was leaving. "Again?" he greeted me.

I nodded sheepishly. I'd hate to think I was, or am, what the psychologists are pleased to call "accident prone," since I always have a good excuse for the things that happen to me, but the fact remains that De Witt had set a broken arm for me, had refused to rebreak my broken nose to set it straight, had strapped a couple of torn ligaments, and had only recently achieved an unconventional bit of surgery, when the dining-room door had stupidly swung closed, taking half my finger with it. Fortunately, it had happened early in the morning while my husband was still at home, so he'd picked the finger up from the floor (it was my smallest, a mere nothing), wrapped it in a handkerchief to keep it warm, raced me over to De Witt, who stopped eating his breakfast to sew it on. One of the truly great surgeons of our time, he had never been called on to do a rush job of impromptu needlework like that before, and for years after, he took great pride in that nicely pieced, slightly cock-eyed pinkie. I don't know how those things get around, but it was sandwiched into a newscast over the radio that I had lost not one but four fingers. It was only a slight exaggeration. By the end of the week, when the nerves began to scream, it felt like four fingers.

Anyway, that was why De Witt said, "Again?" when he saw me come hobbling towards him. "It's just some scraped knees this time," I defended, as I managed to make the examining table, "but I have to use them to go to rehearsal."

He was paying no attention to me. "Call an ambulance," he barked to his nurse. "If I let her walk across to the hospital, she's apt to split the patella, and it's her damnfool luck that she hasn't."

I could tell that he wasn't joking. "An ambulance, you damn fool? I've been walking all the morning!—And don't you dare call my husband!" I yelled after his departing back.

It was too late. The nurse was ringing for the ambulance on one phone and De Witt was cursing my husband on the other. "I don't care if she ate ten lobsters! The right knee is definitely broken, and the left one's so banged up that I can't make a proper diagnosis until I get it under the X-ray! And you let her walk half-way across the city. What the hell's the matter with you! Get to the hospital as fast as you can, you goddam fool!"

I burst into tears. "You're a beast!" I accused him hotly. "You had no right to frighten him like that, it's not his fault, I didn't let *on* that it hurt me, I didn't want to worry him!"

"You're a goddam fool, too," De Witt shouted at me. He clamped my shoulder gently. "It hurts like hell, doesn't it?"

I nodded.

"I'm afraid it'll hurt more before we're through. But when we put you in a cast, you'll feel easier."

"Cast!" I echoed on a bleat. "Why you goddam fool, I told you I have to get to rehearsal!"

I'd better skip all the rest of the hells and goddams and get to the point. Into a cast I went, and overnight in the hospital I stayed. My producer telephoned me the next morning, to say that Adrienne had informed him of my accident, and to assure me, in his softest voice, that there was no need for me to give a second thought to the play. "Just be a good girl, and take it easy, so you'll be able to be on deck for the opening" he ended with a little giggle that apparently, in his deep and hidden delight, he found difficult to repress.

Two days later, I was "on deck" at the rehearsal hall, with my sister in attendance to see that I arrived there safely. I hadn't excelled at the Maxixe and the Hesitation for nothing. I was as agile as a flea, handling my crutches like an expert. Indeed, except for the discomfort of a heavy plaster cast, I was feeling fine. Nor will I ever forget Mr. Beckhard's expression when he looked up and saw me, feeling fine. I could almost hear the mental plunk of the bottom dropping out of the private little world that he thought he had all to himself.

I managed to convince my sister, the next morning, that I could get to the rehearsal hall without her help, and the sooner I learned to manage alone, the easier it would be for everyone. The nice old man in charge of the building shook his head sadly when he saw me, and said it was a shame and a disgrace no one had thought to notify me that they were rehearsing somewhere else.

"Where?"

He looked unhappy, and said he didn't really know.

I gave him a dollar, and he gave me the address, which was only half a block away, within hobbling distance. I arrived just in time to summon my producer to my side with an imperious wave of my crutch. "Please don't hammer the cockroach line like that," I commanded.

"We won't get a laugh on it if I don't!" he returned angrily.

"You'll get more of a laugh if you don't."

"I'll direct this show as I see fit."

"That was not our agreement," I said. "Shall I instruct Miss Hamilton, or do you prefer to do it?"

It was a battle of wits and endurance. I never told my husband, or my sister, or even Adrienne how, day after day, I followed that rehearsal from one place to another, aware that whenever possible, Mr. Beckhard chose antiquated halls that I had to reach by climbing up long flights of stairs. I felt degraded in emulating his devious tactics, but I also felt justified, under the circumstances, in talking to the actors behind his back.

I remember being almost thrown out of—not the rehearsal hall—but Schrafft's Restaurant, where Margaret Hamilton and I were having lunch together in a makeshift coaching session. A thoroughly nice person, she was nevertheless a ready accomplice, recognizing that her characterization of the oldest sister-in-law set the pivotal note of comedy in the play. At that particular lunch, we were trying to rescue two key scenes in the first act from being embarrassingly overplayed. I used some pellets of bread for grapes. "Just push them away quietly, Peggy, and say, 'I don't want a whole bunch,' as you'd say, 'I'm not thirsty.'

—That's fine. Now use the same approach for, 'This is no fight.' "

" 'This is no fight,' " she echoed obediently.

"You've almost got it, but not quite. A little more toneless and matter-of-fact. 'This is no fight.'—No, don't flash your eyes. Try it again, completely dead-pan. 'This is no fight.' "

" 'This is no fight,' " said Peggy.

"Ladies. Please." The hostess stood between us, importunate. "I must really ask you to finish your quarrel elsewhere."

We had lunch at another restaurant the next day, and tackled the cockroaches in discreetly lowered voices.

Like Dracula, I appeared in my cast and crutches only during the hours of rehearsal, and then went home to become a normal wife and mother. Even on the opening night in New York, I preferred to remain out of sight largely because I looked like somebody's poor relative. Having had a rough time of it in Washington, where we played a preliminary week, the massive column of plaster had lost its virgin whiteness and although I cleaned it with soap and water when we got back to New York, it had frayed around the top and bottom, and looked generally down at the heel. So I stayed in the box office, emerging only—and again like Dracula—when the house was darkened, to stand at the back of the orchestra and watch the performance. I was satisfied with the way it was going, in spite of the pinochle game. Peggy's fight was a masterpiece of understatement, and the grapes and roaches were perfect. The audience laughed enough, but not too much. "Let's go home," I said to my husband at the beginning of the third act. "It's foolproof from here on, Dorothy and Glenn carry the big scenes and they won't overplay."

"Better stay," he said. "They might call 'Author.' "

It was wishful thinking. They wouldn't call "Author," because nobody in that whole audience except a handful of friends, knew that I existed. I looked at his intent profile out of the corner of my eye, and wondered if he had lost any weight in the past week. I was so worried about him; he had caught a heavy cold in Washington, and hadn't shaken it. The Broadway opening was an additional strain, but he insisted on waiting for the final curtain. "Listen to that applause!" he exulted.

"They always applaud on a first night. Now stop dawdling or we'll never get a taxi."

"Aren't you going backstage?"

"I'm too tired," I said.

I made an elaborate pretence of exhaustion when we got home. "We ought to stay up to see what the papers say," he demurred as I fell into bed.

"I'm already asleep," I said. "Get a move on and turn out the light."

I kept my eyes closed, but I was far from asleep. I was praying. There have been few times in my life when I pleaded, articulately, with the Omniscience that we call God. This was one of the times. "Dear God—I did what I had to the past few weeks to make the play as good as I could, but please don't think that I care about anything in the world except my husband and children. Whatever else You see fit to give me, please, please let me keep what You've already given me. Don't take it away from me, I don't want to trade success or fame for what I have right here, now, under this roof. God, listen to me. . . ."

"You're crying," my husband said, out of the dark.

"You're imagining things; why should I be crying?"

"I don't know," he replied soberly. "But if it's about the play, darling, no matter what the critics say in the morning, you can be proud of it."

"I haven't given it a thought," I told him honestly. "Worrying about it won't help, anyway."

"No, it won't. But something's bothering you, just the same."

I couldn't fool him, even with the light out. "My cast itches," I said.

He reached for my hand and we slept.

I wakened when he coughed, holding myself rigid against the trembling that shook my whole body. The fear was coming back; I couldn't understand it. For a while, I had conquered it, but gradually it had begun to creep up on me again, standing at my shoulder like an unseen enemy. I knew that it was up to me, and me alone, to destroy that enemy or it would not only invade our own happiness but the children's as well, for security spelled their happiness. Up to now, they did not know that their father had ever been ill. There was no reason for them to know it. When Paul was old enough to understand, I told him to be careful not to roughhouse too hard, and that was all. "Your father had a back injury in college, but he's too proud to give into it. Don't let on I said anything, just try to protect him from doing the things he oughtn't to do."

Protect. Was it right or was it wrong to try to protect the ones you loved? It was a question that I might some day have to answer. But not now. Not tonight. I rose and held a glass of water to my husband's lips. He stirred sleepily. "What is it?"

"We washed the blankets, and the lint has been making you cough a little."

"Oh.—I'm sorry, darling, if I woke you."

"You didn't, but drink a little water, it'll stop it."

"Thanks. . . ." he murmured, and then he slept again.

I don't know how much later it was when I heard the telephone by the bed give a warning tinkle. Blindly, I snatched at it before it could go into a full ring. I recognized Adrienne's voice, richer and huskier than ever with excitement. "We've been waiting for the morning papers to come out. We've just seen the reviews! They're marvellous!"

"I can't talk now," I whispered urgently. "I'll call you tomorrow——"

"But aren't you dying to hear what they say?"

"We're both asleep——"

"But this is no time to sleep! Don't you understand, *Another Language* is a hit! Every critic has given the play a rave notice! Tell that husband of yours to get on the extension while I read the *Times* and *Tribune*, he'll absolutely burst with pride!"

"Adrienne, no, *please!*" I implored her. "We'll see them in the morning——"

Cautiously, I replaced the receiver and lowered myself into the pillows, afraid to breathe. Not a sound from the other bed. My husband hadn't wakened. I was thankful. It must be close on two o'clock. How inconsiderate to phone people at such an unearthly hour! Then I remembered that neither Adrienne nor anyone else, had ever suspected that he was less than the perfect specimen of health that he appeared to be.

It is a very particular satisfaction to watch an audience enjoying one's first play. My husband, shamelessly stage-struck, relished that satisfaction to its fullest. He would have gone to the theatre every night if I hadn't protested that the heavy cast bothered me too much to stand around on it. "I'll go with you after it's off," I promised. "It won't be long now."

"Look. I'm on to you," he rebelled. "I had my check-up, so stop coddling me, I'm fine."

He didn't know that I had talked to the doctor after the check-up, and although the X-rays showed no alarming change, there were râles in both apices, which, he reassured me, could result, temporarily, from a cold. "However, I'll go over his chest again in a few weeks, and in the meantime, I've told him to let up on work. He's agreed to take Wednesdays off from the office."

That was big-hearted of him: Wednesdays were matinée days, and the reaction of matinée audiences fascinated him.

One afternoon I saw him deliberately interrupt a conversation between a man and a woman who were complete strangers to him. "Well," I thought, "he's never done anything like that before." I grabbed my crutches and hurried out of my hiding-place in the box office to find out what was going on. As I approached, the man was arguing indignantly. "Would I say so," he demanded, "if I didn't know what I was talking about? I got it straight from the producer. He told us definitely that the play was originally written in Russian, and he happens to be an intimate friend, I went to school with him."

"My dear sir," I heard my husband reply. "You have been grossly misinformed. I happen to be an intimate friend of the author, I sleep with her." He turned on his heel, and left them gaping.

"What a dirty remark!" The woman finally found her voice. "And I bet anything he's a married man."

It didn't occur to me to try to trace the source of that ridiculous story. I was aware that Mr. Beckhard was guilty of a number of misrepresentations, but I didn't think he could possibly have authored so fantastic a lie. Actually, I saw very little of him once the play had opened. We went to the country early in June, after which he began assembling a Chicago company, loyally using a number of the actors who had been in the Greenwich try-out. As I recall, the second company didn't duplicate its Broadway success. It was public knowledge that the Mayor of Chicago rudely left the theatre in the middle of the second act, and the road tour must have failed completely, because I was petitioned for a loan of two thousand dollars to bring the actors back to New York. I kept the promissory note for quite a while before I realized that it was worthless.

The sale of the film rights should have covered all the outstanding deficits, but it apparently didn't; and as for the subsidiary rights, my producer promptly sold out his amateur and stock interests, and a part of mine as well. I wasn't aware of it at the time. I wasn't aware of many things I probably should have known about, but nothing was important to me except my husband's health. The râles in the left apex had not disappeared.

He had a haemorrhage in August. It was a rainy Sunday afternoon. We were reading on the bed. He gave a sudden, throaty little cough, and then it happened.

The children were playing the victrola in the next room. "Dad's starting another cold, I'm going to make him go back to New York out of the dampness for a few days," I told them later, after I'd telephoned Dr. Miller. Fraulein looked up from her mending. I avoided her eyes.

The collapsing of a lung has become a routine procedure, but the operation wasn't recommended in my husband's case. Even in those days, however, medicine negated climate and rest in favour of a patient's mental ease. "Stay in bed, and take it very quietly for a few weeks," Dr. Miller advised him, "and then if you feel like it, you can go to your office, provided you keep sensible hours."

My husband's face brightened, but fear did not loosen its hold around my heart. I followed the doctor to the door. "Will he really be well enough to practise?" My throat was so tight I could scarcely ask the question.

Dr. Miller hesitated a moment before he answered me. "Yes and no. The sputum's negative, as it always has been, and his

[119]

temperature's normal." He put his hand on my shoulder. "Keep in touch with me, and maybe this winter we'll catch him off guard and get him to take a long vacation somewhere. But not now. He'd only fight it."

I nodded mutely. "I know."

"It's harder for you, this way."

"Yes."

"Try not to worry."

I tried. I relived the days at Trudeau, remembering all the patients who had had "flare-ups," and had got well. I closed my mind against the memory of the patients who had not got well. I had been running from fear for all those years, and now it had caught up with me. It was no longer a shadowy enemy at my shoulder, I was face to face with it. Somehow I had known from the beginning that this was going to happen.

In the autumn, we went to England. It was a put-up job between the doctor and myself, with Gilbert Miller abetting us unwittingly. He seemed to have forgotten that he had turned down *Another Language* because he immediately bought it for London, following its American success. I believe that Adrienne must have intimated that I had played a considerable part in the casting and direction, because he accepted with alacrity my offer to be on hand during rehearsals. At my own expense, I volunteered quickly, but without explaining that I was using the London production merely as an excuse to get my husband to Switzerland for the winter. No one except Dr. Miller knew it. We planned it together. "Don't stay in London any longer than you have to," he advised. "It's too damp for him."

"I'm going to tell him it's too damp for the children," I amended.

"That's better," he agreed.

It was a festive sailing. We were given the Royal Suite on the *Majestic*, though I can't imagine why, now that I look back on it. The rooms were full of flowers, and there were bottles of champagne in buckets of ice. I remember Glenn Anders putting his arm round me and saying, "You're the luckiest woman in the world. You have everything."

I had nothing. A half-hour before we'd left the apartment for the boat, the doctor's secretary called me. "Dr. Miller wants you to telephone him from an outside booth."

I didn't wait to hear any more. "Who was on the phone? Where are you going?" my husband called after me.

"Nobody, wrong number! I have to run to the drugstore, I forgot cleansing cream!"

"You cluck, come back, you can buy it on board!"

"Not the kind I use, it'll only take a few minutes!"

"Don't let him get suspicious," I prayed. He had had his final examination two days ago. "Everything's all right, or we'd have heard by now," he'd mentioned as we'd finished our packing that morning.

"Absolutely." (Oh God, let it be all right)——

But God couldn't have heard me, for Dr. Miller wouldn't have wanted to speak to me in private. My hand was shaking so that I could hardly dial the number, and when I tried to answer his greeting I had the old familiar sensation of my throat being full of ashes.

My voice came out in a croak. "What is it, Dr. Miller?"

He was kind, and he was gentle, but he said that much as he would like to, he could not minimize the gravity of the report that had just come back from the laboratory. "I had a double check made. The sputum is positive. It wouldn't be right to keep it from you."

My lips ached with dryness. "But why, why now, for the first time? Does it mean——?"

I couldn't say it. He said it for me. "Ordinarily, it would not be too significant, but in your husband's case, I'm afraid the presence of active bacilli bears out the suspicion that a small cavity in the apex has broken through."

Cavity. The impact of the word shredded my sanity. It wasn't real, I was only reliving the old Trudeau nightmare when Dr. Heise had misread the X-rays. Or had he interpreted them correctly...?

I was conscious of Dr. Miller's quiet voice compelling me back into the present. "You must be prepared should there be more haemorrhaging from the lesion. I'll send on to you the names of two excellent physicians in London, but try to move on to Switzerland as soon as possible, and use your discretion as to how much, or how little, to tell your husband for the time being."

I told him nothing, because I knew that we would never get to Switzerland.

I was always grateful that he was spared the knowledge that now, suddenly, after so many, many years, his sputum was positive. He would have been afraid of exposing me and the children, and his patients when—or if—he returned to practice. I didn't let myself think that far. For the present, the responsibility to protect those he came in contact with was mine; and I would find ways without his knowing. I wanted only for him to have a wonderful time in London. And he did. He enjoyed every moment to the fullest, and neither rain nor fog could keep him from rehearsals. Auriol Lee was supposed to have directed the play, but she turned it over to me after the first few days, and sat in the back of the theatre talking to my husband. I was glad that they liked each other immediately. She was a plain and lovely woman with thick glasses, and I guess that was why he took to calling her, "Tante." The comfortable intimacy delighted her.

There were no problems in this English production. It is not in the tradition of the British actor to over-emphasize, and the performances were everything I could have asked. During our try-out week in Manchester, the values of the play emerged, and the vast theatre was filled each night to capacity. My husband caught what appeared to be another cold, but he refused to go to bed with it. "He's as well off watching the play as staying in a chilly hotel room," Auriol said. I thought it strange that she should have guessed that it was more than a cold without my saying so until she told me that she'd had tuberculosis. She said, "A lot of people you'd never suspect have had it."

I'd found that out, but I would not have supposed that Auriol was one of them. I don't know what I would have done without the quiet warmth of her understanding. I felt terribly alone and helpless so far from home, for I could sense that he was slowly losing ground. I prayed that it was my imagination that his collar was beginning to look too big on him, but in the endless hours of the night, I knew that it was not my imagination, and my heart broke.

The play was ready for its London opening. It was to be an occasion, with the King and Queen attending the première. My husband had a slight haemorrhage that morning, the first since our arrival in England. He hid it from me, and locked the door of the bathroom.

I was glad that Paul and John had gone out with the tutor I had engaged for them, and that Fraulein had taken Peter to Hyde Park. I paced the floor in mounting anguish. Would the door stay closed for ever?

At last he came out. He was pale, but his voice was jaunty, as if nothing had happened. "Well, what's wrong with *you*?" he demanded briskly.

It was beyond my strength to dissemble. I wet my parched lips. "Much?"

"I haven't the faintest idea what you're talking about." It was his way of telling me that nothing on earth was going to keep him from the opening. I let it rest at that, setting aside, for the first time in our marriage, my desperate, jealous guarding of his physical being. "Don't pay any attention to me," I said. "I guess I must be having a case of first-night jitters."

He remarked pointedly, "You'll be late for rehearsal if you don't hurry."

"I'm hurrying," I said.

"Will you need me?" I asked Auriol when I reached the theatre.

She looked at me for a long moment before she answered. "I expect he needs you more. But let him go this evening, duckie."

I nodded mutely, and returned to the hotel. The air was raw and a fog was drawing in. Perhaps this was as good a time as any to suggest Switzerland. "I think we could all use a little sun," I mentioned at lunch, which both of us pretended, valiantly, to eat.

He shook his head. "After the play is set and running, I want to go home," he said.

I wanted to go home, too, and this moment wouldn't have been too soon. It didn't matter about the play.

But it still mattered terribly to him. We sat in a box. The King and Queen sat in the opposite box. They didn't watch the stage, they kept glancing round at the audience. I didn't look at the stage, either. I closed my eyes, listening for that little cough, and praying. "Oh, dear God, don't let him have another haemorrhage——"

Halfway through the first act, he leaned over to whisper to me. "The Queen is watching the play!"

I blessed Queen Mary for making him so happy.

We went back to America the following week.

His examination showed that his sputum was negative. I didn't fool myself any longer, it could happen that way. But stupidly, I let him think that I was jubilant. "Isn't that wonderful!" I rejoiced.

He frowned. "Why shouldn't it be negative? Did you expect anything else?"

"Of course not, I meant your general improvement is wonderful."

He saw patients every day, but he spaced his appointments farther and farther apart, and began to delegate his hospital rounds. I took to driving downtown with him, always on the excuse of shopping for the children, or the house. Traffic wasn't heavy in those days; it wasn't difficult to drop him off at his office and return to pick him up. I didn't shop though, I always went home until it was time to call back for him, and tried to write against the agony of waiting.

"When are you going to finish *Twice Born*?" he kept asking me.

"Any minute now," I promised cheerfully, and every evening I read aloud to him whatever I had managed to get down on paper. I wanted him to believe that I was happy and interested in working on the novel so that he wouldn't realize how ill he was. And it is merciful that even with the wiliest of patients, the hope of recovery is slower to die than the human body.

Nothing of the outside world affected us very much in those precious two months that followed our return from abroad, except for one disappointment that he felt more keenly than I. When we'd left London *Another Language* was playing to capacity houses, and it was presumably set for a long run until an over-zealous reporter got wind of the fact that Edna Best was going to have a baby. When Auriol wrote us what had happened, she said that Edna was so upset by the premature publicity that she refused to make a spectacle of herself before the footlights that evening—probably, Auriol surmised, because of some unconscious embarrassment in playing opposite her husband, Herbert Marshall. (As I had found Miss Best to be not at all temperamental or difficult to work with, I thought this was very likely true.) At any rate, the understudy had taken over brilliantly, electrifying a disgruntled audience by the simple and strangely moving quality of her performance. "That plain girl became the essence of sheer beauty the instant she stepped on the stage," Auriol ended her letter, "and I promise you the play will not suffer with Edna's imminent retirement from the public eye."

The next thing we heard, Mr. Miller had closed *Another Language*. He gambled only on certainties, and an understudy, no matter how superb her performance, was still an understudy and not a name. It was too bad that he couldn't have taken a chance, just once, on an unknown actress called Celia Johnson.

The days passed gently, slowly, as if time wished to be tender with us during that period of quiet waiting. We saw few people, jealous of any intrusion on our peaceful evenings. We'd read, and listen to the victrola, and take Pat for a walk before we went to bed. The dachshunds hadn't succeeded in endearing themselves to us, and we were back to the single, satisfying package of a Great Dane. Jacob Rupert, a patient of my husbands, had found him wanting as a watch-dog, which made him perfect for us after our experience with Juno. It was too late to change calling him Pat although he deserved something of more stature than Pat, for he was a magnificent fawn, with a noble head. I often wondered how that powerful creature knew to walk quietly when my husband held his leash. It was one of the small miracles of that last tortured, beautiful year of our lives together.

[125]

On a day in late November, I drove him downtown as usual, and I waved to him as he walked, bow-legged, towards his office door. He looked like his old self, I thought with thankfulness in my heart, and he felt well enough to clown. I was almost happy.

There was a message from Max Perkins when I got home. I telephoned him. We talked for a while before he got around to asking about the novel.

"It's almost finished," I said, "except for the very end."

I sat down at the typewriter, and wrote the final chapter, and it came easily and simply, and I had no wish to change it. Then I rose, put on my hat and coat, and drove back to my husband's office. His nurse met me at the door. Her face was white. "Oh thank God you're here, he wouldn't let me call you———"

"I know," I said. "I've come to take him home."

"Dad has pneumonia," I told Paul. "The oxygen tent helps him to breathe better."

The apartment was large enough so that I didn't have to keep John and the baby quiet. "I knew Daddy was tired," John said.

"How?" I asked, sick at heart that I had not succeeded in keeping his world intact, free of the shadow of illness and insecurity.

"I could hear when he walked that he was tired."

It was a bond between us that was never broken.

On the afternoon of December thirteenth, I talked Paul into going to the movies. When he came home, I met him in the hall, and he followed me to the living-room, and I shut the door.

He looked at me in wonder. "You're not crying," he said.

"I have nothing to cry about now. But you can cry, it's right that you should."

I turned to leave him alone with his grief, because there was no way that I could help him. He put his hand on my shoulder to stop me. I shall never forget what he said, and how he said it—"I'll get Dad's things out, Mother. I know the suit and shirt he'd like to wear."

Paul had been a little boy when he went to the movies that afternoon. I had shielded and protected him all his young life, but when the moment came, he grew to manhood.

3

SECOND MARRIAGE. AND WHY

To become widowed is to find oneself alone in the private silences of grief, and no words come to me that would make articulate this ache of loneliness in space. To each woman is the dignity of her own sorrow, and her own means of achieving acceptance and peace. For myself, I sought help from neither God nor man—or so I thought. I could not even cry until long afterwards, and then it was always a little thing like the call of a mourning dove, or the sound of a coyote in the California hills that broke through the barriers that kept my heart frozen from feeling.

I would like to think that my stoicism, if such it was, grew roots from courage and a decent desire to go on living for my children's sake, but the habit of wifehood remained too strong within me. For my husband's sake I went on living, trying, against a desperate longing for the sight and touch of him, to meet the high level of what he would have me be, and do. It was not easy—it had never been easy—to reach beyond the fears that shackled me. As recently as our trip to London, I had shied away from discussing a revised clause in his will, miserably aware that he had uncovered another of my latent pockets of immaturity. "It's high time you grew up and stopped behaving like an ostrich," he told me. "Face it. We all have to die some day."

"With a little luck we can go together in a nice quick accident."

"Great for the children."

"Then I'll die first."

"I'm eight years older than you, why should you have the break of going ahead of me?"

WHEN ALL IS SAID AND DONE

He had had his break, and now, loving him, I could not wish it otherwise. I tried to say a little of what I felt to the two older boys. "We wouldn't want to hold Dad back if he had a chance to go on some wonderful holiday without us——"

"But he didn't go on a holiday," John interrupted gravely. "He's dead in a big box. I saw two men carry the box out of his room."

"Shut up!" Paul glared at him.

"No, don't shut him up," I said. "Listen to me, John. Dad isn't really in that box, it's just a sort of outside shell that was beginning to bother him, and he's much happier being free of it."

"But doesn't he have to have it to walk around with?"

"Not any more."

"Why?"

"Because our bodies aren't meant to last for ever, and the time comes to all of us when we don't need them."

"Like the snake we had in kindergarten that left its old skin on the floor?"

"Very much like that."

He'd said all there was to say about death while I'd fumbled with pretty speeches, which I'd have blushed to utter in my husband's presence. "Women who talk to hear themselves talk give me a swift pain," he always said. Well, I'd come pretty close to giving myself a swift pain, and it augured well for a parental relationship that I had the sense to climb down from my self-appointed pedestal. I could learn as much from the children as I could teach them, but it still didn't alter the fact that they did not, and could not, fill my life. They were on a different plane, in a different world.

Trouble brings out great kindness in people. People who were almost strangers were unbelievably kind. And then gradually, everyone seemed to forget a little, and the days became less crowded. And suddenly empty.

There were things to be done that not even my sister, close as she was, could help me with—the hard things, like clothes, and shoes, and the small, tucked-away milestones of a Trudeau snapshot, or a glowing review, or one of his handkerchiefs, torn to shreds, which I remembered his putting in my hand while John was being born. Yes. These things were even harder to bear than the dreaded reading of the will, followed by the special legalities that death entails. The "key to the vault" emerged from a vague reference to a grim reality, and I can still hear the echo of that hidden cavern in the bowels of the bank, and the loud, noiseless sliding of a long metal drawer full of documents and papers.

The lawyer explained that my husband had left his affairs in perfect order. There were no debts, but unfortunately he, like thousands of others, had lost his life-savings in the stock-market crash, and very little remained beyond his insurance, which, painstakingly, he had increased over the years against the odds of his early illness. His foresight, the lawyer told me gravely, was something to be grateful for.

But I wanted no part of that money. It represented the destruction of my happiness rather than the protection of my material existence, and I instructed the whole amount to be put into a savings account for the boys—a carry-over, no doubt, from the ten-dollar goldpieces of my adolescent birthdays. How much rather would I have had fifty cents to spend as I wished instead of twenty times that much that always ended up as a sterile digit in a small black pass-book. However, it was impressed upon me that some time in the future, I would be very grateful for the accruing benefits of this glittering nest-egg, and sure enough, one day it bought me a squirrel coat.

"But why not a savings bank?" I argued with the lawyer. Because, he pointed out with great patience, savings banks were no longer guaranteed beyond five thousand dollars, which would necessitate upwards of a dozen separate accounts, and secondly, the interest rate was far too low to provide sufficient income to support myself and three dependants.

"But it's safer than the stock market, and besides, I have enough income to get along with," I insisted stubbornly, and I was so lacking in any real significance of money that I believed it, and furthermore believed that I had every reason to believe it.

My cheque book showed a balance of close on twenty-five hundred in the joint housekeeping account, and a little over thirteen thousand in the "literary account" that my husband had fought me to keep in my name. This munificent sum did not even include the final instalment of the motion picture sale of *Another Language*, nor an accumulation of overdue royalties from the Broadway production, to say nothing of the funds that I had advanced to bring the road company back to New York. Out of the vastness of my inexperience, and an untarnished faith in human decency, I regarded these additional moneys as good as paid, and proceeded on the assumption that I was under no financial pressure whatsoever.

I look back upon the illogical decisions with which I reordered my way of life, and I recognize the blind obedience that once more shepherded me through that hazardous period of readjustment. Even now, I am at a loss to find a rational explanation for my sudden decision to give up the apartment and move to California. I knew hardly anyone out there and certainly I had no thought of writing for pictures, particularly since Hollywood had chosen to ignore any contribution that I might have made in adapting *Another Language* to the screen. I had been too harassed by more important problems to notice the slight, but Adrienne Morrison couldn't understand why "Metro" had failed to contact me, and when she heard of my intention to go to the coast, she was the only one of all my friends and relatives who encouraged me. "A successful credit is all you need to land a contract at any one of the major studios, and with Helen Hayes and Robert Montgomery in it, *Another Language* is bound to be good box-office. I'll start the wheels rolling before you leave New York."

"But I don't want to write for the movies," I told her.

She looked nonplussed. "Then why uproot yourself like this if you don't intend to work out there?"

I couldn't tell her why, because I didn't know why. I made the lame excuse that it was a healthier life for the children than being cooped up in a city apartment, to which she murmured something to the effect that she was glad that I was so well provided for that I didn't have to prostitute my talent to pictures. "I'll be expecting a new play from you one week after you find a house and get settled," she told me, only half in jest.

I never wanted to write another play for as long as I lived, but it was my emotional safeguard to avoid the personal. I said instead, "Maxwell Perkins thinks I ought to follow up *Twice Born* with a less controversial book."

"I have the greatest respect for Mr. Perkins, but I don't agree with him," Adrienne stated flatly. "Fundamentally you're not a novelist, you're a dramatist."

I was neither, and I wondered how she could fail to realize that writing meant less to me now than ever. I had no reason to write, nor was the urge for self-expression strong enough to help supplant the emptiness in my life.

There was a night, so full of insupportable longing, that I cupped a dozen sleeping tablets in my palm, thinking how easy it could be to put an end to this ache of being. Then, slowly, I put them back into the bottle. *Great for the children.* No. I didn't have the courage to face his disappointment in me. The weeks, the months, the years, beckoned only the reward of being together again. "Nobody lives for ever," I kept promising myself.

It was my secret and ignominious source of strength.

I learned, in time, that I must banish the shadow of widowhood from my conscious thinking. And yet, as I put these lines to paper, the never quite vanquished memories come flooding back, and incidents, long forgotten, leap into awareness with the astonishing suddenness of one of those toy paintings that lie hidden beneath a blank page until the sweep of a wetted brush brings it to light.

I recall, for example, going into the kitchen early one morning, and James greeting me with a look of glory in his eyes. "Doctor visit me last night before I fell asleep," he said. "He didn't stay long, he just stood by the bed, sort of smiling a little, but not talking one single word. I reckon he didn't have the stren'th yet for talking."

I remember the ridiculous tremor of apprehension that went

[131]

through me—I could never bear the thought of his being tired, or overtaxed. "Don't breathe anything about this to the boys, James," I said with difficulty. "It might upset them."

"No, ma'am, I won't. Anyways, I reckon you is the onliest one Doctor wanted to have know about it."

In that case, I reflected ironically, there was no earthly reason why "Doctor" couldn't have made his presence known to me directly, and I am certain—or almost certain—that I would have attributed James's story to the childlike superstitions of his race, if, that same afternoon, I hadn't received a telephone call from Auriol Lee. She had been in New York for several weeks directing a play of John Van Druten's, and the news of my husband's death had shattered her. Our one short visit together had been hard on both of us, even though I felt that it was a tribute that those who had known him so briefly should grieve so deeply.

Today, however, Auriol's voice was joyous. "Duckie! The most extraordinary thing happened a few minutes ago. Do you remember how he used to call me 'Tante'?"

"Yes," I said over a closing throat. "Why?"

"Because that's how I knew he was with me. I was breaking in the first act business, when suddenly I felt a tug at my jacket. 'That's a nice scene, Tante——' I expect it took a moment to gather my wits, and by the time I turned, he was gone."

I tried to control the most absurd sense of relief that he wasn't tired as James had reported, at least not too tired to hang around the theatre again, being stage-struck. . . . And then the next thing I knew, I heard Paul's accustomed bellow as he came home from school. "Mother! Where are you!"

I was in heaven, spheres removed from his demanding presence in the doorway. "Why didn't you answer me? Mother! What's the matter?"

The sharp break of anxiety in his voice pulled me back from a long, long distance into space. He was an outsider, an intruder, it was difficult for me to keep the impatience out of my reply. "Nothing's the matter."

"You look funny."

"Thank you."

"You were sitting with the telephone on your lap and your eyes closed."

"There's no law against it." I struggled for matter-of-factness, but he continued to search my face uneasily. "Don't you feel well? Were you calling the doctor or anything?"

"I feel fine. And if you must know, detective, I was talking to Auriol Lee."

"From London, with the eye-glasses?"

"From London with the eye-glasses."

A grin finally took over, but still he seemed obsessed by some nameless misgiving. "She must have liked Dad a lot," he said huskily. "She cried the day she came up to see you."

"A lot of people cried. A lot of people miss him, and will go on missing him. It should make you proud."

He swallowed hard. "I guess you miss him more than anybody."

I longed to tell him that his father had at last succeeded in penetrating the high wall of scepticism that he had, himself, built firm and high against my susceptibility, and I had only to open my mind and my heart and there would be no more separateness between us. But I knew that Paul was not ready to share this glorious revelation. "Yes," I said merely, "I miss him."

"Then I wish you'd cry too," he blurted out.

I could have cried, then, because so much that would never be said lay unsaid between us. "Don't you ever feel that he's very close?" I asked with effort.

He didn't answer, and as he stood looking down at me, I thought how strongly he resembled his father. "I think maybe Dad wouldn't want us to feel that he's around," he said finally. "I think he'd probably think it's better to miss people than to believe in ghosts."

The way he said it was at once an accusation and a plea. I couldn't speak for a long moment, and then I gave him the reassurance he so needed. "I don't believe in ghosts either, Paul. Don't worry about me. I promise you I'm all right."

Doubt and anxiety cleared from his eyes, and suddenly he was a little boy again, and flung his arms round Pat who was impatient for his afternoon run. The floor shook with all the scrabbling and

[133]

barking until the front door banged behind them. I was glad that Pat had given himself to Paul above all of us. Paul could show his emotions to Pat without feeling less the man. Pat could take over where I had to leave off.

I listened for the whirring of the lift cables, and then the clanging of the gate and the last rumble of the descending cage told me I was free to return to my private universe. The apartment more than ever was deeply quiet. John was at his play-group, Fraulein had taken Peter shopping with her in his go-cart, and James was off on one of his periodic missions compounded of "an insurance matter" and a sick friend.

Silence and solitude, passport to Paradise, I thought as I closed my eyes again, but the fleeting impression of my husband's nearness had vanished, and against the darkness etched behind my lids, I could not lose the familiarity of the four walls that enclosed me. The very stillness of the room gave back the echo of Paul's voice. "Mother! You look funny!"—Strange that the glow of radiance from within me should have so alarmed him that he would rather have come upon me weeping. He did not want me to be vaguely, disturbingly different from other mothers. "It's better to miss people than to believe in ghosts," he had said.

I was aware of the telephone slipping from my lap. I replaced it carefully on the night table, and rose from the edge of the bed, and walked to the window. The park stretched out skeleton-bleak against the wintry sky, and many stories down, I saw the pigmy figures of Paul and Pat crossing the street to head for a favoured tree. It was not until they blurred from my vision that I realized that at long last I was crying, not in loneliness, but because I knew that I had relinquished my final prop, I knew that I would have to learn not to lean upon that belief of my husband's nearness, or borrow of his strength. It was enough to know that he would always be there, like the sun or the rain or the stars. And if some day we were to be together again, I could not hurry that day, no matter how much I wanted to. I belonged here, in this dimension, with my feet planted firmly on this earth. It was one thing to feel that my children were on another plane, in another world, but it was a quite different thing for me to be on another plane, in another world. I could not afford to trade ecstasy for sanity.

There was a kind of dimension to space in this sudden realization, and I felt lost in a confusion of intangibles. But for the first time in my marriage, I was not afraid.

I wish that I could say that I stayed free of fear, but I was to taste its torment again and yet again in the full years of living that lay ahead.

In retrospect, I marvel at the ease and celerity with which my move to California was effected. I had no difficulty in disposing of the apartment, with a fair price added for the curtains and carpets. The eighteenth-century pieces, of which we had amassed a sizeable collection, went to the Anderson Galleries, and the "little second-hand man" on the corner cleared out what remained. I watched everything go with detachment. I had little sentiment about holding on to a present that held neither past nor future. The lovely things that had made our home had served their purpose.

I was grateful that the children didn't spring a lot of symptoms at the prospect of strange surroundings, new schools, new friends. "As long as we can take Pat with us," Paul said; and John had his cat, and Peter had Fraulein, who couldn't face the thought of parting from him, or from any of us. "Always I have wanted to see California," she lied. "The trip is enough, without the big salary that you pay me. You should cut it in half now. It is plenty."

"Oh, hush!" I told her. "I'm lucky that you're willing to go with us."

I was just as lucky that James evinced no desire to leave New York. He was preacher of his Church every other Sunday, and good fairy to a small segment of Harlem that depended upon him for one thing or another. "You might miss a few groceries occasionally," I alerted one of my friends who was panting to "have" him, "but he doesn't feel that it's stealing."

"He doesn't?" She pondered the distinction dubiously. "What about jewellery?"

"Never." I was emphatic on that score until it occurred to me that I didn't have anything of value except my engagement ring. "If he did, though, he still wouldn't consider it dishonest."

"But it is," she insisted in slight agitation. "Doesn't he realize that he shouldn't take what doesn't belong to him?"

"Not when it all goes to the needy," I returned virtuously.

"The needy don't need jewellery." She closed the discussion with flat lips, being rather literal about the whole thing, but she decided to engage him, anyway.

James, loyal to the last, insisted on seeing us safely on the train. No one else was at the station. I still hate good-byes, and I'd begged everyone, including my sister and aunt, to stay away.

"Everything is going to work out jus' fine in California," he managed a few words alone with me as the guard gave the "all aboard" signal. "Doctor, he arranged this whole business for you to go."

I smiled. "I shouldn't wonder, James." I was content to accept the unexplainable. There are some things which, once acknowledged, are better left unquestioned.

Still, I suppose that even guardian angels lose their grip occasionally. The trip was a nightmare. A drawing-room with an adjoining compartment looked spacious on the tickets, but in the era that preceded the refinements of the Chief and the Super-Chief, our accommodations turned out to be two cubicles of a dusty and horrendous green velour, one of which afforded toilet facilities that permitted barely enough floor space for the cat's pan and a human foot, judiciously balanced. Fortunately, Pansy conducted himself as a gentleman and a scholar, but unfortunately Pat, who was Paul's and my sleeping companion, was all gentleman. I have always hotly denied the legend that Great Danes are beautiful but not bright, but I must admit that Pat's brain could not encompass the idea that, when the train stopped, it was time for him to *go*. When we pulled out of Kansas City, Paul and I were still holding our breaths and it was anybody's guess what Pat was holding. Eventually, of course, something had to give, and he threw up at intervals all through Texas. Paul manfully, if gingerly, tackled the disaster areas, but the power of suggestion lessened his efficiency.

"I don't feel good either," John whimpered.

"I don't feel *well*," I corrected him, and added with asperity, "Look out of the window instead and watch the scenery."

At Albuquerque, all of us, including Pat, were diverted by the novelty of live Indians squatting in the station square, weaving baskets. Rearing wildly on his leash, he scared the poor things half to death, and of course they didn't know that he was the one who was terrified of *them*. Which, in the end, turned out to be a very good thing indeed.

Back in the drawing-room, I breathed deeply for the first time in three days and four nights. "Anyway, I give you 'A' for effort," I addressed my husband silently.

We had left New York in the middle of a blizzard, but when we emerged from the train at Pasadena the air was as soft as mid-summer, and there were roses blooming along a white fence at the far side of the platform.

"Ach, fritty!" Fraulein exclaimed. (She had never quite mastered the lingual intricacies of "pretty.") "See, Peter, the fritty flowers?"

"Where's the snow?" Peter demanded, enchanted not at all by this miracle of misplaced seasons.

John gave him a disgusted shove. "There's no snow in California, dope."

"I am not so a dope!"

"Damn it, cut it out, you brats!" Paul thundered at them.

"You're not our father!" The words escaped John's lips before he could stop them. He darted a quick look to see how I'd taken it, but I had bandaged my heart from feeling. "Listen, the three of you behave!" I commanded. "We're going to a hotel, and I want no fighting or kicking or cursing out of any of you."

The "Château Elysée," which Adrienne Morrison had recommended, was not really a hotel. It was that unique species of hostelry indigenous to Hollywood—a cross between an apartment house and a glorified boarding-house. And rather beautiful it was—a huge, turreted building, hidden away from the bustle of Franklin Avenue by tall palm trees and lovely gardens. The suites were pleasant and commodious, with disappearing beds that fascinated the children, and a kitchenette off the living-room that lured Fraulein like a magnet. The miniscule stove and refrigerator weren't meant to be taken literally, but that didn't deter her from sneaking an onion into her personal meat ball with the smell of it seeping out into the corridors. Why spend good money to have bad food sent up from downstairs?

I, too, found it easier to partake of Fraulein's illicit repasts upstairs, which also served the double purpose of keeping the whole lot of us fairly invisible. Although I liked the Château very much, I had strong doubts as to whether the Château returned the compliment, for I was beginning to suspect that our mass invasion had come as somewhat of a shock to the management. The illegibility of my handwriting having grown more so with age, it was entirely conceivable that the room clerk who had granted my request for accommodations, had mis-read Dane for Dachs, three children for two, and given up entirely on trying to make head or tail out of a Persian cat.

In any event, and all things considered, the sooner we found a house of our own the better it would be for everyone. A real-estate agent, conveniently located across the street from the Château, assured me that she had any number of houses to offer, but with one special listing ideally suited to my needs. "Here it is," she said, whipping the card out of her files. "Six master bedrooms, four baths, servants' wing, three-car garage, landscaped grounds. Monthly rental $200, including services of excellent couple accustomed to assuming full charge."

"What's wrong with it?" I asked distrustfully.

"Neighbourhood," she replied without hedging. "It's on June Street in one of the best residential sections in Los Angeles, but people in the movie set prefer to be in Beverley."

"Oh.—Well, I haven't anything to do with movies, so I'd like to look at it," I said, but with no great optimism. I'd run the gamut of enough summer rentals in the past decade to know that if there was one large fly in the ointment, there were likely to be several smaller ones.

But try as I would, I could find no fault with the house on June

Street. Indeed, the curtailed description in the files had failed to do it justice, having made no mention of the picture postcard magnolias and bougainvillaea outside, and inside, the impressive marble foyer, the brace of elaborate dressing-rooms adjoining the master suite, and last but not least, the mouth-watering perfection of the pink and copper kitchen. "This can't be America," I thought dazedly, for the first but not for the last time in the years I was to remain in California. Hollywood held all the astonishments of a Never-Never Land, a luxurious wilderness where live baby goats were for sale on Wilshire Boulevard, and bakeries were windmills, and restaurants were hats, and flower vendors sold fresh violets sprayed with perfume from an atomizer, and astrologists and palmists hung out their signs on every block, and did a thriving business.

It was only a matter of a day or so before we moved into our new home. "Ach, berdiful!" Fraulein breathed in awe, peering out of the taxi window.

"You haven't seen anything yet," I said, and rang the bell with an air of ownership.

Alas, it was only too true. The door swung open, and Lillian and Bertram, our inherited couple, stood on the threshhold, freezing visibly at the spectacle of the motley entourage of livestock and luggage piling up along the stone entrance path. In one split second, Fraulein developed an instant animosity towards them, and they returned the sentiment in full. Unlike dogs, they didn't even have to nose each other out.

Too late I realized that all is not gold that glitters, or in other words, a very big fly had been hiding in the ointment all along. The competent services of these two impeccably bloodless creatures, "accustomed to assuming complete charge" for their absent employer, were irrevocably written into the terms of the lease, which meant that Fraulein had about as much chance of gaining entrance into the stronghold of that beautiful pink and copper kitchen as the proverbial snowball in hell.

"Supper will be ready at six-thirty, madam," Lillian informed me after a chilly acknowledgment of our united presence. "I've prepared a meat loaf and a tapioca pudding."

"Ugh," John injected with a violent shudder.

"If you will make out your menus each morning," Lillian continued with an unaffectionate glance in his direction, "Bertram will attend to the marketing."

"I'll attend to my own marketing," Fraulein muttered. The beauty of the marble foyer with its winding stairway was lost upon her. Red blotches showed on her neck, which meant danger, and I didn't know whether to hope that the supper would be tasty or nasty.

It was a little of both, but it didn't matter, because Peter developed a sudden cough and a slight fever, which took Fraulein's mind off the meat-loaf's gelatinous texture, and nobody had much appetite, anyway. We slipped big chunks of everything to Pat who stationed himself like a bottomless garbage pail under the table, and our empty plates saved Lillian from also getting red spots. I recognized that she, too, was at that age.

Peter was coughing less the next morning, and his temperature was normal, but Fraulein decided that it was wiser to keep him in bed. "*Gott sie dank* it is not a cold," she said, "but better we take no chances."

"Better we don't," I agreed, and with Fraulein marooned upstairs, I committed the diplomatic treason of giving Lillian free rein and twenty-five dollars to cover our immediate food requirements. Then I asked Bertram to call a taxi, and took the two older boys to enrol in what the agent had assured me was "a very good school in the immediate vicinity." She didn't misrepresent, exactly, it was simply that we weren't talking the same language, for I had yet to discover that there were no "immediate vicinities" in Los Angeles. "This is one place, miss, you got to have your own car in or you'll go broke on taxi fares," the driver volunteered.

He further advised me, when we finally arrived at our destination, that the meter would run up a fortune if he waited for us, and it was a good thing he didn't, because the red tape of enrolment dragged on and on, and only at the very end was I casually apprised of the fact that the grades did not go beyond the eighth year, which excluded Paul, who was ready for "Junior

High." My already sagging spirits took a nose-dive. The days wouldn't be long enough to tote them to different schools every morning, and call back for them at different hours every afternoon. "Isn't there any place I can put both together?" I appealed to the registrar.

She looked over her shoulder as if chary of being overheard. "I send my two boys to Black Fox," she said.

"What's Black Fox?"

"It's a Military Academy about a ten-minute drive from where you live," adding in a seeming *non-sequitur*, "I'm from New York myself. Originally."

"Oh," I said. We smiled at each other, like Americans meeting in a foreign country. "You mean it's really only a ten-minute drive from June Street?"

"Really. No more, and maybe less."

"Thanks. Will I be able to get a taxi on the street?"

She gave me a pitying look. "Poor Easterner," she said. "I'll telephone for one."

I thanked her again.

"What's a poor Easterner?" John asked, as we waited interminably in front of the school.

"Us," I told him briefly.

"What's a Military Academy?"

"Shut up," said Paul. "Mother's tired."

For once, I didn't deny it. The thermometer was climbing, and I wore my winter suit. "You can take your coats off," I told the boys, "and take one off for me."

The taxi came at last. I leaned back against the sticky leather seat, trying not to think of all the small problems that were suddenly bulking up.

"What are we going to have for lunch?" John asked.

"I don't know." (That was one of the problems—I hoped it wouldn't be something like tinned cornbeef hash.)

"Is it chicken?" he pursued hopefully.

"I don't know."

"Do I have to go to that school?"

"I don't know."

Paul cleared his throat. "I wonder where the school I'm to go is."

"I don't know. It's too hot to worry about it now, let's worry about it tomorrow."

There was no need to. The problem took care of itself, not nicely, but conclusively. When we got home, Peter's temperature was up again, and his breath laboured between coughs. Pneumonia! My knees turned to rubber, I felt bereft without the familiar coterie of doctors that had always surrounded me. Now I knew no one to whom I could turn. Except Sonya Levien. Sonya had been the fiction editor of the old *Metropolitan* that had bought a couple of my short stories. After the magazine folded, she and her husband, Carl Hovey, had gone out to Hollywood where Sonya became a successful scenarist, and Carl engaged on some cherished project of his own. Reluctant to thrust my aloneness into their busy lives, I hadn't let them know of my arrival, but with Peter's illness, I had no alternative but to ask their help. I had their private telephone in my address book, and Nanny—their Scotch equivalent for Fraulein—remembered me from New York, and gave me a warm welcome along with Sonya's number at the studio.

Sonya was astonished and delighted to learn that I had moved to the coast, but we didn't waste time over it. "Look, don't worry about Peter," she assured me, "everybody always has colds and grippes and throats in this climate, but anyway, I have the most marvellous doctor in the world, and I'll get in touch with the service, and call you back."

I counted the minutes, glumly mulling over the dubious comfort of her casual allusion to this sunny world of ill-health. Sooner than I dared hope, the telephone rang again. "Dr. Brown will be over within half an hour. I'll phone you later to see how everything is. . . ."

I hung up, feeling less stranded and alone. I went back to Peter's room, and motioned Fraulein aside. "A Dr. Brown is coming over; Mrs. Hovey says he's excellent."

Fraulein said, "That is good. This is not acting like only a cold."

I didn't have to be told that it wasn't. Having absorbed, for better or for worse, a smattering of medical facts, I knew too much for my own good. Nervously, I awaited Dr. Brown's arrival and flew down the stairs when I heard a car turn in the drive.

I opened the door to an attractive woman wearing a leather jacket over a well-tailored skirt and blouse, with a coil of ash-blonde hair in nice contrast to what I had, up to this instant, accepted as the healthy tan of the average Californian. I immediately concluded that she was a friendly neighbour dropping in, but before I had a chance to speak, she said, "I'm Dr. Brown."

I tried to rule the chagrin from my voice as I returned her greeting. Theoretically, I was all for women being what they wanted to be, but faced with actuality, I preferred a traditional physician of the masculine sex (with apologies to the late Dr. Sarah Jordan of the Leahy Clinic in Boston). Nevertheless, I could find no fault with Dr. Brown's medical approach. She examined Peter's ears, nose, eyes, throat, chest, abdomen, spleen, liver and heart, while I stood by, numb with apprehension. And then he gave his first whoop.

Dr. Brown folded her stethoscope. "No need to go any further."

This time my knees went weak with relief. "Do you think that the other two boys are liable to come down with it, too? Neither of them has had whooping cough."

"Have they been in close contact?"

I thought of how they'd been huddled together in the train. "Very close."

She had a nice smile. "Be prepared."

"I haven't started them at a school yet.—Should I?"

"Wait a couple of days." She scribbled a prescription. "This may ease the spasms. Otherwise there's nothing much to be done except to sit it out. Don't hesitate to call me if you have any questions."

"I won't. And thank you."

"You did not tell me——" Fraulein began at once, with thin lips.

"I was just as surprised as you were."

"It is a good thing it is nothing serious," she averred elliptically.

That evening, when Sonya telephoned to find out how Peter was, I asked, "Is Dr. Brown just a paediatrician?"

Sonya said, "Oh, no, she's our family physician, we have her for everything. Isn't she wonderful?"

"Yes," I said. I hung up the receiver thoughtfully. I was more firmly grooved in convention than I'd realized, and if I wanted to adjust to this new life, a woman doctor probably wouldn't be the only hurdle I'd have to make. Paul had informed me at supper that the boy next door had a "nifty secondhand convertible," and drove himself to school every day. "There's no other way to get to places," he said. "All the kids have cars here."

My blood ran cold.

"I hope you're not going to be a sissy about it, Mother. . . ."

It was a tactful way of begging me not to be the one to make him into the sissy. But he's only fourteen, I thought bleakly, and compromised by buying a car for family use, and teaching him to drive it. I might mention in passing that in due course I taught all three boys how to drive. My licence is older than they are, but you'd never know it. To them, I'm just another female at the wheel.

The next morning John started with Peter's symptoms, and it wasn't long before Paul followed suit, which settled more than the immediate problem of schools. Fraulein had her hands so full with the three of them coughing it up in blatant competition, that she couldn't have taken over the reins of housekeeping no matter how much she longed to. Lillian and Bertram had both had the disease when young, but nevertheless they kept themselves conspicuously isolated, even to the point of not waiting at table, lest, by some perversity of nature, they catch it again.

And so it was that a kind of false truce descended upon the domestic scene, and in the lull of hostilities, I finally got round to straightening out my finances. I was in for a rude shock, for I soon discovered that a bank balance can deplete at an alarming rate if it is not periodically replenished. Travelling expenses alone had made a big dent in my original capital, to say nothing of two months' rent in advance, wasteful servants, Fraulein's salary, doctor's bills, and sixteen hundred dollars for the new Buick. To offset these expenditures, I had received not a cent of the moneys that were owing to me, and whereas I had counted on a considerable sum from the sale of the furniture, a freak blizzard, combined with an end-of-the-season slump, had conspired against the high prices that the Anderson Galleries expected the collection to bring. After the fees for the insurance, cartage and cataloguing were deducted from the total, there remained a very modest sum indeed to deposit against my rapidly dwindling funds.

Although I told myself that I had bid in a lot of bargains myself at auction, it was a purely moral sense of retribution, and did not alter the fact that I was suddenly confronted with the serious problem of not only supporting and educating three children but providing as well against the exigencies of illness and catastrophe. This meant that I would have to buckle down and master the one trade at which I could conceivably earn a livelihood. I could no longer afford to regard writing as a pastime or a hobby. I hired a typewriter, and bought a ream of paper, and started on my third novel.

Always an early riser, I began work at six in the morning before the demands of the boys and the household converged upon me. At first I couldn't concentrate in the loud noisiness of uninterrupted silence, and I missed desperately the blessed crowning of each day's batch of pages—there was no one to read what I had written, or to encourage me to go on with it. I suppose, in a way, it was subjective writing, for I told a story that was in direct contrast to my own marriage, the story of a woman who very nearly permitted a career to wreck her home and happiness. How humour ever crept into the lines I shall never know, but at any rate the pile of manuscript grew into a sufficient number of chapters to send on to Maxwell Perkins.

With the intuitive gentleness that I had come to know in him, he put in a long-distance call to tell me how much he liked it. His approval lifted a heavy load of doubt from my heart, but when he spoke of scheduling publication for the following autumn, I realized with a dull thud of significance that a novel was a luxury form of writing that would yield no immediate income and possibly very little future renumeration. As if he sensed my dismay, he remarked casually that it was not uncustomary to make an advance payment to an "established author," but with a puritan horror towards unfulfilled obligations and possible indebtedness, I refused his generous offer. It was a lucky thing that I did, because Scribner's never did publish that novel, and it wasn't until many years later that I renewed my professional contact with Max.

In the meantime, I ploughed ahead on the book, doggedly intent upon finishing it before the summer, when my sister planned to visit me with Donna and Margot. My days were regimented solely to the combined demands of typewriter and children and I felt guilty in fostering the illusion to those at home that I was leading a glamorous Hollywood existence, when I hadn't so much as budged from the house, except on the single occasion when Sonya asked me to have lunch with her at the studio.

We had a lot to catch up on, against the bizarre surroundings of the Twentieth Century Fox café, and I was thankful that she said, merely, "He was a wonderful person. Carl and I always loved the way he was so proud of you"—and then she went on to talk about *Twice Born.*

"I asked Scribner's to send me a set of page-proofs," she said, "hoping there'd be a movie in it, but there isn't a chance. It's a fine, adult piece of work, but it's ahead of its time.—You never had a movie sale out of *Pattern* either, did you?"

"No. My agent submitted it, but the studios were afraid of a story that was fundamentally the study of a neurosis."

"Well, maybe the picture industry will grow up some day." She broke off to greet with affection a pleasant, freckled-faced man who paused to drop a kiss on the top of her head. "Spencer! Have you finished lunch, or are you about to begin——?"

"Finished."

"Sit down anyway, and have some coffee with us.—I don't think you've met Rose Franken yet, she's just come on from New York——"

"I'm delighted," he said, as if he knew who I was. He drew up an empty chair, and gave me a warm, twinkling kind of smile that seemed vaguely familiar.

[146]

"Keep a watch for her new book, it'll be out in a few weeks," Sonya told him. "It'll surprise you. To look at her, you wouldn't think she knew anything about such things."

"In that case, I'll certainly make a point of buying it." He withdrew a small memopad from his pocket and removed the top of his fountain pen. "What's the name of it?"

I waited for Sonya to carry on what she had begun, but she was busy catching the attention of our waitress. I was on my own. "*Twice Born*," I croaked uncomfortably, and not wanting to dominate the conversation, I added politely, "Do you write, too?"

"Do I write?" He moved his head in rueful negation. "I'm sorry to say I don't."

I wasn't good at small talk, and Sonya was still occupied with the problem of ordering another cup of coffee. "Then what do you do in pictures?" I pursued a trifle desperately.

"Well," he admitted, "I act a little."

I'm sure that he has no memory of the incident, but I've never forgotten it. His hair has turned white, and his face and his body show age, but to me, he retains all the dynamics and charm of his early stardom. And even then I unashamedly, in my letters home, made great stock of my encounter with Spencer Tracy. It fostered the impression that I was meeting all sorts of celebrities, and having a gay and wonderful time.

And yet, knowing just one person as I knew Sonya can sometimes open up strange doors, and lead to a series of events that determine a whole new way of life. A few weeks after our luncheon together, she gave a cocktail party for me. I begged her not to go to all that trouble (I didn't add that it was trouble for me to buy a new dress, which I could ill afford, and get my hair set, which I loathed), but she said how else was I ever going to get to meet people? It would have sounded ungracious to protest that I didn't especially want to get to meet people, so I thanked her effusively, and hied myself to a nice little shop that Lillian told me about on the corner of Hollywood and Vine. It was called "Magnin's." She also told me about a nice little beauty parlour on the corner of Wilshire and Rodeo, and as she was an ardent follower of the society columns, it so happened that she didn't

[147]

steer me wrong on either place. I bought a lovely gown (I kept it for years and years, and wore it for my Genthe photograph) and yielded to the persuasions of a slim young man who, with light, graceful hands, wrecked the serviceable bun at the back of my head.

"Stop it. What are you doing!" I screeched in horror.

"Nothing, dear, be quiet. Just snipping off an inch or two here and there."

"You snipped at least six inches, I'll never be able to roll it up now!"

"Of course not, dear. Who wears buns any more? I'm going to give you a nice long bob with a very light permanent."

"But I have a small natural wave of my own!"

"Yes, I know, dear, it's very small and there's not enough body to it. Just trust Shelly, dear, and close your eyes and relax."

I closed my eyes, but I didn't trust Shelly and I didn't relax. While I was chained up to the ceiling in sizzling spirals, he brought me a cup of tea and a biscuit on a tray with a lace doily. I pushed it away. "I don't want it. You're a snake in the grass, you're going to make me look like Shirley Temple."

He dropped a light kiss on my cheek. "I'm going to make you look absolutely divine," he said. "Your husband won't recognize you when he sees you. Does your scalp feel hot anywhere?"

I shook my head. All of a sudden, I couldn't feel anything except the slow, sick beat of my heart all over my body.

As it was the first time that I had gone out in the evening since my arrival in California, I had about as much privacy as I dressed as a goldfish. Lillian added to the crowd, drifting to my bedroom door on the pretence of bringing in some freshly laundered towels. "You sure look nice," she said, with the pride of sponsorship.

"She looks berdiful!" Fraulein amended loyally.

The two younger boys said I looked funny. I really didn't care how I looked. Less than ever I wanted to go to this party that was being given in my honour.

Paul followed me to the garage. "Gosh, Mother, is nobody going to call for you?"

"I don't know 'nobody' to call for me," I rejoined flippantly, "and besides I'm a big girl. I can take care of myself." I felt sorry for him, I knew he couldn't help but worry about me. He was too old to be a little boy and too young to be a man.

It was a long ride into Beverly Hills, and Sonya's large drawing-room was already crowded when I arrived. "Would you believe I didn't recognize you as you walked in?" she exclaimed. "You look ten years younger than when you first came out here!" She linked her arm through mine. "Come on and meet everybody. . . ."

I didn't realize until the next day that the place was jammed with notables, along with a collection of Sols and Sams who were apparently quite important too. In fact I worked for no less than three Sols and four Sams during my Hollywood career, and that's what their names really were—not Solomon or Samuel, just undiluted Sols and Sams. Sol Wurtzel was the first Sol I was introduced to. "This is the dearest person in the world," Sonya said, leading me up to an unremarkable man with thick glasses and a fleeting spasmodic smile, to which I needn't have kept smiling back, as it proved to be not a smile, but a tick. "He taught me everything I know about pictures," she went on. "I'll always be grateful to him for my apprenticeship at Fox Western." I'd already gathered, when I'd had lunch with her, that the Fox Beverly Hills Studio was the rich relation of the Fox Western Studio of which Mr. Wurtzel was evidently in full control.

"I hear you wrote a couple of good novels," he began at once, offering me a succulent morsel of stuffed fish on a toothpick. "Dip it in some of this red horse-radish."

Sonya's rambling white clapboard house sat stubbornly behind its picket fence like a protest against the surrounding mansions of Spanish architecture, and the fish, too, was a kind of protest on the sumptuously laden buffet table. Mr. Wurtzel seemed to prefer it to the more delicate and expensive delicacies, but I didn't happen to like the taste of it. Surreptitiously I dumped it on a transient plate and selected a caviar canapé instead, which, taste for taste, if you get right down to brass tacks, is worse and more of it except that it's caviar. "I don't know how good they are," I temporized modestly. "The novels, I mean."

He helped himself to another bouquet of fish and horseradish, and carefully broke the toothpick into an ash-tray before he spoke again. "Who's your agent?"

"Adrienne Morrison is connected with someone out here called Rosalie Stewart——"

"I know Rosalie," he broke in. "I do business with her."

"I've never met her, but she's telephoned me——"

"What's the matter. She couldn't get you a job?" he interrupted again.

"I haven't wanted a job."

"Why not? You're too rich to work for the movies? Or maybe too highbrow?"

"Neither," I assured him, and before I could explain that I was writing another novel, a tall, sandy-haired man joined us, and Sol introduced him sketchily and drifted off to find himself a glass of water. "Hardest thing you can try to get at a party," he grumbled.

"It is, isn't it?" I smirked woodenly at my new companion, anguished for the warm, familiar presence of my husband to whom I could always gravitate when small talk froze on my lips. "I'd like to have some too, but ginger ale will do," I said.

"With what in it?"

"Nothing, thanks."

"On the wagon, eh? Good girl."

I let that one pass. He corralled a passing waiter. "A bottle of ginger ale and a scotch and soda in the library. . . ." I felt a firm hand beneath my elbow. "Come on, let's get out of this mob. I don't belong here either. I just blew in from New York for a couple of days. . . ."

Thankfully, I followed him to the comparative quiet of Carl's study; I accepted a cigarette, careful not to put the wrong end in my mouth, and when he lit it for me, I unobtrusively didn't smoke it. I'd never learned to inhale without making unbecoming faces and sounds, but my gown and hair-do dictated a certain amount of sophistication. I cleared my throat, and made perfunctory conversation. "Have you known Sonya long?"

"Back in the old newspaper days when I was a cub reporter.

Tell me, I'm very curious to find out something. Are you by any remote chance related to this Franken woman who wrote *Another Language*? A fourth cousin twice removed, perhaps?"

What a bore he was! "Not even a first cousin," I replied with heavy-handed humour.

His eyes swept over me like a broom. "I didn't think you could be. I gather she's a pretty gruesome specimen, although that's one hell of a fine play, don't you agree?"

"I didn't care for it too much," I kept up my end of it.

"You didn't? Well I did. But when I asked to set up an interview with her, the producer told me to spare myself the disillusion. It seems she's a big fat dame who lives up in the Bronx somewhere, and speaks with an accent you can cut with a knife."

This was carrying small talk, or any other kind of talk, a little to extremes. He'd probably had more to drink than was good for him.

"Shall we go back to the other room?" I suggested coldly.

It didn't even remotely occur to me that he might have been perfectly sober, with no intention whatsoever of trying to be funny. Had I realized it, I doubt that I could have resisted the dramatic fillip of astounding him with my identity.

I was in the society columns of Lillian's newspaper the next morning, and she was much impressed. So was I. I bought a few copies to send home as proof positive that I was having a wonderful time. And the funny part of it was, that I really could have started going out and having a gay time. Following on the heels of Sonya's party, I was besieged with all sorts of invitations, but I was too reticent to accept hospitality from people who were complete strangers to me. Besides, it was only right to spend my evenings with the children, since I felt under pressure to stick to my typewriter during the day. With the last half-dozen chapters I had sent on to Max, he'd written me a letter saying that he thought that the story had more chance of a motion picture sale than either of my other novels, and he also had a strong feeling that it might be serialized in a magazine before publication. And he liked it.

With every incentive to finish it, and to finish it quickly, I printed a small placard in big letters and hung it outside my door during working hours: DON'T DISTURB. I could hear the boys hooting in the hall when they saw it. I didn't blame them; I'd never needed quiet to work in before, and it was a huge joke to them that I should suddenly begin to put on the airs of an author. Maybe I should have apprised them of the fact that from here on out, our very existence depended on my writing, but I decided that they had had enough to face without sharing my financial worries.

I was well into the middle of the book when Rosalie Stewart telephoned one morning. "Hello there," she greeted me in a voice that sounded like Ann Watkins' (there's a limited variety in the distaff end of the business) "how about getting off that lazy little rear of yours and doing some work for a change? Sol Wurtzel wants to see you in his office this afternoon, and my guess is that you're about to land yourself a job, my girl."

"But I've got a job. A couple of jobs," I added silently.

"When did this happen? What studio?" she demanded, a trifle sharply.

"No studio. I'm working on a novel."

"Oh." She sounded relieved. "I'll pick you up at your house at three sharp."

"I'm just finishing a chapter," I demurred.

"Finish it when you get home. Sol Wurtzel doesn't ask to see an author unless he means business."

She'd shot holes in my first job, so I fell back on the other. "I can't anyway, this afternoon. I just remembered, I have to take the children to the dentist."

"Let somebody else take them."

"There isn't anybody else. Who can drive, I mean."

"You know something? This doesn't sound kosher to me. How is it they all have toothaches at the same time?"

"It's a prophylaxis," I admitted. "They haven't had their teeth cleaned since they left——" I started to say "America," but changed it hastily to "home."

Miss Stewart didn't notice the slip. "Then it won't hurt them to wait another day. Good God, this is the first time I've been in this business that I ever had to coax a writer to see a producer!"

I didn't want to sound as if I had to be coaxed. What with all the invitations I had refused, the first thing I knew I'd be getting a reputation of playing hard to get. "I'll change the dental appointment, and be ready at three," I gave in.

Miss Stewart, when I finally met her face to face, turned out to be the sort of person who could have been anybody's aunt or high-school teacher. "So this is the way it is," she remarked, as she took in the marble foyer, Bertram's white coat, and finally Fraulein's long blue veil.

"She feels naked without it," I said apologetically, "and the butler came with the house."

Miss Stewart ignored the explanation, and delivered a friendly slap between my shoulder blades. "Now I see why you haven't been on my tail for an assignment. Well, that's all to the good, it's a pleasure not to have a hungry writer for a change. I intended asking Sol five hundred as a starting salary, but things being the way they are, I'll make it seven-fifty."

She'd lost me at that point, but then nothing in this part of the world seemed to make much sense. "I'll follow you in my car so that you won't have to bring me all the way here again," I suggested.

"That suits me fine," she said. "I have an appointment with Sam Marx at Metro at four-thirty."

Another Sam, I noted silently, and counted up a few more that I'd met at Sonya's, including Sam Berman and Sam Jaffe, and Sam Speigel, all of whom seemed very nice.

"Humph. One of the new Buicks," Miss Stewart commented as I backed out of the garage.

I remained discreetly silent, in order not to foster an impression of grandeur. Every time I opened my mouth in this town I seemed to be putting on airs.

For once, it was a reasonably short distance to our destination. "Fox Western" was comprised of an undistinguished group of low buildings in the middle of a busy intersection, but Mr. Wurtzel's private office was sumptuous beyond description. "Have a seat," he said. He motioned us into cavernous armchairs, and opened gold boxes of cigarettes for our pleasure. Then he selected a long black cigar from a humidor as big as a small coffin, and settled his unassuming body behind a vast expanse of mahogany desk. "Well," he said, through quick puffs of odorously expensive smoke, "let's get down to business. What are you asking for her, Rosalie?"

"A starting salary of seven-fifty on a three months' contract," she replied promptly.

"Out of the question."

"Then it's no deal."

I felt as if I were a piece of merchandise or a tract of land they were negotiating. "I'm really too busy with my novel anyway," I interceded firmly, which elicited an odd look from Miss Stewart, and caused Mr. Wurtzel to address his further remarks in my direction. "It's a gamble with a beginner even for peanuts. You have to remember that it could take the whole three months to get the hang of this medium if you never wrote for it before."

"I don't know the first thing about pictures," I agreed. "I'd be a total loss to you."

He chewed his cigar, and waved me to silence with a surprisingly well-cared-for hand. "That doesn't worry me. I'm teaming you up with a man who's been in the business for years, with a couple of dozen screen credits behind him."

"Well, in that case he certainly doesn't sound as if he needs any help," I said amiably.

Again, Miss Stewart glanced at me, this time with a faint smile. "It's customary to put two writers on an assignment," she explained. "Who've you got in mind, Sol?"

"Phil Klein."

"Very solid," she approved.

"I'll say he is." Mr. Wurtzel turned to me again. "You too young to remember a play called *The Auctioneer*?"

Momentarily intrigued, I assured him that I also remembered *The Music Master* and the *Return of Peter Grimm*, and the memory carried me back to fifty-cent seats in the second balcony of the old Belasco Theatre on Saturday afternoons. "David Warfield was wonderful in all of them," I said dreamily. "At least I thought he was when I was sixteen."

Mr. Wurtzel had no recollection of the veteran actor, and cared less. "The man who wrote those plays," he informed me weightily, "was the father of the man you're going to work with. I'll make it six hundred with an option to renew in three months at seven-fifty," he concluded in the same breath.

"Nothing doing, Sol." Miss Stewart competently took over where she'd been left off. "Seven-fifty, with an option to renew at a thousand."

Mr. Wurtzel placed his cigar on a large bronze ash-tray. "Tell me, Rosalie, please, why I should pay a big price for a beginner without a single screen credit?"

"I'll tell you why, Sol." Miss Stewart stamped out her cigarette into an ash-tray a little smaller, and brass. "You're not buying just anybody from the east. This girl is a great writer, she's a *name*! Her new novel is sensational. I've read it and I'll send you a copy."

"Okay, okay. Is there a picture in it?"

"No," I answered for her. "And I don't think you'd like it, Mr. Wurtzel."

"Not if it's smutty," he said. He picked up a book from his desk and gave it to me. "Here. Read this tonight, it's a good clean story. Mary Roberts Rinehart's latest. But keep it under your hat, it's a vehicle for Joan Crawford, so we'll build up the part of the girl even more than it is. Settled."

Everything had moved too fast for me. "Wait, please, nothing is settled yet. I can't possibly accept this assignment——"

"Why not?" he demanded. "We just came to terms, didn't we? It's against my will, but all right, your agent can draw the contract for three months at seven-fifty——"

"I think Sol is being very fair"—Miss Stewart hastily stopped me from answering—"And I'm sure you'll do such a great job on the script that he'll be equally fair when the time comes to renew." She glanced at her watch. "Shall we go?"

"Not yet," I said. "We can't go until you both understand that a three months' contract isn't what I want——"

Mr. Wurtzel blew his breath out between his rather generous lips. "Come on. Let's have it. You're angling for a six months' contract? Okay. I'll take a chance." He banged the desk for emphasis. "But I'm telling you it's robbery!"

"You still don't understand," I protested. "I don't want any contract at all! What I mean is, the longest I could possibly afford to work, if I did accept the assignment, is three weeks."

He stopped banging slowly. "Maybe I didn't hear you right. Say it again, please."

Obediently, I repeated that I only wanted to work for three weeks because my sister was going to spend the summer with me, and it was important to me to be free during her visit.

He continued to favour me with a blank stare. "No person in his right mind," he averred eventually, "gives up a fine contract like this because their sister is coming."

"I do," I said. "Besides, the people I'm renting my house from are getting back from abroad sooner than they expected, and I'll have to get settled in another place by the end of May. So you can see why working any longer would cut my time too short."

"Your time? What about my time!" Mr. Wurtzel began banging again. "I happen to have a picture I would like to go before the cameras early next year!"

"Oh, that's a long while away," I placated him easily.

Miss Stewart quickly collected the salient points of the nebulous conversation and presented them to me in simple terms. "Mr. Wurtzel means that he needs a shooting script, and in three weeks you won't even have a first draft of the screen treatment."

"A first draft? But that's ridiculous, I can't see why the job shouldn't be all finished in that time. If I can write a play in a week, I can certainly get somebody else's story down on paper in three."

"Listen to her," Mr. Wurtzel injected hoarsely. "A lot she knows about Hollywood."

Miss Stewart said, "She'll learn fast enough." She rose to her feet and patted Mr. Wurtzel's shoulder with the air of a conspirator. "In the meantime, I say we should play along with her. Sure it's a crazy deal, but three weeks it is." I caught the wink she gave him. "She'll change her mind."

"I don't like it," he grumbled. "On general principles I don't like it. What is she, the King of Sheba? All right, I told you I'd take a gamble. Go ahead, make it a six months' contract, at seven-fifty straight."

It was frustrating after all this talk to be right back where we'd started. Only now I really wanted the job, and I was loath to lose it on a mere technicality. I'd done some mental arithmetic while the argument was going on, and it had suddenly occurred to me that it would be very nice to have that unexpected sum of money in the bank for my sister's visit. Clearly, it was up to me to make the next concession. I said, "If the story shouldn't be finished in three weeks, I'll stay on an extra few days."

"An extra few days," Mr. Wurtzel echoed in a bleat that ended in a roar. "Get her out of here!"

It served me right. By my sheer stubbornness and stupidity, I had talked myself out of something over five hundred dollars for less than a month's work, and wasted Miss Stewart's afternoon as well. I was prepared to proffer my abject apologies as soon as the door closed behind us, but she swiftly propelled me down the hall away from the vicinity of Mr. Wurtzel's office. "Beautiful!" she congratulated me. "You've got him eating out of your hand! And for a start, seven-fifty's not a bad deal, believe me. If I had to, I was willing to settle for three-fifty a week——"

"Three-fifty a *week*?"

She grinned. "And Adrienne Morrison told me you were a babe in the woods. All I can say is you can give the two of us lessons in driving the hardest bargain in Hollywood."

This was not the moment to disabuse her high regard for the shrewdness with which she credited me. I managed a feeble smile in spite of the fact that my head was whirling. I couldn't believe that my "less than a month's work" added up to more than two thousand dollars! Why, I hadn't earned as much as that from a whole year writing *Pattern*!

Rosalie was right in saying that it was a crazy deal. A crazy deal in a crazy town.

Nervously, I arrived at the studio at nine o'clock the next

morning. There was no one around except the man at the gate who had a pass ready for me, and who directed me to the bungalow I was to share with my collaborator. It was very small, with two rooms sparsely furnished and a secretary's cubicle in between. One of the rooms showed signs of occupancy—stacks of manuscript, a bottle of aspirin, and a couple of pipes spilling out on to an ashtray. I concluded that the other room was to be mine, so I sat down at the bare desk with my coat on. There was something sneaky about California weather, you never knew where you were with it. There was a stove contraption beneath the window, but it was as cold as I was.

Eventually I decided that I might as well start writing. The novel that I had read the previous evening lent itself to a progression of scenes that didn't seem too difficult to put on paper, except that I couldn't find any paper in my desk, and there wasn't a typewriter, either. I waited a few more minutes for Mr. Klein to appear, and then went back to his room and used his paper and machine.

"What in God's name are you doing!"

Some things make me madder than others, and being startled, whether intentionally or not, is one of them. I wheeled round in a fury. "You damn fool, you scared me half out of my wits. I'm writing, what do you think I'm doing?" I exploded wrathfully.

It was Mr. Klein, of course, and after so unconventional a departure from the usual amenities, it was impossible to revert to a formal introduction. "You're nuts," he informed me merely, as he peered over my shoulder at the page in the typewriter.

"And you're late," I retaliated, adding more civilly. "I was just experimenting until you came. I don't know the first thing about a movie script."

"You seem to be doing all right," he remarked drily. He sat down in a wooden armchair opposite me, reached for the remaining sheets on the desk, and scanned them in silence. "I wish you wouldn't," I objected. "We haven't begun to collaborate officially, so why don't we tear those up and start fresh?"

He paid not the slightest attention to me until he had finished the last of the pages I had written. "Keep on like this," he said, "and you'll be the most unpopular writer that ever set foot in this studio."

I swallowed my dismay. "I will? But why?"

"For the unforgivable treason of turning out a month's work in half a morning."

"But I have to finish the whole job in three weeks——"

"What do you mean, three weeks! Who the hell is your agent to let you get screwed on a lousy deal like that?"

I quickly exonerated Miss Stewart from all blame, and explained about my sister's visit. Phil Klein was a small man with a large glower; he stared at me out of very brown eyes beneath bushy brows. "You're nuts," he said again. "I didn't have any breakfast, let's go out for lunch."

The idea appealed to me, especially since I had eaten a very early breakfast and not much of it. Remembering my enormous salary, though, my conscience bothered me more than my appetite. "What about getting some work done first?"

"You've done enough for both of us. Besides my secretary is off sick. Where do you want to eat?"

"I don't mind."

"Vendome, again?"

"Again? I've never been."

"Stop kidding your Uncle Phil. You were there yesterday."

Yesterday I hadn't stuck my nose out of the house until my interview with Mr. Wurtzel. "Don't be silly."

He shrugged and tossed me a newspaper that he had brought in with him. "Here, read it for yourself."

Sure enough, I was in the Columns again, wearing a simple but expensively tailored beige suit with a silver-fox neckpiece. This was ironic. During the run of *Another Language*, people had caught passing glimpses of me on my crutches without knowing, or particularly caring, who I was. Now everyone seemed to know me without ever having seen me. "I don't even own a silver fox," I told Mr. Klein.—"Is there a washroom hidden somewhere in this bungalow?"

"There's a door behind the door where you came in. But the paper towels are all used up."

"It doesn't matter, I don't have to wash. I just wanted to find out where it was on general principles."

"You're my idea of a dame," he approved me finally. "The last female I worked with spent hours in there, what doing I wouldn't know.—I think I'm going to like you."

I had a feeling that I was going to like him, too. He wasn't exactly what I'd expected the son of an illustrious father to be, but then who is?

We walked out into the blazing sun of a California noon, and I wished I could have shed a lot more than my coat. The studio, no longer deserted, buzzed lazily with the activity of a small village. Writers lolled about in front of their bungalows, and Mr. Klein introduced me as we passed. To my surprise, they all had very pretty names, with not a Sol or a Sam in the lot. One slim young man was called Doré Schary, another Dudley Nichols, still another Dalton Trumbo, and the prettiest of all was Nicolas Joy, who took pains to tell me that he wasn't a writer but the story editor from Fox Beverly Hills. "He's slumming today," Mr. Klein enlightened me.

Mr. Joy conceded that he was, holding my hand longer than was comfortable. "And I'll have to pull some wires, little girl, to get you away from here over to where the important pictures are being made," he said.

I hadn't been called "little girl" since kindergarten.

"It's nice of everyone to make me feel so welcome," I told Mr. Klein on our way to the parking lot and his Rolls-Royce roadster.

He scowled at me. "Don't be deceived. If you don't mend your ways, they'll boycott you to a man."

I giggled. It was a long while since laughter had passed my lips, and the sound stopped my heart with the first sharp pain of healing.

In spite of Mr. Klein's grumbling, the script of *Elinor Norton* was completed within four weeks, although we were called back for another week of rewriting in September. However, that was only because the main scene of action had to be switched from Newport, Rhode Island, to a ranch in New Mexico, due to Mr. Wurtzel's sudden decision to star a young unknown called Claire

PAUL at Quincy

PETER, the young
Professor

JOHN—on the farm

The farm house at Lyme. The effect of the first hurricane is visible

The log cabin on Preston Mountain

The new farm buildings after the fire

Trevor, and since the dialogue and locale had been fashioned to the shape of things in Joan Crawford, certain changes had to be made.

I know that many writers feel that the climate of motion pictures, in which the author becomes fifth wheel to producer, director, cast and budget, is detrimental to the output of a creative artist, and in professing that I found the exercise invaluable in teaching me discipline and facility, I am, of course, laying myself open to conjecture.

Apart from the experience, though, I confess to being grateful for that first rewrite job for other reasons. My sister had returned to New York, and the spacious house that I had rented on Canon Drive (primarily because Paul could attend the Beverly Hills High School) was full of a new kind of loneliness. Even more important, I needed the additional seven hundred and fifty dollars to tide me over the combined expenses of Peter's tonsils and a recently broken shoulder of my own.

"Who threw you out of bed?" Mr. Wurtzel lewdly inquired when I reported in at his office with a bandaged side.

I said, "Pat did. He's so big, he doesn't know his own strength."

Mr. Wurtzel blinked, and I let him make of it anything it pleased him to make of it. Nevertheless, it was exactly what had happened. For some perverse whim, Pat had seen fit to appoint himself my personal night-watchman in the new house, and with the first clink of the milkman's bottles at dawn, he would leap on the bed and gallop heroically across me to the window, from which safe vantage point he would stomp and bark in one of those "Hold-my-coat-while-I-kill-him" daydreams that Great Danes frequently indulge in. Pat, especially, was all front and no back. He looked ferocious, but a burglar would have reduced him to a quivering mass of nerves.

On this particular morning, his frenzy to protect me from the milk bottles caused him to miss his footing, and we both tumbled to the floor. Luckily—very luckily—I landed on my left shoulder, which didn't interfere too much with typing—or driving.

"You're nuts." Mr. Klein greeted me with what had become a familiar refrain. "You can't handle a car with your arm in a sling!"

"You manage your business and I'll manage mine." We were good friends by this time, and the week of re-vamping the script went by quickly and pleasantly. On the last afternoon, he said, "Sol has another job for us. And don't give me that business that you haven't finished your novel yet."

"I haven't, quite."

"Rats."

"Don't say 'rats'."

"I will say 'rats.' You'll make a lot more money in less time on this new assignment. Make Sol sweat a little before you say you'll take it, and I bet he'll come across with a thousand a week on a six-month commitment. And if he picks up the option, that's fifty-two thousand a year, my good woman."

I knew that Phil wasn't getting any more than that, and he'd been at Fox Western for years. "I'm not worth it," I said. "Why should Mr. Wurtzel be willing to pay me so much?"

"Because you're difficult."

"I don't mean to be."

"Keep it that way," he advised. "Also, Sol's willing to spend money on this story because it's his original idea. He's already had a team of writers working out a treatment, but he isn't satisfied with it.—Incidentally, I have to hand it to him, he's got a hell of a title—*Dante's Inferno*."

Phil had a wry sense of humour. "It is a hell of a title," I agreed, and inwardly I couldn't help feeling a little excited. This wasn't just another popular novel, it was in the nature of a challenge, something really worth while doing. *Dante's Inferno*. Odd that I should have selected a stanza from Canto I to use in front of *Pattern*.

> In the midway of this, our mortal life,
> I found me in a gloomy wood astray,
> Gone from the path direct; and e'en to tell
> It were no easy task, how savage wild
> That forest; how robust and rough its growth,
> Which, to remember only, my dismay renews
> In bitterness, not far from death.

I'm not superstitious, but I do believe in signs. And this was a sign, if ever I saw one.

I took a copy of the rejected screen treatment home with me that evening. Fraulein had to go off for some reason or other, so I had no time to read it until I'd got the boys in bed, and gone to bed myself. I didn't have to read far. I skimmed through the first half-dozen pages, reached for the telephone on my night table, and called Phil in a huff. "If I woke you up, I'm not at all sorry," I opened up on him.

"What's wrong?"

"What's wrong? You have a nerve to ask me what's wrong. This isn't Dante's Inferno, it's nothing but a story about a gangster who runs a gambling den in San Francisco——"

"Sure it is," Phil said, quite unruffled by my tirade. "His name is Dante, and he calls the place 'Dante's Inferno.'—What the hell did you expect, *Dante's Inferno?*"

"Yes, I did," I admitted defiantly, "and you can have your damn signs."

"What do you mean, 'signs'?"

"Oh, shut up," I said. "You wouldn't understand."

He sounded resigned. "I told you the first time I met you that you were nuts.—Look, don't do anything hasty until we talk it over tomorrow."

I promised him that I wouldn't, and we kept on talking it over all during the last of our lunches at the Vendome. He had an exasperating habit of grabbing the bill before I could reach for it, so I always ordered the cheapest thing on the menu, which was spaghetti or ravioli, but today I tried the cheese-blintzes that Phil liked, and offered to split with whatever he ordered. Perversely, he had to go and lose his appetite, and settled on soft-boiled eggs and a pot of tea. "This time you can pay," he said bitterly. "Celebrate finishing the Great American Novel."

"That's not the only reason I turned down the assignment. Nobody will ever get a script out of such a shoddy story that won't be more of a waste of more of Sol's time and money. It's distilled banality." (I believe that it was eventually distilled, quite successfully, into a series on television.)

[163]

"So now you're an expert," Phil cut in with the first display of temper he had ever shown towards me. "Hollywood is full of producers with shoddy ideas, and who says a little banality ever hurt the box office? Let one story happen to click, and the guy's not a damn fool, he's a bloody genius."

"I hate to be the one to clip Mr. Wurtzel's wings," I retorted, "but I still have a degree of integrity towards what I do, or don't do."

He gave a short laugh. "Me, I can't afford that luxury. I guess I've stayed in this goddamned town too goddamned long."

"Phil, if you feel that way, why don't you leave?" I asked him seriously.

"Leave? That's a joke. Where would I go, and what would I do?"

"Write. On your own."

"And make a decent living at it?"

"Other people do."

"Not after you've sold your soul to Hollywood for ten years. I've got a way of life and a family to support."

A way of life. Everyone had a way of life out here. I looked round the crowded restaurant—the rendezvous of Hollywood's fortunates—and gathered up my gloves and purse. "If you've finished your tea, let's go."

"I've had all I want."

When he left me at my door, he said, heavily, "Well, I guess there's nothing I can do about it if your mind's made up."

"It is, Phil, I'm sorry."

"I'll miss you. How am I going to get this damn piece of tripe written without you?"

"But if you think it's tripe, why do you write it?" There was no use asking him. I knew the answer. He didn't say it in so many words, but once you've lived with fear, you recognize it when it looks out at you from someone else's eyes.

Two years later while I was on a trip east, I received a letter from his wife. I pondered the name and address on the back of the envelope. Why should she be writing to me? I opened it. The letter was very short. "Phil went to Tia Juana to be alone for a few days.

He died there. The doctors tell me it was his heart. He would
have wanted you to know."

I grieved. But not for him.

It was just as well that I had decided against Dante's Inferno,
because I had a small inferno of my own to contend with. Household crises never seem to come singly. Peter started off the
fireworks by tumbling, head first, down the stairs, and having to
have six stitches in his scalp. John added his bit by getting into a
fist fight in school and losing two front teeth. Not baby teeth, but
permanent teeth, which, alas, no longer were. Overlapping this
major disaster, Paul, replete with driver's licence, fell in love and
broke out in hives. And last, but by no means least, Fraulein
suddenly took leave of her senses. And us.

With no rumblings or forewarning of any nature, she erupted one
evening into a sobbing declaration that she was overworked,
underpaid, and generally mistreated.

"I think she's sick, Mother," Paul whispered, as I hastily
hustled all the boys out of the room.

With a perception that was so like his father's, he recognized,
as I did, that here indeed was an illness as virulent as any physical
disorder, and when she insisted wildly that she was going to pack
her clothes and leave at once, I realized with a sinking feeling in
the pit of my stomach, that it was the inevitable solution for all
of us. "I can't stop you if you really want to go," I said, "but I
brought you out to California, so at least wait until I can put you
on a train back east to your cousins in New Jersey."

Her face grew purplish; I feared for her blood vessels. "I don't
need your charity," she spat at me. "I can buy my own ticket if
I want to go home. But I am not going home, I have plenty of
friends right here!"

It suddenly occurred to me that perhaps it was true. Her days
off never used to matter, but recently they had become a ritual, an
urgency, from which she would return with a glow of exalted
secrecy, and tins of vegetable juices that she would harbour
privately and jealously in her own room, rather than in the
refrigerator. I suspected, now, that she might have got mixed

[165]

up in one of the many cults that offered hope, health, happiness and God on every boulevard in Hollywood, and I knew that I could pit neither reason nor compassion against this unbeatable combination of menopause and fanaticism. Numb with shock and helplessness (and a vague thankfulness that it was not I who had fallen victim to these spiritual snares), I went upstairs to make out her cheque for an extra month's salary. I folded it and gave it to her when she emerged from her room completely packed and ready to leave. My conscience stopped nagging me. This was no irrational impulse that I might have argued her out of. Her move was of a considered and paranoiac deliberation.

I told her as quietly as my raw emotions permitted, that money could never repay her for all she had done for us over the years, and gave her the cheque. She tore it up without looking at it, and stalked down the stairs with her two heavy suitcases clunking behind her. The children hovered in the lower hall, but she walked out of the door without so much as saying good-bye to them.

"I want Fraulein to come back!" Peter whimpered, while John confronted me in an agony of conflict. "She said you were mean to her, Mother!"

"Oh, grow up," Paul snarled at him. "Mother never ill-treated anyone. I'm glad she's gone. She was getting to be a mean old bitch."

"That's fine talk," I rebuked him automatically, but again I was surprised at his sentience. Increasingly, in the past months, I had chafed beneath the yoke of her well-meaning but Teutonic dominion, but her devotion would have forever swayed me from suggesting a parting of our ways. However, since the decision was hers, I made up my mind to accept it philosophically, like a dose of castor oil. "Swallow it down," my mother always tossed it off for me. "It'll make you feel fine afterwards."

This time, I was a long while "feeling fine." My spotlessly clean but stony-hearted Finnish houseworker walked out the next morning, irretrievably poisoned by the seeds of distrust that Fraulein had sowed before her own exit. I replaced her the next day with one of those soft-voiced, deft little Filipino men that Hollywood abounded in. He cooked strangely, but quite elegantly, played tennis with Paul in the afternoons, and gambled away his wages in the evenings. But I suppose it would have been asking too much to have replaced Fraulein as painlessly. In the endless procession of ignorant nursemaids, lofty governesses, and proudly decayed aristocracy, I missed her megalomaniac energy, and dreamed shamelessly of her appearing, cured and penitent, on the doorstep.

Finally, I engaged "Mademoiselle" in the hope that a little French would rub off on the boys. German hadn't, and eventually I was forced to resign myself to their being nice children but not linguistically inclined.

Mademoiselle took some getting used to. She was a mousy little woman, painfully proper and virtuous, who, for some god-forsaken reason had recently become enamoured of the "violin". She hadn't progressed beyond scales and finger exercises, and practised religiously an hour every morning and every evening. Linked to this barren perversion, she was completely dispossessed of the slightest vestige of humour. Her flaccid, gentle face was as imperturbable as a soft, rubber mask, and to further the illusion, she wore an upper plate which was of such dazzling perfection that she might have been kissing-kin to a halibut.

It can be an education to live with a truly literal person, and Mademoiselle was literal to the point of sadness. One evening, after she had proved to be competent and trustworthy, I accepted an invitation to one of the big parties I rarely went to, but now I felt that I needed a little respite from my various harassments. "You do all the worrying for me this evening," I entrusted her, as I stabbed an unlisted telephone number to her pincushion. "If Paul isn't home by eleven, let me know so that I can do some myself."

I thought I was being pleasantly droll, but sharp at eleven, she called me. My heart jumped in my throat when I heard her agitated voice hissing softly through her dentures. "Master Paul has not yet come in, madame, it is time for you to worry."

It was as good an excuse as any to thank my bleary-eyed hostess, and unobtrusively slip away. Paul was coming out of the garage as I turned into the driveway. "Why are you back so early?" He hopped up on the running board, peering in at me to see if I was all right.

"Too many people, all getting tipsy," I prudently modified actualities. "Why are you?"

"What?"

"Back so early."

"You said I should be home by eleven," he said accusingly.

"So I did, and it's not even midnight," I commended him. "Did you have a nice time with Bee Jay?" (Her name was Beatrice Jane.)

He didn't say he did, and he didn't say he didn't. "She wanted to go to one of those miniature golf places. It wasn't much fun, but God, I drank like a fish."

I tried for nonchalance. "How come?"

"I dunno," he answered debonairly, "I guess I must have been thirsty, I bet I polished off four bottles of ginger ale, maybe five."

"You're going Hollywood, son, better watch out."

How often, in the long wakeful nights, I prayed to hold my balance on the tricky tightrope between too much wisdom and too little wisdom. One of the hardest decisions I had had to make was letting Paul have his own car, but other problems that came up day by day were not as concrete, or as drastically solved. Sometimes I preferred to err on the side of not magnifying passing phases into important issues, it was easier on the children if I didn't aspire to playing God and analyst in one. And sometimes I wished that castor oil had not gone out of style.

This particular period of readjustment was a little rough on all of us, and I was glad that I didn't have to report to a studio every morning. At least the boys always knew where to find me when they came home from school—a small enough sense of security, and they were entitled to it.

It was the main reason why I was disinterested in another assignment when Rosalie Stewart called me up a couple of months after Fraulein's departure. "Harry Cohn wants to see you this afternoon," she announced.

"Who's Harry Cohn?"

"Oh, for God's sake! How can you not know who Harry Cohn is?"

"Well, I don't," I said patiently. "There's lots of Cohns and Harrys in Hollywood."

"Well, this Cohn-and-Harry happens to be Columbia Pictures. The Big Cheese himself."

"Then why should he want to see me? He doesn't know me any more than I know him."

"No, but he caught a sneak preview of *Another Language* last night at Pasadena, and he thinks it's great. Absolutely great. —What did you think of it?"

"I wasn't there. I didn't know anything about it being previewed."

"You didn't? Somebody from the studio should have notified you. I'll ask Metro to run it for you any time you want."

I didn't want. It would stir up too many memories, but I didn't say that to Miss Stewart.

"Oh, and two more things," she remembered. "Harry's had word from the underground that *Elinor Norton* is going to be a swell picture, and he's had a resumé of *Twice Born*, which means you're sitting pretty. Look, I'll be at the Beverly Brown Derby for lunch, so I might just as well pick you up at your house at two-thirty."

She rang off before I had time to explain that I couldn't properly manage another job at the moment. I tried to call her back, but she wasn't in her office and wasn't expected until late in the afternoon. Apparently she had telephoned me from outside, and I had no alternative but to be ready for her at two-thirty.

She should have prepared me, on the way to Mr. Cohn's office, but probably she didn't think to, because she was used to him. At first glance, he was just an ordinary stocky man, good-looking, after a fashion, rather than good to look at. A heavy cane lay within his reach, not to walk with, I soon discovered, but to clobber his desk with. "I have a sensational idea," he began at once, in the rich superlatives to which my ear was growing accustomed. "Never been done before. Absolutely sensational. An all-woman picture, cast included."

"No men?" I inquired obligingly.

"No sir," he said, and proceeded to enlarge upon the project with gusto. He'd lined up Dorothy Arzner to produce it, the dame who did *Maedchen in Uniform* (he forgot her name) to direct it, Marlene Dietrich to star in it, and me to write it.

"Well, what do you think of it?" He leaned far back in his revolving chair, rotating restlessly as he waited for my response.

I told him what I thought. "I can see the possibilities, but it doesn't happen to appeal to me."

He grabbed his cane, swung it whizzing through the air, and hit the desk a shattering blow. "Why doesn't it appeal to you? What's the hitch?"

"Too many women," I said briefly.

"But that's the whole point! I'm making an all-woman picture!"

"That's my point, too," I explained. "I don't mind them singly, but I don't think I'd care to work with them in droves."

His knuckles grew white and his face red. "Nobody's going to turn Harry Cohn down!" he shouted. "Name your price!"

"It isn't a question of price——"

"It's always price!" he proclaimed loudly. "Money buys everybody! So what do you want? A thousand, fifteen hundred, two thousand a week? Or a flat guarantee for the whole job? Name it!"

I don't like loud noises. I cringe and cover my ears when I even see a pistol, whether it's loaded or not, and every time the hard knob of Mr. Cohn's cane came in contact with the hard edge of his desk, I shrivelled inside. "I wish you'd stop doing that," I said.

His face got redder. "See here, young lady," he shouted at me, "nobody ever told Harry Cohn what to do and what not to do!"

"I'm telling you," I said, "and if you bang once more, I'm leaving."

He banged, and I left. "I'll phone you later!" Miss Stewart called after me.

The telephone was ringing as I walked into the house. As if I were a magnet, John drifted towards me from out of the air. "You weren't home when I got home," he said aggrieved. "Where were you?"

"Out. Any objections? See who it is on the phone."

"I can't."

"Why can't you?"

"Because you don't like it when children answer the telephone," he replied righteously. "You never let us."

"I'm letting you now," I started to add, "And if it's Miss Stewart, tell her I haven't come in yet."

I thought better of it. In the natural course of growing up, he'd lie enough without my teaching him.

"It's Miss Stewart," he reported back, preening with responsibility. "She wants to talk to my mother, she said."

"You're a big help. Your mother thanks you." I gave him a whack in passing, which restored his world to normal, and picked up the receiver with a bravado I was far from feeling. Although I hadn't instigated the interview with Mr. Cohn, I had given Miss Stewart a hard time of it nonetheless. "Why don't you just write me off your list?" I began contritely.

I expected her to be anything but jubilant. "Write you off my list?" she echoed. "When Harry Cohn is willing to pay you two thousand a week?"

"Two thousand a week! He's an idiot!"

"So are you, but on you I like it. When can you start?"

"I can't. I mean, I can't take a job now, but you didn't give me a chance to tell you before."

Irony balanced impatience in her voice. "What's the matter, your sister coming again?"

I laughed. "No, but my aunt is, she's going to spend Thanksgiving with us.—But that's not what's holding me back," I added quickly. "And, anyway, no good would ever come of Mr. Cohn's offer, because he doesn't really want me at this point, he just wants what he can't get, and when he gets it he'll stop wanting it."

She both accepted and dismissed the possibility. "What if he does? Don't you realize that it's a fabulous fluke simply to have established your salary at that figure? Usually, you'd have to work a couple of years, if not longer, to climb up to two thousand a week!"

"I know it," I admitted.

[171]

"Look. If it's the woman angle that's bothering you, frankly I don't think it'll pan out. For one thing, I happen to know that he can't get Dietrich."

"But it isn't only the woman angle, you make me sound like a prima donna, and I'm not."

"Glad to hear it," she retorted drily. "May I ask just what reason you have, then, for calmly throwing a chance like this away?"

I didn't want to drag the children into the discussion—plenty of mothers went off to their jobs every day—but I had no other logical explanation to give her except that I didn't like Mr. Cohn enough to dislike him with any degree of satisfaction, and I could imagine nothing more boring than to work for him. On second thoughts, though, it might not sound so logical to Miss Stewart, so I resorted to the time-worn but reliable excuse that I was up against a deadline to finish my novel for Scribner's.

She made no reply for a very long moment, and her silence convinced me that I had exhausted her forbearance and alienated her interest once and for all. I was about to tell her that I didn't blame her in the least, when she finally spoke. "Okay," she said. "Could be you're smarter than I am, maybe in the long run it'll pay off for you to establish yourself as a legend of unavailability. Anyway, I'll buy it, and I'll play along with you on it."

I didn't try to set her straight on my motives. It didn't matter whether I did or not, because to my surprise, she had taken no umbrage, and was as nice as ever.

I hung up, meditating on a quirk of human behaviour that I had found indigenous only to Hollywood. It seemed impossible to antagonize people here, if they didn't choose to be antagonized.

I suppose it took less courage than stupidity to disdain Mr. Cohn's "fabulous" offer, but whichever it was, it turned out for the best. My novel was no sooner finished than it was accepted by *Redbook* as a one-shot, and besides the immediate income, a magazine circulation strengthened the likelihood of a motion picture sale. Once more my bank balance was generously replenished, and once more I felt that money was the last thing in the world I had to worry about.

Since Max Perkins had himself suggested that the story might lend itself to serialization, I took for granted that he would be especially pleased that it was to be cut to a single issue, thus obviating postponement of the book publication. To my distress, however, he wrote me a long letter, saying that although he was happy for my sake that a sale had been effected, he was deeply disturbed because Scribner's, along with the majority of other publishing firms, had recently signed an agreement to reject any novel appearing as a one-shot. He made no intimation that I should withdraw from my commitment to *Redbook* but I wasn't sure but what it was the right thing to do. "If only I weren't three thousand miles away," I talked it over with my aunt, who had arrived a few days before, "I might be able to straighten it all out, because both publications mean a lot to me, financially."

"Then why don't you go to New York while I'm here to look after the boys?" she suggested.

It wasn't a bad idea and, if I flew, I wouldn't have to be away more than a week. But I couldn't leave until the following Tuesday, because I was stuck with a cocktail party I had planned for Sunday, ostensibly in my aunt's honour, but actually to show her that I wasn't lonely or unhappy in California. I had a suspicion that she and my sister had been hashing me over, and I still wasn't strong enough, or perhaps mature enough, to accept sympathy without being destroyed by it.

It was the first real party I had given, and like all Hollywood parties, it was a catered and painless affair, and everybody came, including a raft of people I'd never laid eyes on before. It was a great success.

"I didn't dream you had so many friends here," my aunt said the next morning. I refrained from telling her that I didn't, and went on tidying up the usual after-party mess by thriftily emptying all the remaining driblets of a large assortment of liquors into one Scotch whisky bottle, which I was pleased to see it just about filled to the top.

"What are you doing that for?" she asked curiously.

"Nobody's touched any of it with their lips, so why not? I'll be glad to have it in case someone happens to drop in for a drink."

An occasional glass of sherry was the limit of her own indulgence, but even so, she looked doubtful. "But how is all that stuff mixed together going to taste?"

"It's all alcohol, it should taste fine, like different herbs you put in a soup," I said, unaware that I might be forever uncementing what few friendships I had made.

"I don't think it's the same theory," she persisted.

"Oh, don't be so pig-headed. Look, how would you like to see a print of *Another Language* in a projection room at the studio?" I suggested suddenly, wishing to further impress her with my influence as well as my popularity.

"Could you really manage it?" she exclaimed, as goggle-eyed as a schoolgirl.

I shrugged. "Perfectly simple. No problem."

I telephoned Rosalie Stewart, reminding her of her promise to arrange a screening. "It's all set for tomorrow at three," I announced to my aunt fifteen minutes later, and with an air of tossing gift after gift into her lap, I added, "And on the way to Metro, we can stop in and have lunch at the Vendome."

"With all that food from the party?" she demurred.

"This is no time for thrift," I said grandly. "Let the children and Mademoiselle and Fermin eat the left-overs."

I hadn't been to the Vendome since that last day at Fox Western, but I counted on the head waiter remembering me, and I was also pretty sure of running into a number of writers from the studio, including Phil. Talk about name-dropping, I reflected moodily—I'd never put on a false-front for anybody in my life, and here I was staging a big show for the benefit of my unsophisticated little aunt. But I had to do it. I wanted her to report home, with first-hand conviction, that I was completely contented and happy in the new life I had made for myself.

I accomplished my purpose. "I have something to confess to you," she said, as we left the restaurant to drive out to Culver City.

"What?" I had an idea what was coming.

"Well . . ." She cleared her throat, finding the admission awkward. "We've been a little worried about you at home.

Especially after Fraulein left. I mean you'd never been alone like this, so far away from everyone and with the responsibility of the boys, and having to earn a living besides."

"It bothers you more than it bothers me," I rejoined flippantly, which made it easier for her to come to the point.

"That's just what I want to tell you," she said. "This trip out here has put my mind completely at rest about you. I think it's just wonderful how you've changed. You never used to be a good mixer, to my knowledge."

Nor to my knowledge. I always died a little of shyness when I was with people I didn't know well, and I probably always would. I felt more than ever a hypocrite.

In the darkness of the projection room, I wept. It didn't matter that I disliked the picture—it mattered only that my husband wasn't sitting beside me. Memories tore me to pieces.

If my aunt noticed that my eyes were red when the lights went on again, she made no mention of it. "It was a beautiful play," she said, staunch in her loyalty, "but this isn't the play you wrote."

"No it isn't, is it? In spite of a star cast it seems to be more the play that was done in Greenwich," I said, and I was puzzled about it.

Miss Stewart had told me that Mr. Griffith, the director, had asked that I call in at his office after the screening, and although I would rather have avoided any discussion of the picture, there was no way out of it.

I was surprised to find him as nice as he was. His first words were, "Did you like it?"

I had never successfully mastered the art of diplomatic evasion. "No," I said, but because he was so essentially a gentle person, I added, "But of course authors are always difficult to please."

"Not necessarily. There are certain aspects of the picture that don't please me, either, and I'm wondering if we agree on them. What, specifically, did you object to?"

I told him. He frowned. "I don't understand. Those were the major points I checked with you."

I frowned back at him. "Checked with me? How?"

[175]

"Over the telephone. I called your producer's office on several occasions. He said you were unavailable, but that he would relay my questions to you and give me whatever reactions or suggestions you might have."

"I never got any of your messages," I said slowly. "I shouldn't wonder if you thought I couldn't talk English."

Mr. Griffith looked embarrassed. "Well, to be truthful," he admitted, "I expected to meet someone entirely different."

I bit my lips. This was no joke any longer. But what was to be gained by blowing off at this late date? *Another Language* had served its purpose, it belonged to a part of my life that was over and done with.

I was wrong on one count—*Another Language* hadn't quite served its purpose, for I was to owe my future happiness to the slow reverberation of my erstwhile producer's infamous lies. He was a man of varied enterprises and limitless ego, but I doubt that he ever fancied himself as miller to the gods.

Anything could have happened, but nothing did, to stand in the way of my trip east. The flight was supposed to take sixteen hours in those days, but even with delays, it was a miracle of speed compared with pretty nearly a week on the train. It seemed as if we were hardly in the air before we landed at Albuquerque to refuel.

I raced to a phone booth. My aunt was tremulous with relief when she heard my voice, she'd implored me to take the train. "Are you all right? Where are you?"

When I told her, she couldn't believe it. "Already? Just imagine that!"

I called her again at El Paso, and then it got too late, and too expensive to keep on telephoning at every stop. Eventually the overhead lights in the plane dimmed out, and the passengers settled down to sleep, wrapped in blankets like papooses. I couldn't sleep. I stared out into the flying blackness, feeling the first flutter of anticipation that I was on my way home. I lay back in my seat and closed my eyes, reviewing the year that lay, thank God, for ever behind me. It had been a period of marking time—

The FITZGERALDS—Ed and Pegeen—were frequent visitors at New Canaan

Our mail-order Wolf-hound and one of the Danes at the farm. The guest-house in background

a moment in space and an eternity in living. And now it was over. I had proved that I could stand alone, earn a fair living writing novels, and there was no longer any reason for me to remain in Hollywood. A climate of easy friendships and alliances, I would feel no wrench in leaving California, for I had put down no roots. I was as truly wed as though my husband had but stepped ahead of me into another room. . . .

I was aware that dawn was breaking through the darkness. Passengers yawned and stretched and leaned against the windows to peer below at a miniature world emerging from the clouds. "We're coming in to Columbus, Ohio," the stewardess confided to us one by one. "There'll be a stop of twenty minutes for breakfast."

We were grounded there for three hours. The waiting-room was full of icy draughts, and the wooden benches were hard. I wired my sister and brother-in-law not to meet me at the airport, and it was a good thing that I did because it was after midnight when I arrived at their apartment. I was cowardly enough to have preferred to stay at a hotel, but they wouldn't hear of it. We talked for a while, and then I went to bed and slept from sheer exhaustion.

The Kenilworth was only a block away. In the morning, before I went downtown to see the editor of *Redbook*, I made myself pass the building on the park side of the street, and from there I looked up at our old windows that faced the lake. And I looked until the agony of remembering subsided into the dulled ache of acceptance. It was one more step to have accomplished.

But I accomplished little else as far as the business end of my trip was concerned. *Redbook* had completed the condensation of the novel, and had scheduled it for an early issue. Scribner's was bound to the agreement they had signed, and there remained very little choice of publishing firms who hadn't entered into the war against one-shots. "It's a pity," Max told me with the deepest regret. "A great pity."

I was equally depressed, and not only because our professional relationship had met disaster. Soberly, I realized that my months of hard work would now add little to my stature as a novelist,

M   [177]

and not a great deal to the balance in my bank account. A weekly pay cheque in Hollywood had at least offered a degree of security, but thanks to my own stubbornness, or independence, or ignorance, or whatever it was that had guided or misguided me, the total income from the one assignment that I had deigned to accept, amounted to exactly seven hundred and fifty dollars a week for four and a half weeks—minus agent's commission: I may have proved to myself that I could stand alone, but I had yet to prove to the world in general that I could support and educate the three young lives that were dependent upon me. The vision that I had had on the plane of returning home for good, vanished abruptly.

"I think I'll go back a couple of days earlier," I told my sister.

"I was hoping you'd stay a couple of days longer."

I shook my head.

"Maybe next time," she said. "It'll be easier for you the next time."

I think she knew what I had not acknowledged even to myself— I didn't belong in New York any more than I belonged in the white brick house on Canon Drive. I loved being with her, and it was good to see old friends, but beyond that I felt like a stranger in a strange city.

The rebuilding of a way of life was not as easy as I had thought it would be. Moving from place to place was of little avail, it merely postponed the inevitable acceptance that grief was a kind of death in which the spirit must be reborn. I was far from achieving that rebirth. Coming east on the plane, I had comforted and deluded myself with the thought that I had survived a year of painful readjustment. Simply, I had survived. And nothing more.

On the evening before I returned to the coast, I had dinner with Dr. Menas Gregory, one of my husband's oldest friends. I would have preferred to spend the little remaining time with my sister, but he had gone to great pains to arrange for me to meet at last "Missy" Meloney. He had spoken of her often, certain that both my husband and I would find her a fascinating and wonderful person, but because of one thing or another, the intimate little dinner parties he planned had always fallen through at the last moment. I wished that this little party could have fallen through, too. Now there would only be three of us. "Nobody else," he had enticed me. "Just you and Missy." He must have known that providing another escort in my husband's place would have hurt even more than going alone.

In the taxi on the way down to my host's huge bachelor apartment on top the Buckingham Hotel, I racked my brains to recall all the things he had so glowingly recounted about Mrs. Meloney, and the record of her achievements loomed formidable. She had been decorated by almost every country in the world, she had been responsible for bringing Madame Curie to America, and she was one of the most influential editors in America. Menas himself was an alienist of great repute, having established the psychiatric department at Bellevue. Time and again, he had taken me on blood-chilling tours through the wards, as patiently instructive as if I were a fellow physician. Even my sister, much as she hated to forgo our last evening together, said that Menas had always been such a warm and loyal friend that I couldn't very well refuse him without seeming ungracious.

Mrs. Meloney was already ensconced in a great Charles II needlepoint wing chair when I arrived, and my first impression of her was that her feet scarcely touched the floor. She was extremely tiny, and I wondered, vaguely, as her hand so firmly pressed mine, how such vitality and strength could be packaged in so small a body. And a delicate body, too, I recollected tardily. Menas had mentioned that she was badly lamed from a fall off a horse, and had been plagued by ill health from the age of seventeen. "She's a woman who's turned all her liabilities into assets," he had described her ardently, and looking at him in her presence, I thought, "He's in love with her." I felt sorry for him because I knew, looking at her, that she could never return his love— or the love of any other man. Many times, during the evening, she spoke of "Big Bill," as if he were alive, and I wondered at her fortitude in bringing her husband's name so often to her lips.

"I wish you'd look up Little Bill when you get back to Hollywood," she said, as we rose from the dinner table. "He's at Twentieth Century Fox."

"I will," I promised, but with little interest in the mission. "What does your son do at Fox?"

"A variety of things, I gather. He's only been in California a couple of months, he went out to recuperate after a bad case of the 'flu, and Winnie, Winfield Sheean, an old friend of Big Bill, felt that he could make a great contribution to pictures, and asked him to stay on for a while and learn the ropes."

"It sounds like a wonderful opportunity," I murmured politely.

"At least it will keep him in the sun for another month or so, until this dreadful winter is over. You won't forget to get in touch with him, will you, darlin'?"

"She's really quite Southern," I recognized in surprise. It had hardly crept in, except for the "Missy," in lieu of "Marie." "No, I won't forget," I said aloud, hoping that I'd remember. Looking up people for other people was usually a graceless procedure, but I could understand her concern for a young son who had been ill, three thousand miles away in a strange city. "I'll tell him I met you, and that you're fine," I promised.

She drew me to her, and kissed me. "God love you," she said.

I agreed with Menas that she was a very extraordinary little woman, and her melting brown eyes in contrast to her snow-white hair, and the strong, firm cast of her face were intensely arresting. I liked her without any sense that I could ever feel close to her.

I was booked for the early morning flight. With the difference in time, I was due to arrive in Los Angeles some time after midnight, and if there hadn't been a Columbus, Ohio, we might have made it, but we were grounded there again. Luckily, the family didn't expect me until two days later, so I didn't have to worry about them worrying.

Dawn was breaking as I stealthily fitted my key in the door, thereby reducing Pat to a cowering mass of jelly at the top of the stairs. Once he was certain that I was not a burglar, he reared up, with his great paws on my shoulders, and licked my face in his customary wet greeting. A moment later Pansy appeared from nowhere to rub up against my legs. "Everybody all right?" I whispered, and they said "Yes," and I thought, "It's nice to be home, anyway."

It wasn't worth while going to bed, so I unpacked, took a bath and surprised the children and my aunt at breakfast. "Madame!" Mademoiselle exclaimed softly, clasping her hands against her breast, and Fermin bowed his head off when he saw me, and again I savoured the warmth of homecoming. It was as if, at long last, I belonged somewhere.

"You're a different person, the trip did you good," my aunt said.

"I am, and it did. Has a Miss Stewart phoned?" I asked hopefully.

"I have a whole string of messages written down. Rosalie Stewart? Yes, she did call."

"Did she say what she wanted?"

"No, she just asked when you were expected, and said she'd ring you again."

It was part of the new leaf I had turned over that I didn't wait for her to telephone back. "Well, great!" she said, very gratified at my calling her. "How'd you like to go to work for Universal?"

"I haven't been to bed for two days——"

"Well, we'll let you get a little sleep first," she said good-naturedly. "Do you know who Maggie Sullavan is?"

"I think I met her at Sonya's. A lovely girl with blonde bangs and a husky voice I'd be afraid of adenoids in with the children."

"That's the one. Universal has her under contract for a two-picture deal. They haven't been able to find the right property for her, so they'd like an original. Something young and fresh. No blood and thunder. Just a good love story. Think you'll be rested enough to start in next Monday? No collaborator, you're on it alone. The deal's all set."

"But how can it be when I haven't even talked to Universal yet?"

"It's better for you not to. The producer you're going to work with knows all about you, and he definitely wants you. I warned him you were a little cuckoo about contracts, and not tackling anything unless you believed in it, but I also told him that you stuck with a job until you were satisfied with it."

"It sounds as if you'd oversold me," I said dubiously.

[181]

"You can't oversell a writer at two thousand a week. It's only when they get five hundred that you have to talk yourself blue in the face. I have a call on another wire," she broke off. "Monday morning, in Carl Laemmle's office."

Her whole approach to the assignment seemed to me a little elliptical and hurried, but I concluded that she had had enough of my shenanignans in the past, and since Mr. Cohn had already offered the same salary, I accepted it thankfully and without question. My aunt was flabbergasted, though. "The President of the United States doesn't earn that much!" she exclaimed.

"Why should he? The President works in Washington and this is Hollywood."

She left for New York on Sunday night, and on Monday morning I drove out to Universal. A youngish sort of woman or an oldish sort of girl—I was never quite able to decide which—was talking to the man at the gate as I pulled up to a stop. She leaned across the car window. "Welcome," she said. "I got here early so that I could walk you to your bungalow. I'm Grace Dudley. Your secretary."

I liked her right away. She had twinkly blue eyes in an irregular face, and her teeth were slightly bucked and pleasantly Irish. "You know why we're going to get along?" she demanded that afternoon. "You're Capricorn and I'm Gemini."

Although I couldn't accept the explanation as a basis for compatibility, Grace stuck to me like glue over the years—a combination secretary, watchdog and general buffer; and I loved her in return. I think that the devotion of people who work for you and with you, is no accident, even if I can't go quite as far as the stars to find a reason.

I didn't get much accomplished that first day at Universal, chiefly because Grace turned the studio upside down to make the bungalow comfortable and attractive. She sat at the telephone like a dictator. "I want a sofa. I don't care where you get it, get one. And it's got to be comfortable. While you're at it, you can take these chairs away, I want a couple of upholstered ones instead and send over a new stove, the one in Miss Franken's room smokes. Look, I'm going to need some vases for flowers, also a decent rug, for God's sake. And get these lousy ashtrays out of here."

In between moving in and throwing out furniture, she raided the supply room for boxes of soft pencils, reams of paper and carbon, and a new typewriter. ("Who do they think you are, giving you an old wreck like that!")

At noon she escorted me to the studio commissary. Since it was a long ride into town, everyone usually ate on the lot, and it was no hardship—the food was wonderful—rye bread, and noodle soup, and herring in cream, and new dill pickles and rich desserts.

Apart from the fact that calories were something I didn't have to reckon with yet, I was quite happy in my work at Universal, and before a month had passed, I had finished a draft of the screen play. I wrote it entirely in dialogue, simply because it was easier for me to write it that way. "This is practically a shooting script!" Grace told me as she typed the final pages. "No wonder you got two thousand at Fox, you were worth it."

"What makes you think I got two thousand at Fox?"

"Well, I deposit your pay cheques every week, don't I?"

"But what's that go to do with it?"

"Look. Who are you kidding? Don't you suppose I know a writer always starts off with the salary he got in the last job?"

There were no secrets between us. "Not always," I said. "Because I only got seven-fifty at Fox. I was raised to a thousand, but I didn't accept the assignment. And I was offered two thousand at Columbia, only I didn't accept that assignment either."

She whistled, long and significantly. "Either somebody slipped up or somebody must have wanted you for this story awful bad. Anyway, take it and shut up about it, and I'll forget you ever told me."

I couldn't forget it, though. After I'd handed in the script to Mike Boylan, my story editor, I went over to Mr. Carl Laemmle's office. "It's very important," I told his secretary. "I have to see him."

I'd had no contact with him since he'd welcomed me on the day of my arrival; his son-in-law, Stanley Bergerman, was the active if not the titular head of the studio.

[183]

Mr. Laemmle settled back in his chair, and I quickly stated the purpose of my visit. "Maybe I'm to blame for the mix-up, but I didn't mean to be," I summed up. "In any event, I'm not entitled to the salary you've been paying me, so I owe you the difference between seven-fifty and two thousand for the four weeks I've been here."

He said, "I see." I waited for him to say something else and, when he didn't, I added helpfully, "You have no contract with me."

"Are you happy at Universal?" he said in reply.

"I like it very much."

"Then we're very happy to have you. And as for your salary——" He smiled. "I'm quite certain that one or two of us in the studio must have known what Sol Wurtzel had been paying you, but perhaps they eased their conscience because you were writing an original for us. Stanley tells me it sounds like a very good story, by the way."

"I'm rather pleased with it. I just handed in the first draft to Mr. Boylan. I hate having nothing to do while I'm waiting to hear from him, so perhaps I could be working on something else in the meantime?"

His smile widened. "It's an unusual request. Are you really serious about it?"

"Of course."

"Then if you don't mind, Stanley tells me we're in trouble with a script about a woman mayor. We've got the shooting date set up, and it would help us if you'd read it, and give us any suggestions you might have on how to fix it up?"

"I'd love to," I said.

That was the official beginning of my career in Hollywood, and such success as I achieved testifies not so much to my ability as a scenarist, as to the fact that I ignored the pursuit of the almighty screen credit, in favour of my self-created job of script doctor. I also continued to ignore the security of contracts. I held to the contention that a written agreement served only as a protection against incompetence, nor have I since, with a single regrettable exception, submitted to a contractual obligation. Later, much later, I wrote *Claudia* for Mr. Balmer of *Redbook* for over a period of twelve years with nothing to bind either of us beyond a relationship that was mutually satisfying. Not until he had been retired did I feel morally free to accept an offer finally from a competitive magazine, thereby evoking a blistering editorial in one of the more literary publications, which excoriated me for putting money above loyalty.

The article was mailed to me anonymously, and it was with great difficulty that I resisted the temptation to set that particular gossip-monger straight on his facts, since another of my firm beliefs is that it is futile and undignified to explain one's position. I must admit, however, that an occasional disappointment in the integrity of the human animal causes me considerable conflict in remaining silent. All in all though, I've been pretty fortunate in my haphazard business dealings, because once, and only once, have I been deliberately "double-crossed." I use the word thoughtfully and precisely, for I do not mean it to imply the dishonest manipulation of funds or some equally flagrant and, to me, insignificant transgression, but rather a breach of trust and affection. It was an experience that has left me not a little bruised, and if more than one person squirms when he reads this, then I would rather not know about it.

Certainly I had no cause to be other than grateful for my long and happy association with Universal. I enjoyed the variety and the sense of accomplishment that came with working on two or three scripts at once with separate producers, and yet I was not subject to studio régime. On Thursdays, with Mademoiselle off for her violin lesson, I'd write at home, and once I stayed away from the studio for two full weeks when John went down with a membranous croup. My salary cheques, which I hadn't earned, were delivered by special messenger.

This was Hollywood at its best, Hollywood as it used to be in the old days of the Vendome and the Trocadero. Gradually, as I lost the sense of being a transient from the east, I began to feel as if I belonged and the people I met became a part of my daily life. I remember, in particular, and with affection, George Kelly and Gene Markey, but I doubt that either of them has the faintest memory of why they remain in my mind. I had always had the greatest admiration for George, but I'd never known him until I came to California. I liked him straight off because he didn't talk about himself or his plays. Instead, he took me on long, late drives through the canyons, and along the ocean, regaling me with ghost stories, which he believed in, and I, shivering for more reason than because the heater in his car didn't work, tried not to believe in them.

"I had a lovely time, George," I'd thank him dutifully at the end of each chilling drive.

"I enjoyed the evening too. The ocean air should make you sleep like a top. We'll do it again very soon."

I didn't have the heart to tell him that his eerie tales always kept me awake hours after I went to bed. His stories were as vivid and persuasive as his plays, and as an audience of one, the slightest creak in the house would scare the wits out of me.

Gene Markey, on the other hand, was not a mystic. He was one of the most attractive men I ever met, and it is a dubious comment on my own charms that his kindness to me should have shown itself in intensely practical terms. He said, one day, "I have something serious to discuss with you. What have you done about the food shortage?"

"Nothing. I didn't know there was one."

"It's not acute so far, but it will be. I'm laying in a big supply of stuff for my household and I'll duplicate the order for yours."

"That's awfully nice of you, but I wouldn't dream of bothering you," I refused politely but hastily.

"Nonsense. It's no bother. All I have to do is pick up the telephone——"

"No, don't, I'll do a little extra marketing," I promised him.

"A little extra marketing with a big family to feed isn't enough," he insisted.

"Then I'll do a lot," I said, lacking the courage to tell him that there were a few little chores I liked to perform for myself, and a judicious stocking of my pantry was one of them. I made a mental note to buy a half-dozen cans of corn for the boys, some jars of hot tamales for Fermin, and some tins of tuna fish for

Mademoiselle, which would more than take care of our immediate needs. I could panic over almost anything, but not over food shortages, or any other kind of shortage, with the possible exception of paper. I was hysterically grateful when Missy pulled wires to get me a big supply of toilet tissue before World War II, and even so we couldn't use it up. Some of it must still be knocking about in one place or another because every so often I come across a label, long out of date, and yellowed with age.

I was hysterical but not grateful when Gene Markey got me the groceries. The first I knew of it was when Mademoiselle telephoned me at the studio. "Madame, where shall I have the man put it all?" she wanted to know in quavering perplexity.

Not wanting to add to her agitation, I suppressed a bawdy suggestion. "Is it in boxes or bags?" I fenced for time.

"Cases, madame. There are many large wooden cases and some barrels."

"Oh no!"

"Mais oui, madame!"

"I can't bear it. Have everything put in the cellar."

The flour and sugar grew mouldy with disuse, but as far as I know, those large wooden cases are still in the cellar of the house on Canon Drive, waiting for someone to come along who likes tinned stringbeans and tinned carrots and cut-up fruit—tinned. —But just the same, Gene Markey, it was sweet of you.

I had been at Universal for well over a month before I remembered contritely that I had forgotten to telephone Mrs. Meloney's son. "See if he's still at Fox Beverly Hills," I told Grace. "He may have gone back to New York by this time."

No such luck. He hadn't. Moreover, he didn't appear to be any more pleased about hearing from me than I felt about looking him up. And anyway, how was it "Little Bill" had such a grown-up and frightfully cultured voice? I disliked him sight unseen, but I explained, quite civilly, why I was calling him, and suggested that he drop in that afternoon on his way home from the studio for a drink—a generic term that could have meant anything from alcohol to a cup of nice hot cocoa. Judging by his hoity-toity manner, the cocoa was definitely out. And so was my bottle of party mixture that everyone seemed to gag on. Just from the sound of him, I'd have liked to see him do a little gagging too, but very politely he regretted that he had a previous engagement. Merely because of his mother, I said that I would get in touch with him again.

It was a couple of weeks before I did so. I'd send Mrs. Meloney a reassuring note that I'd finally seen her son, and that would be that. "Get that Meloney boy on the phone again, will you?" I asked Grace.

"He's tied up," she reported back.

"Try him later, then."

He was still tied up, and like a fool I believed it, until I managed to reach him the following afternoon to talk to him myself. "How about calling at the house tomorrow or the day after," I said, giving him plenty of leeway to "untie" himself.

"It's very kind of you but I'm afraid I have engagements for the remainder of the week."

It didn't take a second ton of bricks to fall on me. Just how many convenient "engagements" could anyone have? I could feel a slow boiling of my blood as I realized that I was being politely, but definitely, snubbed by this supercilious young man. "You can go plumb to hell, even if your mother is a good friend of Menas Gregory's," I muttered as I hung up the receiver.

Revenge was sweet, when he telephoned me several weeks later at home, and asked if he could see me that same evening. Sorry, I was busy. Sorry, I was also busy the following evening, the week-end was quite out of the question, and I was never free for lunch. I hung up with the unworthy, but pleasant satisfaction of having paid him off in full. His mother had doubtless reprimanded him for his rudeness, and it served him right.

The next morning he telephoned the studio. "That Meloney fellow is getting around to calling you back," Grace announced.

"He's already phoned me at home," I enlightened her. "Tell him I'm not in my office."

"But I told him you were."

"That's your tough luck. Tell him you made a mistake."

"Oh. Okie-doke."

"Say, he doesn't sound so young, and he's getting to be a pest," she remarked, after his third call in as many days. "What excuse shall I give him now?"

"Who?" I asked absently, as I jotted notes on margins of an inept script.

She gave a small snort. "He's changed his tune from Bill Meloney to William Brown Meloney, if you please. Maybe he thinks three names is going to impress you."

"He thinks wrong. I'm allergic to three names." I was yet to discover that his book-plate bore testimony that there was a "fifth" thrown in for good measure. His father was William Brown Meloney the fourth, his grandfather the third, and I suppose it went all the way back to zero. (In our family, we'd never, to my knowledge, gone beyond three namesakes, and then we didn't remember them.) However, the comment is irrelevant. "I'll fix him once and for all," I decided abruptly. "Put him through."

"Okie-doke."

"Can't you say 'all right' for once!" I yelled after her. My temper got shorter as I grabbed the receiver. "Look here, Little Bill, I'm terribly rushed on a script," I opened and closed the conversation in one terse dismissal.

"Now hold on a minute, that's hitting below the belt," he protested. "You've been talking to Missy!"

"Naturally. Why did you think I called you in the first place? And by the way, why haven't you gone back to New York? Your mother said you were only going to be here for a short time."

"I'm leaving this Friday. That's why I'd like to meet you before I go. I have a particular reason," he added. "You might be interested in hearing it."

"I doubt it," I said. "What is it?"

"It's a little too involved to go into over the telephone."

Curiosity was my undoing as always. "It's Mademoiselle's day off on Thursday, so I have to be home anyway," I capitulated ungraciously.

"Splendid," he said.

"Splendid," I aped him under my breath. "Oh, come off it."

He couldn't have come off it, because it was the way he was born to talk, and anyone looking at him could tell that he wasn't putting it on. I suppose my ear had grown partially inured to the careless short-cuts of Hollywood speech, just as I had learned to regard the open-necked shirt and sandals as the accepted male attire. Mr. William Brown Meloney, however was impeccably garbed in a Harris tweed (my husband had bought a Harris tweed in London, so I recognized it) and polished Oxfords. Because I noticed hands, I saw that he was not given to manicures, although he looked as if he might have been. And far from fitting the name of Little Bill, he was extremely tall, extremely thin, with an immaculate hairline above a good forehead, and a very clipped and tidy black moustache. He had an outstanding nose, almost beaked, but it contributed to, rather than detracted from, what I had to concede was his rather distinguished bearing.

"I thought you'd be younger," I rebuked him, as we shook hands. "Much younger.—This is Peter," I broke off. "What is it, Pete?"

"Can I use your typewriter?"

"No. Say how-do-you-do to Mr. Meloney, and start your bath."

He said "How-do-you-do," and Mr. Meloney said, "I have a little boy called Peter, too."

This was another surprise. "Your own? You're married?"

"I was." He waited judiciously for Peter to depart. "I hadn't meant to embark on my personal life," he apologized. "But you see, I'm not very good at making conversation with children, and it was one of those inane gambits, like 'What grade are you in?' "

"I know," I sympathized, wondering if he might have lost his wife in childbirth, and if so, why his mother hadn't mentioned it.

"I'm divorced," he said, as if he'd read my mind.

"Oh. I'm glad. Not that you're divorced, of course," I stumbled over myself awkwardly, "but that you didn't have anyone you loved very much, die."

"It must be pretty tough," he said soberly. "I'm sorry."

I stiffened. "Would you like a drink?" I asked from behind a quick shell of defence.

"Nothing thank you.—Forgive me."

I didn't pretend not to understand his apology. "It was over-sensitive of me to have shut you up like that. I didn't stop to think that your mother must have written you."

He shook his head. "I haven't even that excuse to offer. My mother hasn't mentioned you in her letters."

I felt distinctly miffed. His mother hadn't bothered to mention me, and I'd been fool enough to go out of my way to look up her silly son. "I try to keep my private affairs to myself. Very few people know anything about me out here, and I prefer it that way."

"Then I'm afraid I owe you another apology."

Oh, Lord, he was going to be the apologetic sort under all that brittle veneer. "Why should you?" I rebuffed him.

"Because I deliberately found out everything I could about you this past week. I even managed to get hold of everything you've ever written from your first short story to *Twice Born*. That's a fine book, but the photograph on the jacket isn't very flattering. Still, I could tell from it that you weren't an enormously fat woman."

I suffered his juvenile overtures until the "fat" part made me prick up my ears. Maybe there was more than idle flattery behind all this. "Please stop being mysterious," I said impatiently. "What made you so interested all of a sudden in finding out about me?"

"Curiosity. I wanted to see for myself if you weighed two hundred pounds."

"And couldn't speak English," I finished grimly.

He stamped out his half-smoked cigarette and lit another one. "And now that I've read your books, and seen exactly what you look like," he said at length, with measured intent, "I shall be most happy, with your permission, to punch an erstwhile acquaintance of yours on the nose."

I was still mystified. "But when did you meet him, and where?"

"About ten days ago. At lunch. In the studio café."

"Please go on.—Now I'm the one who's interested," I said.

"I imagined you would be. Because this fellow painted a pretty grisly picture of you. 'It's a funny thing,' he volunteered, 'my being at the director's table when I'm actually a writer.' Then he waited for someone to ask him what he'd written—and said, 'Oh, just a little thing called *Another Language.*' The New York theatre being as remote from Hollywood as it is, nobody disputed his authorship very strenuously, but it so happened that I had gone to the opening of *Another Language,* and then I remembered that you'd telephoned me, and it just didn't add up. I said, 'I thought Rose Franken wrote the play.' 'Well, her name is on it,' he admitted, 'and it's a fascinating story, if you'd like to hear it.' This time he didn't wait to hear if we'd like to hear it, he launched into a detailed account of how this poor immigrant woman, badly crippled from childhood——"

"Me?"

"You—came to him with an idea for a play which she—you—had jotted down in Polish."

"He made a mistake. Russian."

"I don't want to misjudge him, maybe he did say Russian—— Look. Be serious. This isn't anything to laugh at. I think I'll punch that slimy bastard on the nose anyway," my visitor announced with relish. "Or perhaps," he added thoughtfully, "I owe too much to him."

"How?"

It sounded more coy than I'd intended it to, and I didn't give him the chance to reply. "I loathed you over the phone," I reminded him obliquely.

"I don't blame you. My mother's friends who look me up bring out the worst in me. Especially professional women. When may I see you again?"

"Meaning that, in your estimation, I don't fall into the professional category."

"You don't. No."

I regretted having opened the door once more to personalities. "You won't be seeing me again," I said with finality. "I don't think I'll be going back to New York until Paul—he's the oldest—is out of high school."

"I meant here, not in New York."

"But you told me you were leaving?"

"I was. But Jesse Lasky has offered me an assignment to translate and adapt a French play, and I've just decided to accept it."

"Oh.—But don't you have a job that you have to get back to in the States——? I mean, in the east?"

He laughed. "That was a nice slip of the tongue.—You don't like California, do you?"

"I'm learning to.—Does any easterner really like it?"

"I like it."

"But what about your job at home?" I asked primly.

"I have a buyer."

"A buyer?"

"I thought my mother might have mentioned that I own and publish a string of newspapers in Dutchess County. She usually does."

"No, she just said that you'd come out here to recuperate. Is it because of your health that you've decided to give up newspaper publishing?" I asked with diffidence.

"Good Lord, no! Missy's blown up a simple little 'flu attack into a major debility."

"Mothers are entitled to worry," I pointed out with severity, feeling a belated kinship with Missy.—"Are you actually going to make a career out of pictures?"

"I doubt it."

"Then what will you do?—I don't know why I'm asking all these questions, it's none of my business what you do, and honestly," I added frankly, "I don't especially care."

A smile twitched at his lips. "That's base ingratitude," he said, "for the punch in the nose I was going to deliver on your behalf."

"You're not the type, you're much too natty. I'm being really nasty, and I'm not usually," I broke off contritely. "Let's start again. Suppose you don't like being a Hollywood director or producer or whatever it is you intend doing out here."

"I won't starve, if that's what you mean," he interrupted with his smile coming outright. "I can always go back to law, or teaching."

"Go back? Or begin?"

"I thought you weren't going to be nasty."

"But you couldn't have been all those things."

"Why not? I was an attorney in Bill Donovan's office, and before that, I was a professor of English at Columbia University."

I felt a renewed surge of annoyance. "You don't seem to stick at any one thing very long," I remarked. "Lawyer, Professor, Publisher."

"I worked in a lumber camp for a year," he supplied mildly, "and I've written quite a bit."

"I don't think I'd brag about being a dilettante," I said, and felt as if I looked like my mother all of a sudden.

"I'll let the 'dilettante' jibe pass," he returned, without umbrage. "More important, you have a conventional streak in you, haven't you?"

"I was brought up conventionally," I acknowledged, slightly nettled by his perspicacity. "Marriage and the responsibilities it entails require a certain solidity."

"There were other contributing factors in my divorce," he said quietly.

My cheeks grew warm with embarrassment. "I wasn't prying. Whatever obligations you have, and however you approach them, is your own affair. Are you sure you won't have a drink before you go?"

He was quick to take the hint. He rose and held out his hand. "Perhaps next time."

There isn't going to be a next time. It would have sounded childish had I said it. "Perhaps," I agreed noncommittally.

Paul popped out like a jack-in-the-box as the door closed upon my departing guest. "Hey, who was that?" he demanded with unwonted avidity.

"Nobody," I said. "I mean, just somebody I was supposed to look up. It's a long story, forget it."

"Gee, when I saw him, I thought it was Basil Rathbone."

"That's true, there is a resemblance, isn't there?"

"Sure. Even their voices sound alike. Too bad."

"Sorry I let you down."

"That's okay.—Can we have an early supper?"

"Bee Jay on a school night again?"

"I'm helping her cram for a history exam."

"You told me she passed it. With an 'A.'"

"That was an English exam. Gosh, with Ambrose Bierce for a grandfather, why shouldn't she?"

"Your literary background doesn't seem to have helped you very much," I remarked pointedly. I was just as glad that he didn't show any aptitude or desire to follow my footsteps, nor John either. I wasn't so sure of Peter, although I suspected that his bent for words lay chiefly in banging the keys of the typewriter. In any event there was a great deal to be said for the more substantial if humdrum approach to life, and I neither liked nor approved of what Mr. William Brown Meloney V stood for. I changed my mind about writing to his mother. If I couldn't say anything complimentary about her son, it was better not to say anything at all.

"Did Whoosis show up last night?" Grace greeted me the next morning.

The thin walls of the bungalow didn't contribute to privacy. "If 'whoosis' is who I think you mean, he did."

"He must be quite a guy from what Maisie told me happened at the studio last week."

"Who's Maisie?"

"Herb Blachman's secretary."

"Who's *he?*"

"I'm going to have to make you out a Who's Who of Hollywood. Blachman's a big producer at Fox, he's doing this French picture, and Sheean—You know who Sheean is?"

"Don't be so sassy."

Her face crinkled into a grin. "Well, anyway, Sheean knows Meloney from New York it seems, and he wants him to see what the motion picture business is like, so he starts him off as assistant director to Blachman. Everything's going fine, until they come to a sequence with pigeons——"

"I can guess the rest. Let's get some work done."

"It's not what you think with the pigeons, so hold your horses.

Blachman wants a shot with the birds in flight, so he has them thrown down from the top of the church roof, which smashes the poor little things when they hit the ground. Well, Blachman should worry about a couple of dozen crates of pigeons as long as he gets the effect he's after, but Meloney sees red. 'You son of a bitch, quit that!' he yells at the top of his voice. 'I'm directing this picture!' Blachman yells back at him, and climbs up on the roof and throws down a pigeon to prove it. Meloney's up after him like a bat out of hell, grabs Blachman by the throat, and tells him if he doesn't lay off he'll get the same treatment as the birds——"

"Is it true?" I broke in, "or is it just one of those Hollywood yarns?"

"So help me." Grace lifted a hand in solemn oath. "Maisie was right there on the set, bringing Blachman his ten o'clock glass of milk and Graham crackers. She said Blachman scurried down off that roof like a scared rabbit, swallowed a couple of pills, and stalked off to Sheean's office to get Meloney thrown off the lot, by God, if it was the last thing he did. It looks as if he did it, too, because Maisie says he's going back to New York. Meloney, I mean."

"He didn't come out to stay," I said, wondering why I bothered to defend this hot-headed young man.

"He's smart, he knows a dumb guy like him doesn't belong in this town. Want to hear another story about him? I got it straight from Sheean's secretary who's a buddy of Maisie's."

"No. I think we've minded other people's business enough for one day."

"Now don't get huffy, the girls wouldn't have said a word if I hadn't happened to let drop at supper last night that he was going over to your house. Guess what he did when Sheean offered him a job?"

"What?" I surrendered feebly, because I'd met his mother, and perhaps it was something I ought to know, in case I changed my mind about writing her.

"This is rich. Listen." Grace licked her lips with an effect of shoving her buck teeth out of the way. "Sheehan says to him,

'Would four hundred a week pay your expenses while you're learning the ropes?' And the cluck turns it down. 'It's too much,' he says, 'I don't know the first thing about pictures, and I'd feel more comfortable if you made it two hundred to start off with.' And Edie—that's Sheean's secretary—says she knows for a fact that that's all he's getting when he could have had twice as much. Did you ever hear anything so crazy?"

"I don't think it's crazy at all. He didn't want to take advantage of Mr. Sheean, and I'd have felt the same way."

"Then you're both nuts. Nobody thanks you for giving them anything in this racket. The more you earn, the more you get. Your two thousand a week makes you a big shot and you could ask for an increase any time, and get it. Only don't do it for a while yet."

"I have no intention of doing it now, or later. But why shouldn't I?"

"Because I keep tabs on Capricorn, the same as Gemini, and there's going to be a change for you in a couple of months. Maybe sooner."

Sometimes I took a peek at her astrology magazines, although I certainly put no stock on such nonsense. "What kind of a change?" I asked, a little apprehensively.

"Nothing bad," she assured me, "nothing with the kids or anything, just in your professional life."

"Better phone home and see how everything is, to be on the safe side," I said. "And then let's stop gossiping for heaven's sake, and get some work done."

"You're not kidding. Just a jiff till I get my pad."

"Jiff." "Bye-now." "Be seeing you." I wondered, for no good reason, whether Mr. Meloney spoke with a British inflection, or if it only sounded that way compared with Hollywood diction. Not that I cared. I couldn't have cared less. In fact I was rather annoyed when Mademoiselle, very pleased, informed me on my return from the studio, that a gentleman had telephoned who had spoken to her in her native tongue. "Very fluent, madame, and a perfect French accent. He said he would call back in a little while."

[197]

He didn't have to leave his name. A "perfect French accent," was a trifle galling when my own French was spectacularly domestic. "Haven't you gone back to New York *yet*?" I asked him pettishly when he telephoned later.

"No, I told you I'd decided to accept an assignment with Jesse Lasky."

"Oh. So you did. Is it an interesting one?"

"I don't know, I found out today that I didn't get it," he returned cheerfully.

"Why not?" (I thought I knew the answer, but I was curious to hear the pigeon story from his point of view.)

"I'll tell you when I see you," he put me off. "I could be over in about three minutes, if you're not busy."

"Where are you, at the corner drugstore?"

If he noticed the edge in my voice, he chose to disregard it. "No, I'm at home," he said.

He'd told me that he was staying at the Château Elysée. "And you can drive all the way down from Franklin Avenue in three minutes? Your capabilities continue to amaze me."

"I thought you weren't going to be nasty any longer."

"I know, but I can't help it, you irritate me."

"I wonder why?"

I disregarded the implication and changed the subject. "I'll call your bluff and time those three minutes of yours."

"All right, let's bet on it. If I win, you'll have to go out to dinner with me this evening."

It couldn't have been more than two minutes when the front door bell rang. "So you lied. You weren't home," I eyed him coldly.

"The 'Château' answers a certain purpose, but I wouldn't go so far as to call it 'home', " he returned, quite unruffled by my accusation. "I moved out last night."

"Where?" I asked with immediate distrust.

"I spent all day Saturday house-hunting, and found a nice little place, fully furnished and ready for occupancy."

"Where?" I repeated sternly.

"Crescent Drive."

No wonder he could sprint over and win his bet. Crescent Drive was not only one short block away from Canon Drive, but the two avenues shared a common alley leading from the back-gardens, thus supplying an effective short-cut between the rows of houses. It was on the tip of my tongue to lash out at him and ask him what sort of person he was, with his divorce hardly cold, to move in practically next door, and what sort of person did he think I was to tolerate such impudence when there were plenty of other streets he could have chosen at a respectable distance away! However, I knew what sort of person he thought I was. Conventional. Well, I would disarm him by being indifferent to whatever he did, or didn't do. It was no concern of mine; let his mother worry about his renting houses when he didn't have a job, and going around punching people in the nose.

"Come in," I said, affably. "And don't make love to Pansy, he's moulting like mad. Fermin has a roast in the oven, and Paul has company for dinner, so I can't go out with you."

"I insist on collecting part of the bet, anyway. I don't mind cat's fur. Couldn't I stay?"

I shrugged. "If you'd like to. You look skinny enough to do with a little home cooking. Tell me about your new house?"

"You're completely unpredictable," he said elliptically. "Anyway, I promise not to make a nuisance of myself. Living so near, I mean."

"I just think it's a little stupid to have saddled yourself with housekeeping responsibilities when you didn't get the Lasky assignment," I said, with another shrug.

"But I didn't discover that I'd lost it until after I'd signed the lease," he explained, with what I felt was too much equanimity under the circumstances. "And guess why I didn't get it?"

I smiled enigmatically. "Tell me."

"It couldn't happen anywhere else but Hollywood. The deal was all set as far as I knew, Sheean was delighted that I was staying on at the studio, Lasky was delighted to have me on the picture, until he happened to find out what my salary was."

"Too much?" I murmured, reaching the peak of my nastiness.

"Too little. 'I'm sorry, old boy,' Jesse told me, looking very

[199]

uncomfortable about it, when he called me into his office this morning, 'but I'll have to ask you to bow out from the assignment I offered you last week. The fact is, we're going to spend a great deal of money on this production, and I couldn't possibly justify engaging anyone to work on it who isn't earning at least a thousand dollars a week, and preferably upwards of that.' "

I knew Jesse, he was a kind man, and I could see and hear him in all the nuances of his unhappy dilemma. I suppressed a laugh. "Let this be a lesson to you, my dear quixotic Mr. Meloney," I advised him. "Next time, don't be so quick to cut your salary in half."

He was astonished, and slightly abashed. "How did you hear about that?"

"You've yet to learn that nothing is a secret from anybody out here. Not even the things that aren't true. What are you going to do now?"

"Fly home, wind up my newspaper deal, come back and look for another job," he replied without hesitation.

"It won't be easy at two hundred a week."

"I know it. And yet it's a fair bit of money—in America, that is."

We both laughed. Laughter is a pleasant thing to share. On the whole I decided that he was rather a nice person, not because of what he said, but because of what he had left unsaid. He could have bragged about taking less salary and saving the lives of those pigeons, and he hadn't even referred to either incident.

I liked that.

He wrote me from New York and I also liked a definite signature in his handwriting. Possibly a little too compact, but firm and decisive. "I'm returning by train, because I'm bringing Freya with me, and I don't think she'd enjoy flying. You'll love her, I hope. And I'm sure that she'll love you, and the little house on Crescent Drive."

Freya. He'd never referred to her, either. I had no idea who she was, or what she meant in his life, but I was too involved with a script problem at the studio to give it much thought. For the

[200]

first time, I was up against a story I couldn't lick, and my pride balked at acknowledging my limitations. It was a vehicle for Boris Karloff—a dramatic departure from his horror roles—and it was all about dust storms in the middle west, and grain elevators, and a lot of other things I didn't know anything about. "This is something I can't tackle," I told Mike Boylan. "It's a background that needs a male point of view."

"But it needs the woman's angle too," he argued. "How about if we put someone else on it with you?"

It was my initial collaboration at Universal, and I suppose I'd become accustomed to working alone, because I found it was difficult to match wits and rhythm with an alien mind, and a weary one at that, full of clichés and time-worn situations, with the dust storms superimposed on the action like a wart. "We're not getting anywhere," I reported to Mike in discouragement.

"What a girl!" he said good-humouredly. "You've only been on it a week. Give yourself a little more time."

"It won't do any good. The scenes are limp and they lack validity. Read the little we've written so far and you'll see what I mean."

"I see what you mean," he admitted, after he'd skimmed through the handful of pages. "Same old stuff. Go to Palm Springs for a couple of weeks' vacation, and let me see who else I can come up with for you to work with."

I'd already taken the children to Palm Springs over Christmas, and I didn't want to go again. It was unbuilt-up and unspoiled in those days, consisting mainly of The Desert Inn surrounded by dusty, winding roads against a backdrop of sand, and purple mountains, and you could bicycle for hours. It had reminded me too much of Bermuda, and loneliness had shadowed the sun. "I have the last version of the script about the woman mayor to go over," I compromised. "Maybe I'll come back to the dust storms with some fresh ideas."

Mike Boylan was a big, rough, gentle Irishman, and I remember the way he looked at me. "You're in a bad way, honey," he said gravely. "You don't let yourself relax."

He was right. I was in a bad way, goaded by an incessant

compulsion to work. I was afraid not to work. I tackled script after script with an omnivorous hunger to cram full every empty hour. Once more it was the way it had been in the beginning—the children could not fill my life, nor could I participate in the small, private worlds they were building for themselves. I needed only the knowledge of their well-being and they needed only the pervading sense of my nearness.

"Skeezicks got tired of waiting, he went home," Grace said when I returned to my office; she did not bestow the dignity of a name upon anyone she didn't like, and she didn't like my collaborator. "What did Boylan think of the script?"

"Not much. We'll drop it for a while, and polish off *Her Excellency, the Mayor.*"

"That's a little stinker, too. Can I get you a cup of coffee?"

"No, thanks."

"A bar of chocolate? For energy?" she wheedled.

"If you insist. But just for energy!" I threw after her.

The telephone rang. She paused at the door. "Shall I answer it before I go?"

"No, I will." I pushed a couple of the wrong buttons before I connected with the right one. It was Mademoiselle. She was weeping, and her voice, when she finally got it out of her throat, sounded as if it were wringing its hands. "Oh, madame, madame, something terrible has happened!"

". . . this is a bad dream, one of the bad dreams I sometimes dream . . ." I wet my lips. "What is it———? Mademoiselle! Tell me! What's happened———?"

"It is the little Pansy, madame, he has been run over by a car and killed! Oh, madame, I am so sad to have to call you like this, but Master Paul is not yet home from school, and Johnnie is crying so hard I can do nothing with him. . . ."

My mouth felt as if it were full of ashes. Had I heard her right? Had she said "the little Pansy"? Somehow, I got Peter's name to my lips, and waited an eternity for her quavering voice to reach my ears.

"Peter does not know yet, madame, it was Johnnie who carried the poor little cat in from the street."

[202]

"Oh, God, thank you! Tell John I'm coming home as fast as I can."

I scribbled a note for Grace and ran the long length of the studio grounds to the car park, with each breath slitting my chest like a knife. The man at the gate waved me out, and I waved back at him, just as if Pansy, who was a part of our very lives, had not been run over and killed. The road blurred before me. The drive into Beverly Hills was endless.

It was strange that I should have found words of comfort and strength for the children when their father died, but now I could only share their sorrow, with the tears rolling unashamedly down my cheeks. The neighbour who had inadvertently hit Pansy as he'd backed his car out of the garage, came to express his regret, and offer his deepest sympathy. "I wish there was something I could do. I didn't even know what had happened until I was halfway down the street, and your little boy ran out to pick the poor thing up. He screamed that he wanted to kill me, and I can't say I blame him."

"You didn't mean to do it," I said. "I'm sure John knows that as well as we do."

He knew it, but it didn't assuage his grief. "But I loved Pansy, I loved Pansy, why did it have to happen!"

I put my arms around him, and he didn't squirm away. "Darling, I wish I had the answer why it happened."

"His eyes were open," John kept on sobbing. "He was looking at me, but he didn't see me."

"I guess Pansy knew you were there, anyway, Johnnie," Paul said huskily.

"I want Pansy to come back," Peter whimpered.

"We all do," Paul told him. "I guess we just have to be glad we still have Pat."

I had a sudden sense that Paul must have said the same thing about me when his father died. "I guess we have to be glad we still have Mother."

Fermin announced dinner in a muted voice. We sat at the table, but none of us could eat. Mademoiselle came to the door. "Monsieur Melloney is on the telephone, madame."

I noticed dimly that she called him "Melloney." I didn't want to leave the children sitting alone at the table, and I didn't want to talk to anyone. I was afraid I would cry. "Tell him I can't speak to him now."

"Yes, madame."

I wondered vaguely if he was telephoning from New York, or if he had come home. A few minutes later, Mademoiselle appeared again. "Monsieur Melloney is here, madame. He is waiting in the living-room."

"He should go away," John said angrily, as if he didn't want an outsider to disrupt our unity.

"Shall I see him for you, Mother, and tell him to come back some other time?" Paul offered.

"No, I'll see him for a minute."

He was standing by the window. He turned as I came in. "Mademoiselle told me over the phone."

I began to cry. "I feel such an idiot," I gulped.

"You're not. I could cry, too."

I looked at him, and saw that he meant it. "I can't cry for people," he apologized. "But I cried when my Irish terrier died. Where have you put Pansy?"

"On the patio, covered with a towel until we decide what to do."

"Let me take him over to my place. It's better not to bury him here."

"I didn't want to on account of John. But I didn't want to just——"

"No. That wouldn't do." He saved me from saying it. "I'll be back in a little while."

"I'm so grateful to you."

I wiped my eyes and blew my nose, and he put his arm around me the way I had put my arm around John, and later I realized that I hadn't squirmed away either. It was the first warm, human touch that I had welcomed. It was easy to call him Bill after that.

When he came back from his grim mission, John and Peter

were in bed, ready to sleep from emotional exhaustion, and I had
encouraged Paul to seek an hour's respite with Bee Jay.

"Is it all right to leave you alone?"

"I won't be alone. Bill's coming back."

He looked relieved. "That's good." I could see that I was a
weight off his mind. "Is that his first name?"

"Yes. William. William Brown——"

He grinned. "It sure dresses up the Meloney end."

"It sure does."

I had changed from my office tweeds to a dark blue slack suit.
Bill noticed, "Good," he said. "You're all dressed to take a ride.
It's a lovely night."

I thought of the long, chill drives with George Kelly. "Have
you a heater in the car?" I demurred. "That heats, I mean?"

"It heats very hot."

"Do you believe in ghosts?"

"I do not," he said firmly. The look he bent upon me was
probing and severe. "Do you?"

How odd, I thought. His eyes were brown, and he was tall and
dark. My husband's eyes were blue, and he was not tall, and his
colouring was very nearly blond. And yet, suddenly, there was
a strong resemblance between them. . . .

"You haven't answered me.—Do you?"

I pulled myself back from a long distance. "Do I what?"

"Believe in ghosts."

"On and off," I admitted. "But mostly off.—Is everything
attended to?" I hastily changed the subject.

He nodded. "The gardenia tree. With a white stone to mark the
place."

"Thank you."

"My car's in front of my door. Why don't we walk over? I
want you to meet Freya."

"Oh. You spoke of her in your letter."

"Did I? Probably. We're not happy away from each other.
She's the only reason I went back east. I could have sold my
newspaper business from here."

"Then you did sell?"

"Yes. I've got a lot to tell you about my trip, but it'll keep till later. First, Freya."

No one could have helped but fall in love with her. She was a beautiful police dog, with a slim, lovely head, and melting eyes. "I'm anxious to see if she growls at you," Bill said. "She growls at Missy.—She growls at most people," he added fairly.

Freya didn't growl at me, even when I knelt and put my face against her soft ruff. "She likes me. I feel as if someone's left me a million dollars."

"So do I," he smiled. "I was afraid she might be touchy, because she's going to have puppies."

"Oh, how wonderful! I've never had puppies."

"You haven't? Neither have I. We'll have them together."

"This is a very nice little house," I said.

"Shall I show you through?"

"Do. Houses fascinate me. I'd have liked to have been an architect."

It was typically a bachelor's house, with a small bedroom and sleeping-porch upstairs, and a combined living- and dining-room on the first floor. "The kitchen's very tidy," I complimented him.

"Max seems to be the tidy sort, I'm glad to say."

"Who's Max?"

"My Filipino boy. I called up an agency early this morning, and he was here an hour later."

"You work awfully fast, don't you?"

"Why not? Life is awfully short. Shall we get started for our drive? And do you mind if we take Freya?"

"I'd mind if we didn't."

It was a luxurious roadster—a yellow LaSalle. "I just bought this, this afternoon too. No sense hiring a car any longer. Is it too flashy? It has a beautiful engine."

"It makes my black Buick look stodgy. But then, I have three boys to tow around in it," I mentioned by way of reminder.

"Stop bragging. I've got two."

"I thought you only had one. Peter."

"He's the younger. Bill is the older."

"That would make him William Brown Meloney VI," I said. "I'm sorry. You've been too nice this evening for me to begin being nasty again."

"Were you?"

"A little."

"Why?"

"Conventional."

"It's half the battle to know your own limitations."

"Do you know yours? Or haven't you any?"

"There you go again."

"This time I really didn't mean to be.—You said you were going to tell me about your trip to New York."

"Oh. Yes. I telephoned your sister."

I tried to remember if I'd asked him to. "I didn't, did I?"

"No, but you telephoned me for my mother, so it was only fair to let your family know that you were well. And happy."

"But how did you know my sister's name was Lindsay and where she lived?"

"I asked Menas Gregory.—She's a lovely person."

"Much nicer than I am," I said humbly.

"And very beautiful."

"Did you see her?" I demanded, astonished.

"She invited me to dinner."

"And you went?"

"Of course. Your aunt was there. She's a lovely person, too."

"Well, now that you've sized my family up, I'm glad they passed muster."

"You're being nasty again," he said pleasantly. "Be reasonable. They love you and they worry about you, and they were glad to get some first-hand news of you."

"From someone who hardly knows me?"

"I know you."

"What are you going to do about a job?" I changed the subject prudently.

"Winnie Sheean told me before I went east that he'd be glad to have me back."

"At that figure, I don't wonder.—Let's turn round and go home.

[207]

It's getting late, and I have a horrid day ahead of me at the studio."

"Why?"

"I have to polish somebody's script about a woman mayor."

"That sounds really nasty."

"And I flubbed a script of my own about dust storms.—Do you know anything about dust storms?"

"Certainly."

"Is there anything you *don't* know?"

He grinned. "Very little."

"Then tell me about grain elevators."

He told me. "I hope I can keep it all in my mind until tomorrow," I said. "And the soil being thirsty—that's a good title: *Thirsty Soil*."

"I'll make notes for you when we get home." He switched on the dashboard light to look at the time. "It's not even ten o'clock."

"Is that all it is?"

"I must have bored you."

"You didn't. What I meant was, it seemed so much later because such a lot has happened in a few short hours."

We didn't speak again until we turned into Canon Drive. He said, "I'd better leave Freya in the car until she can be formally introduced to Pat."

"Yes, you'd better. He'll put on a show and wake the children up.—Paul's not home yet, the garage door is still open."

"Don't worry about him."

"I shouldn't?"

"No.—He's all right and he's a nice boy. You can be proud of the job you've done."

"He's like his father.—Make yourself comfortable in the library, I want to take a peek at the other two."

When I came downstairs again, he was typing away like mad. "Your machine needs cleaning," he said, without stopping. "There are crumbs in the keys."

"That means Peter's been using it." I looked over his shoulder. "Page three!" I exclaimed.

"I'm just setting the scene for you. Throw it out if you don't think it's right."

"You don't belong in Hollywood, you write as fast as I do. That is, when I know what I'm writing about."

"How'd you like your villain to set fire to the grain elevators?"

"I'd adore it!—When did you think of that?"

"Just now." He slid a fresh sheet of paper into the machine. "Use it as your opening, start off with a bang. Then go into a flashback."

"That's brilliant. And I mean it."

Paul came home a little before midnight. He was surprised to find us in the library. "What's all the writing about?"

"Bill's helping me with a script.—Did you see his dog out in the car? She's going to have puppies."

"Gosh, I was talking to her. She's a beauty."

He regarded Bill with a new respect. "What does a fellow have to do to get one of those pups?"

"Ask Mamma," I injected promptly. "You don't clean up after Pat any too well."

"You can have the choice of the litter," Bill said. "If Mamma lets you."

"Gosh thanks. It'll almost make up for Pansy."

Pansy. For a little while, I had forgotten. I felt the silly tears well up in my eyes. Paul gave me his handkerchief. "I never saw my mother cry before," he told Bill, half in apology, half in wonder. "Not even after Dad died." His voice broke. He turned abruptly, and went upstairs.

I tried not to take sleeping pills, but I took one that night, and was late in getting to the studio. Mike Boylan was already in his office, and I stopped on the way to my bungalow, and gave him the sheaf of pages that Bill had written the night before. "Can you glance through this beginning while I wait?"

"Sure," he said. "*Thirsty Soil.* That's a great title.—Say, I thought I told you to lay off for a while? What's the idea of driving yourself? You look like death warmed up."

"Just read and never mind what I look like." I couldn't bring myself to tell him about Pansy. He was a nice man, but he wouldn't have understood. I sat down and picked up a *Hollywood Reporter*, watching his face from behind it. He put the last page down, quite excited. "This is great. Absolutely great. You don't need a collaborator, my girl!"

"On this script, I do. Because I didn't write what you've just read."

He looked at me blankly. "Are you pulling my leg?"

"No, I'm not," I said, and explained that a friend of mine had happened to know all about dust storms.

"He happens to know how to write, too," Mike said. "What are we waiting for? Who's his agent?"

"I am," I said promptly. "I'm asking seven-fifty for him."

"You've got it," said Mike.

I was diffident about telling Bill he had the job, not wanting to demean his maleness by having taken the initiative without consulting him.

Therefore, I didn't know whether to be pleased or disappointed when he showed nothing but pleasure in our prospective collaboration. "He either has no pride at all," I pondered, "or he's big enough not to be petty or jealous." It remained a small, niggling question in my mind until time, and more living, finally answered it for me.

Thirsty Soil established us as a writing team, although I felt that I contributed less to the story than I should have. The "woman's angle" was necessary, but minor in relation to man's highly dramatic struggle against the elements. Unlike my collaboration with Phil Klein, in this one Bill took over the physical writing of the script, while I sat opposite him on the other side of the desk, suggesting scenes and throwing in lines of dialogue. At the end of the second week, when we had the story-line fairly well mapped out, he said, "Do you like sailing?"

"The nearest I've sailed is on an ocean liner. And a canoe in the Adirondacks."

"You don't know what you've been missing. Let's fly to Catalina tomorrow. We can be back early Monday morning."

"I can't. I've never left the children for a whole week-end."

"It's time you did. Anyway, there are telephones, and it's no more than an hour's flight. I'll leave my car at the airfield."

"I wish you'd go, Mother," Paul took sides with Bill. "It'll do you good."

I had a suspicion that he browbeat his brothers into also urging the Catalina jaunt, because they stood waving us off at the kerb, and yelling at the top of their lungs, "Have a nice week-end with Bill, Mother!" I don't know what the neighbours thought, but as for myself, I intended to have as pleasant a week-end as if I were going away with my sister.

And I did—except for trying to be graceful and nonchalant in following Bill's shouted instructions in a small sailing boat on a wavy sea combed with a brisk wind. "Duck!" he kept yelling at me every time the boom swung round and bumped my head. "You don't duck fast enough!"

"Why should I learn new tricks like ducking at my advanced age?" I demanded at lunch.

" 'Advanced'!" he scoffed. "You look indecently young to be the mother of three sons."

"It isn't how old I look, it's how old I am." This boat business presented a highly opportune moment for us to face the fact that our respective birth dates were even more at variance than they actually were, for not only had I added three years to my age, but his mother, for sound professional reasons, had subtracted two from his. According to our driver's licences he was thirty-three and a half, and I had just turned forty. "My three extra years are on my last passport, too," I mentioned. "What about your two?"

"They're off," he admitted. "Missy fixed that when I hit six feet at sixteen. And passports are hell to change," he added bleakly.

"Well, there's no reason to," I closed the discussion with asperity. "I simply wanted to remind you that with my elderly bones you can't expect me to duck with your agility."

"Let's get into our bathing suits and I'll race you to the dock," he replied.

I wasn't a bad runner, but I suspected that he almost let me win. I wasn't sure to what end he thought he was building my confidence.

On Monday morning I found that I needed as much of it as I

could get. We'd planned to catch the earliest flight, which would have got us to the studio for a ten o'clock story conference. I came down from my room to find him waiting in the lobby. "How'd you like to skip breakfast?" he inquired in lieu of a good morning.

"I wouldn't," I said, affronted at the very thought of it. "We have a half an hour before our plane leaves."

"It's not leaving. The flight's cancelled."

"I don't believe it," I said flatly. "Why?"

"Fog."

My voice curdled with irony. "Now isn't that nice," I said, "to be caught with our pants down like this."

Like a gentleman, he let the inaccuracy as well as the inelegance of my statement go unchallenged. "Don't worry," he said. "I'll get us back on time, I've hired a speedboat. It's going to be fun."

"I like your idea of fun," I rejoined scathingly.

It really was fun. We arrived at the office ahead of Grace, which made us feel, for no good reason, delightfully illicit.

"My, but you both got a beautiful tan over the week-end," she observed.

I peered into a mirror that she had filched from a truck-load of props. "I did, didn't I?"

"It must have been that last spurt of ocean wind and sun this morning," I said on the way over to the story conference.

"I'm terribly sorry."

"What are you sorry about?"

He looked down at me. "Then you didn't mind Grace saying that?"

"About my tan? I'm very pleased with myself. I never burn as a rule. Why should I have minded?"

As I was beyond the age of naïveté, I suppose I was just stupid.

On the following Saturday morning, he appeared bright and early at the front door. "Good. You're dressed. Come along, I want you to look at a present I've picked out for you."

"I don't want a present, I don't like presents."

"You'll like this one."

"Now you've got me curious."

"I was counting on that."

I was pretty sure that it was going to be either a new briefcase or a sensible wrist-watch, both of which I needed, but, like groceries, I preferred to buy them for myself. However, he didn't seem to have that sort of a gift in mind, for we headed straight out towards the valley, and after miles and miles of flat, parched countryside, drew up in front of a small white cottage with a red sign on it: Katy's Kattery. Pedigreed Siamese Kittens.

"I hope it isn't too soon after Pansy," he said anxiously.

"No," I said. "It isn't." How could he have known that I liked pets in pairs?

He stayed for dinner that evening, and for the first time, the boys really warmed up to him, and so did Fermin. Mademoiselle was already smitten, but chiefly because of his excellent French. I cannot, with any degree of honesty, pretend that he was the sort of man who had that special talent of immediately ingratiating himself with servants and children. Hollywood abounded in males with winning personalities, but he was not one of them.

It would be a nice addendum to this saga of the Siamese kittens to say that they grew up to be an everlasting delight and comfort, but it would be an unconscionable falsehood. They were fiends. With their tiny claws and teeth they scratched, bit, and tore our flesh to ribbons. They were the only animals, two-legged or four-legged, that I ever remember being intimidated by. We gave them a week of unadulterated trial and error, and then returned them to Katy's Kattery.

On that same afternoon, Freya started having her puppies, and at midnight she was still at it. Late as it was, I knew that Mademoiselle would still be squeaking away at her scales, so I telephoned to let her know where I was. "I'm going to stay until it's all over," I said. "Tell the boys not to worry, in case they wake up and I'm not home."

"Yes, madame." Her voice was faint with embarrassment at so unseemly a situation. "I can't tell whether she's more shocked at where I am or what I'm doing where I am," I reported to Bill.

It was three o'clock in the morning before Freya delivered

her eleventh puppy, and set about washing them and putting her house in order. "You won't get much rest if you go home now, with Pat waking you up at dawn," Bill said. "I'll sleep out on the porch, and you take my room. I've got a new toothbrush, and a pair of silk pyjamas Missy gave me for Christmas that I haven't worn yet."

The pyjamas didn't lure me, but I suddenly discovered, to my dismay, that I had no alternative except to stay. Mademoiselle locked even windows at night, but it never entered my mind that I'd be out late enough to need my key, so I hadn't bothered to bring it.

I don't know about Bill, but I fell asleep right away, and wakened a little after seven to Peter's and John's shrill voices hollering up to me from the alley. "Mother! Are you there! Can we see the puppies!"

I opened the window. "Be quiet!" I called down hoarsely. "It's Sunday morning, you'll have the whole neighbourhood on its ear. Go home, it's too early to see them!"

Bill came in from the porch, tying up his bath robe "The little darlings," he said.

"I'd like to wring their necks."

"The pyjamas are very becoming. Max will be here any minute. What would you like for breakfast—pancakes and sausages?"

"I'm having breakfast with the boys. Did you say pancakes and sausages?"

At the last minute, when I heard Max moving about in the kitchen below, I felt self-conscious. "Did you tell him why I stayed all night?"

"I just told him I expected you for breakfast. If you're uncomfortable about it, why don't you put your coat on, tiptoe downstairs, go out, ring the bell, and when he opens the door for you, tell him you came to see the puppies?"

"That's devious but clever," I said. "Roll up your blankets from the sleeping porch and put them back in the cupboard. I'll keep the toothbrush as a souvenir, and I only used one small towel, once over lightly.—What'll I do with your pyjamas?"

"Just leave them on the bed. I didn't wear any, so it evens it up."

We worked stealthily, and efficiently. "If you're ready to leave," Bill whispered, "I'll go down ahead of you and keep Max talking in the kitchen while you step out."

"I suppose you think I'm conventional again."

"Anything but." He tipped my face and gave me a brotherly kiss on the forehead. "Did Freya and I forget to tell you how grateful we are? How can we ever repay you?"

"I'll take it out in sausages," I said.

Everything started off beautifully, without a hitch. "Good morning, Max," I said brightly, when he opened the door for me. "I hear the puppies came——"

He smiled broadly. "I count ten, Mr. Meloney say 'leven."

"'Leven.—I mean, that's what Mr. Meloney told me, too," I corrected myself hastily, as he took my coat to hang it up.

Bill appeared. "Good morning!" he said, also very brightly. "I'm glad you hadn't had breakfast when I phoned you."

"So am I," I said.

Iced grapefruit halves were already on the table, lightly sugared, and exquisitely pinked around the edges, Filipino-fashion, with a glass of fresh orange juice at the side. "All this and pancakes too?" I murmured, covering my perfidy with small talk.

Max whisked away the chilled plates and replaced them with hot ones. "Hope you like," he beamed.

"Oh, I do," I beamed back at him, and proceeded to gild the lily of guilt with a supreme show of nonchalance. "How's the weather this morning, Max?"

Max blinked, Bill choked on the last of his orange juice, and I knew then and there that I was not cut out to lead a life of sin.

It seemed to be an unwritten law in Hollywood for everyone to go somewhere else on week-ends—everyone, that is, of any importance in the motion picture industry. I always found the town singularly pleasant after the general exodus, and I certainly had no intention of making a habit of Catalina—or its equivalent —but we did plan to take the boys to Arrowhead the following Saturday for a breath of bracing air and a glimpse of snow. At the last minute, though, I had to call it off. "Dr. Stetten just flew in

[215]

from New York for a consultation, and he's leaving again to-morrow, so I asked him for dinner this evening. He's an old friend, and I simply couldn't not do it," I explained to Bill.

"You couldn't possibly not," he agreed. "Is that de Witt Stetten?"

"Do you know him?" I asked in surprise.

"I met him at Menas Gregory's a couple of times."

"In that case, you can come to dinner, too."

"I should hope so. It's the least you can do after standing me up this way. Are the boys very disappointed?"

"No, I think they were relieved when I told them. The expedition was a little too chummy for them, they weren't brought up to be 'close companions'."

"Lucky them," said Bill. "And lucky you."

I had no embarrassment or reservation about having Bill for dinner with de Witt, and as they'd known each other before, the evening, for them, passed quickly and pleasantly. But for me, it was a step back into the past, and I felt newly and forever widowed.

Strange, that through de Witt's eyes, I could see that he felt I had found a degree of happiness and adjustment, and he was glad for me. And I was glad I had deceived him. "Call home and tell them I'm fine when you get back," I reminded him as, regretfully, he rose to take his leave.

He put his arm around me. "I will. You bet I will."

"You'd better let me drive you back to your hotel," Bill said. "It's hard to get a taxi in this town."

"I've noticed that. Thanks. I've got an early plane in the morning, so I'd appreciate it."

"I'll come too," I said. "It's not out of his way to drop me off again, he lives right round the corner."

"That's good," de Witt said. "You keep an eye on this girl, see that she doesn't break up any more bones.—By the way does the knee ever kick up?"

"No," I said. "And you can hardly see any more where you stitched my finger back."

He put on his coat and examined his handiwork beneath the

hall light. "Well, I'll be damned! But I have to share the credit. If your husband hadn't had the presence of mind to wrap that digit in a handkerchief and rush you to my office, I couldn't have saved it."

"Mother!"

It was Peter, looking like a drowsy angel at the top of the steps.

"What are you doing up, you should have been asleep hours ago!"

"I had to go to the bathroom. Are you going out?"

"Yes."

"Where?" Anxiety pierced his drowsiness.

"Just to drive Dr. Stetten to his hotel."

"Are you coming back for breakfast, or are you going to sleep with Bill again?"

"I'll be home," I said. "Run back to bed."

"I thought perhaps you'd explain to de Witt——" Bill offered unhappily on the way back.

"There was nothing to explain."

"Yes, there was. About the puppies. It took courage not to."

"Whatever de Witt thought, it's all right. He loves me because he loved my husband."

"I could tell that by the way he talked about him.—I wish I could have known him."

"I wish so, too."

"He must have been a very wonderful person."

"He was."

"Was." It was a word that had never entered my consciousness or passed my lips before. It was at once an acknowledgment and an acceptance.

Perhaps, I thought, healing happens to us without our knowing it.

I remember that de Witt's visit marked a milestone in my thinking. I stopped fighting against the fact that Bill supplied a companionship that carried on, in some small part, the spiritual and physical unity that I had lost. And I acknowledged that I gave to him a kind of fulfilment that he had never found. It was as if I realized suddenly how wrong it was to dam back the stream of human love, and I began to relax in the harmony of our enjoyments and our contempts. The newspaper columns linked our names constantly, and not always in kindness. I was a wealthy widow—he was a fortune-hunter. I had to smile at that. He knew the exact amount of my inheritance and my stubborn insistence on keeping it intact for the boys. And of course he knew what my salary was, and how I divided it equally, each week, between my bank-account and the local savings bank, with the former steadily growing a balance that was far in excess of my modest needs, and more than enough to meet my income tax without drawing on my reserve.

He was horrified when he discovered that I made out the tax returns myself, without an accountant's advice, or even a verification of my cancelled vouchers. "I always do it this way." I told him airily. "I remember everything I spend."

He stared, incredulously, at the neat listing of my expenses and deductions. *Travel—about twelve hundred. Medical—about fifteen hundred. Car, professional use of—about seven-fifty.* "My God," he bleated. "*About!* And in round figures? You'll land in gaol!"

"Gaol!" I echoed indignantly. "Why, I pay a fortune in taxes!"

"That's not the point," he argued in mounting agitation. "Your figures aren't accurate!"

"You mean, instead of putting down twelve hundred, I should put down eleven-hundred sixty-two dollars and twenty-nine cents?" I scoffed.

"If that's what you spent, yes!"

"That's silly, why complicate it?"

"Because you'll end in gaol!" he repeated hoarsely.

"Don't worry about it," I calmed him down. "You just make out your tax your way, and I'll do mine my way."

"You're an imbecile, and I don't like imbecile women, but I adore you," he remarked gloomily.

"It irks me to be adored, but if you must do it, try not to let me notice it. I'm too old for such nonsense."

"If you say that once more, I'll swat you one," he warned me.

I must admit that I was beginning to feel younger than I should have, what with sailing at Catalina, and dancing at the

Trocadero, and playing roulette at Redondo Beach, and I only hoped I wouldn't break out in girlishness. Fortunately, though, our intensive hours of work at the studio acted as a kind of ballast. We wrote two scripts following *Thirsty Soil*, and then Sam Goldwyn borrowed us to do a story on the Irish Uprising. I suppose that "borrow" isn't the right word, since neither of us was under contract to Universal, but we functioned as if we were, and so did the studio.

I viewed the new assignment with misgiving, for I didn't know the first thing about the Dublin of 1921. "You didn't know anything about dust storms either, and you turned out one hell of a piece of work," Bill reminded me.

"It was mostly your work." I made no secret of it, but even the studio thought I was bending backwards to give him credit for it.

"It's unfair," I railed. "Doesn't it bother you for everyone to think that it's the other way round?"

"Why should it?"

I never failed to marvel that there was no falseness in his pride, but his lack of ego only imposed a greater burden on my sense of integrity. It was a vicious circle, because I soon saw that my insisting that he contributed as much as, if not more than, I did to a script, sounded as if I might be protesting a little too vehemently, and tended to diminish him in the eyes of others. "You'll just have to take time off to write a novel on your own," I told him. "Then everyone will know how clever you are."

He said, "You puzzle me. One of the things I respect in you is that you don't give a damn what people think."

"For myself? No."

"Then stop caring what they think about me," he said, "because I don't."

"I guess it's a question of my own pride," I admitted miserably.

"Well, why didn't you say so?" He laughed, "In that case, I'll write you a novel as soon as we finish this Goldwyn job, and in the meantime, just don't minimize what you give to a script."

Bearing his injunction in mind, at the first story conference with our new producer, I said gaily, "I'm wonderful at dogs, I'll do all the dog scenes."

[219]

"Dogs? What dogs?"

"All those Black and Tans that keep running in and out of the picture."

Our producer's bewilderment vanished in a loud guffaw. "Black and Tans! What a sense of humour, if we can get a few comic touches like that into a dramatic script, we've got it licked!"

"Tell me something," Bill said afterwards, looking rather strained. "Were you trying to be funny about the dogs?"

"Certainly not. I don't see what's so funny about dogs, anyway."

"There usually isn't, my love. Except that these Black and Tans happen to be soldiers."

"Now, how should I know that?" I demanded indignantly.

"You shouldn't," he assured me. "And no one ought to expect you to for the miserable little salary you get."

He was teasing me, but he was right just the same; there was no justice in an industry in which my aborted education could earn me such huge dividends. Only the success of the Goldwyn picture eventually eased my conscience. The original title was *Covenant with Death* but I suggested *Beloved Enemy* instead, which lifted the heaviness of the theme into a fairly moving love story. "Information they can buy," Bill bolstered my confidence, "but inspiration comes dear."

At any rate, it was another of our collaborations that moved fluently and painlessly into the yellow binding of a shooting script. "I'll be glad when we get back to Universal," said Grace, who resented hotly the impersonal sepsis of the Goldwyn Studio, and our being cooped up in three large adjoining offices on the writers' floor. "Not even your own private toilet," she grumbled.

I didn't care for that part of it, either. Having to walk the length of a long corridor to a door that said "Ladies," made me think twice before going, because once there, I knew I'd be caught in a convivial gathering of female writers and secretaries, so I made it a practice to powder and things in off hours; unfortunately, some one else evidently had the same idea, and we kept bumping into each other, "You first," I'd offer with a falsely

SECOND MARRIAGE. AND WHY

polite smile, and she'd say, "No, you first, I'll wait." And then one day, after this had happened a number of times, she held out her hand and said, "I'm Lillian Hellman."

I sure she hasn't the faintest recollection of our first encounter, but being allergic to the sweetly antiseptic smell of public lavatories, I've never forgotten it.

So we shared Grace's pleasure in returning to the cosy privacy of Universal, but we remained there only long enough to turn out an adaptation of a short story with Charles Boyer in view. Production having slowed down virtually to a standstill on the lot, it was mutually advantageous for us to accept another outside assignment when it came along. "This one looks as if it's going to be fun," Grace said. "You've never done a musical before."

It wasn't strictly a musical, it was to be a kind of Hungarian Porgy and Bess with music, and in colour—the initial venture of Pioneer Pictures. Few heard of the studio, and less than few remember it, but during its short-lived existence it wore the stamp of immense prestige, and simply bulged with available monies. It was headed by John Hay Whitney (everybody called him Jock in those days) and his enthusiasm and excitement over what was, for him, a new and provocative enterprise, was boundless and contagious. "George Gershwin is going to compose the score," he told us in our opening conference, "but he's tied up in rehearsals and can't come to the coast. So if you two would consent to go to New York and work out your story-line with him there, I'd appreciate it very much."

It was I who appreciated the chance to go, for my ill-fated novel was at last being brought out by Longmans Green, a firm predominantly engaged in the publication of text books, and therefore not subject to the one-shot agreement. The publicity department had been asking me if I could possibly arrange to be available for a brief promotion discussion, but it had seemed unlikely that I could leave during the initial weeks of a new assignment. Now both projects dovetailed beautifully.

"I'd like to see Missy," Bill obligingly fell in with the plan. "I gather from her letters that she's been put to bed on an enforced rest, which means that something's gone hay-wire with her hip again."

"Then you'd certainly better go," I advised him.

Jock was delighted at our willingness to take the trip. "Stay as long as you wish, and spare no expense."

I told him that, since I had personal business to attend to, I would pay my own fare, and Bill felt the same way because of his visit to his mother, but Jock rejected the offer. "This is a production cost," he said firmly. "Everything will be taken care of by the office, including your secretary, if you want to take her along."

It was a lavish gesture, but I vetoed it on Grace's behalf. "She doesn't like New York and we wouldn't really need her there anyway. But I happen to know she's been waiting for things to slow up so that she could go on a two weeks' holiday to Honolulu that she's been saving up for, and this would be a good time."

"Is she a satisfactory secretary?"

Grace's virtues were too numerous to list. "I don't know what we'd do without her," I said.

Jock made another note on his pad. "Then that's attended to. She can save her savings for something else. We'll send her to Hawaii while you're away, and she'll be here for you when you get back."

There were a lot of little men in Hollywood in those days, but they were lost among the giants.

At the last minute, I had qualms about leaving the boys. Bill said, "Mademoiselle and Fermin are perfectly capable."

"Mademoiselle loses her head in an emergency."

"But there won't be any emergencies."

I relaxed, the way I had relaxed on that first trip to Europe when my husband said that it was all right for me to go without the children. It was a long while since I had shifted my worries to another pair of shoulders.

Jock recommended the Super-Chief, but Bill thought it was wiser for us to fly, and I did too, because it saved so much time.

"That was not my reason," he informed me patiently. "I think Jock has an idea that we're secretly married."

I pooh-poohed the idea until I discovered that one large suite had been reserved for us at the hotel. It was awkward. I couldn't even go to my sister's to stay because the girls were home for the spring holiday. But Bill was already explaining to the desk clerk that we had some writing to do and needed extra space. "A single room will answer the purpose nicely," he added.

"I'm afraid, sir, that I have nothing on the same floor. Not at the moment, that is."

"It doesn't matter," Bill told him.

I was grateful to him for having handled the situation so deftly, but I wished, inconsistently, that we could have been on the same floor. I hadn't been aware until this moment that I was getting used to having him around.

Several times, during those weeks in New York, I couldn't help comparing this trip with the desolate aloneness of my first journey east. The days were busy, and passed quickly, with Bill always at hand to pick me up and take me somewhere in a cab, and call for me again. We had dinner often at my sister's and the first evening I pointed out our old apartment, where a lighted lamp cast a glow across the crimson curtains that still hung at the windows.

"I can imagine you living there," he said.

Whenever he dined with his mother, I wanted him to go alone, but she wouldn't hear of it. "You must come too, darlin'." She had been quite ill, but she was well enough now to work with a crew of secretaries from her bed at the Waldorf, and to join us at the table that was set up in the drawing-room by a possessive and foreignly obsequious head-waiter, who made a great fuss of her. Everyone made a fuss of Missy, and if I had been the sort of person who could, I probably would have, too.

"I wonder if you know how rare it is for two strong-minded women to like each other?" Bill remarked as we walked to our own hotel afterwards.

"How did you know I was beginning to like her?"

"Because you resisted all the openings she gave you."

[223]

"I didn't want to trade on her generosity. And understanding."

"But she meant it when she said it was the first time she'd ever seen me really happy."

"Why did I let myself in for that radio publicity tomorrow?"

"Why are you changing the subject?"

"Because it's the most important thing on my mind at the moment."

"You lie."

"Have a little more respect for your elders."

"Which reminds me. Get yourself a decent photograph taken while you're here. Don't give that god-awful one on the jacket of *Twice Born* to Longmans Green."

"I don't happen to be photogenic. I'm worse than Mrs. Roosevelt."

"You haven't gone to a good photographer. Arnold Genthe's your man. Do you know him?"

"I know of him," I said coldly. "He took pictures of the San Francisco disaster."

"He also photographed the Grecian Isles in moonlight. And Isadora Duncan."

"I thought he was a quite old man and had retired."

"He is, and has. But he's a great friend of Missy's, and I'll phone her first thing tomorrow and ask her to ask him to see you."

"It's only going to be a waste of time," I prophesied glumly.

Nevertheless, I kept the appointment that Missy made for me, and Arnold Genthe gave me a sitting.

Our evenings were leisurely, devoted to family and one or two old friends, but our days were given over to the professional chores which had primarily brought us to New York. I met my new publishers at long last, Mr. and Mrs. Edwin Mills—and to them I am indebted for a very handsome presentation of *Gold Pennies* (complete with one of the Genthe photographs), and for whatever part they played in facilitating the sale of the book to Constable's of London. Also, I am certain that, if they had not published the novel, David Selznick would not have purchased the motion picture rights.

I spent an all too short half-hour with Maxwell Perkins, who said he had heard how successful I was in Hollywood, and it was very sad. "Aren't you ever coming home again? Aren't you ever going to go back to serious writing?"

"Yes," I said, without knowing when—or how.

He glanced at his watch. "It's half-past twelve. Can you have lunch with me?"

"I wish I could, but I have to meet my collaborator at George Gershwin's at one o'clock." I rose, with the uncomfortable feeling that he might think that I had absorbed the taint of Hollywood pressure and importance. I was glad when he said, as he held my hand in leave-taking, "You're happier than the last time I saw you, but you haven't really changed."

"I was afraid you'd feel that I had."

He shook his head. "No," he said, "I'm satisfied that you're the same. And please, write another novel as soon as you can."

"I'll try," I promised.

In the taxi, going uptown, I was filled with nostalgia and a nameless yearning, but it did not destroy me; the pale green shimmer that lay upon the park did not cause my heart to sicken with the excruciating pain of beauty. Max was wrong about my not having changed. The trees were putting out delicate new leaves, and the birds were beginning to sing, and yet without bitterness, I welcomed another spring.

Bill, invariably prompt to the point of being ahead of time, was waiting for me in the downstairs lobby of the Gershwin apartment. I had met George only once, years before, when he had first played his *Rhapsody in Blue* for a group of close friends, and my husband and I had been included. George referred briefly to that far-off evening, and then broke off to exclaim, "What a wonderful colour you're wearing—my children in Porgy and Bess would love it!"

"Oh," I said, more crestfallen than elated. I'd bought the dress especially for the trip and only because Magnin's—or rather my guardian angel of the gown department—had browbeaten me into a departure from my usual beige or grey. "But this is too gay for me," I'd objected. "I never wear red!"

"This isn't red, it's a cross between heliotrope and scarlet, and it's absolutely divine on you, so take it, and be quiet," she'd shut me up with the familiarity of long association. "Besides it's perfect for travelling, it'll never crush, and won't need pressing."

That settled it for me. I'd even begun not to mind the colour, but now I was self-conscious about it again. "If anyone of 'your children' would really like the dress, I'm going to send it to you," I promised.

"You're fooling," he said flatly, and when he discovered that I wasn't, he was as childlike in his delight as the childlike people he loved and worked with.

I learned a lot on that short trip. My session with Arnold Genthe had taught me a lesson in the supreme art of simplification, and the luncheon with George Gershwin taught me the sublime modesty of conceit. "My mother is a very remarkable woman," he told us, as we rose from the table. "You'd never know I was her son, she's not the least swell-headed about me." He sat down at the piano to improvise a thread of melody for the story we were writing. "And you'd think she would be," he went on, and suddenly stopped playing, spreading his fingers on the keyboard to look at them. "Why, even I can hardly believe that these hands can make such wonderful music."

I thought then, and still do, how rightly it becomes an artist to acknowledge himself as a mere instrument of whatever beauty it is given to him to create. But there are few, alas, who achieve the detachment of a George Gershwin, few who can observe, so simply and humbly, the magnificence of their own genius.

With a modesty borrowed for the occasion, I can say that the screen play of *Hurdy Gurdy* lent importance to a distinguished package, and it was a lamentable waste of time, talent and money that the Pioneer Studios did not survive long enough to produce the picture. The venture was one of Hollywood's costly and inconsequential catastrophes.

Bill had left his car parked at the Burbank Airport, and I thought how much nicer it was to drive home instead of hailing a taxi by myself in the middle of the night.

It was a relief to find everyone safely asleep and in bed when we tiptoed in and Pat let Bill carry my suitcase upstairs with only a token growl to keep his hand in, so to speak. A pile of letters and messages lay neatly stacked on my bedside table. I riffled through them, my attention arrested by an envelope with "Hidden Valley" engraved on the flap. I slit it open. "It's an invitation for both of us to spend next week-end with Winfield Sheean and his wife—wasn't she Maria Jeritza?"

"Yes. You'll like her."

I was lost for a moment in a stirring of hero-worship as I remembered a performance of *Die Walküre* in which Jeritza had fallen off her horse, and without a break in the aria, had picked herself up and remounted. The applause had been thunderous.

"I'm sure I'd like her," I said, "but I'm not going to spend a week-end with people I don't know."

"I know them."

"Exactly. That's why I was invited. And I don't like it. Our names are being linked too much, and for no reason."

"I want there to be a reason," he said. "I want to be married to you more than anything I have ever wanted in my life."

All these months I could not have helped but know how he felt, but it was the first time he had put it into words, and I was aware of the strangely gentle phrasing of his proposal: "I want to be married to you. . . ." It was as if he were asking neither a diminishment nor an invasion of the love that had filled, and would always fill, my life. I tried to match his gentleness with my own. "It wouldn't work, Bill. I'm a preparation, but I'm not an answer to what you want. Or need."

"I expected better of you." His gentleness vanished. "That sort of twaddle belongs in a movie script."

This was easier ground, not having to be tender of his feelings. "It would be highly unsuitable from every aspect," I said with finality. "It's late and we're both tired. Don't you think you'd better go?"

"Not until we've settled this."

"We've settled it. You'll wake the boys if you keep talking."

He closed the door to the hall, and came back to plant himself firmly in front of me. "What's unsuitable about it?"

"Do I have to go into detail?"

"Yes."

"Age, for one thing. How are you going to whistle away my being seven years older than you are?"

"You're not. We've gone into that. Subtract the three that you added, add the two that my mother snitched off, and we're practically even."

"You might have been a college professor but your arithmetic leaves much to be desired.—Which brings me to another impractical aspect. The whole pattern of your life is against your taking on the responsibilities of a family man. I'm not criticizing you for it, I'm stating a fact. So far I haven't discovered anything that you haven't done, can't do, and won't do——"

"I do it well," he injected without rancour.

"I grant you that. And as soon as you succeed at something you've exhausted your interest in it and go on to something else."

"Have you been discussing me with Menas Gregory?" he demanded quizzically.

"Certainly not. In the first place, I wouldn't do a thing like that, even if I were interested, which I wasn't. In the second place, I don't need a psychologist to interpret what I can see for myself. You may have gathered a lot of moss, but you're still a rolling stone, and you always will be."

"That's where you're wrong. I aim to stop rolling."

"That's a perfect basis for a successful marriage," I snorted. "No, thank you, I have no desire or intention of trying to make you conform to my idea of what a man should be."

"A very sound attitude for a woman," he approved. "But you see I'm gambling that you'll take to a little rolling yourself."

"With three children? You're an optimist."

"We'll set them an example. Or do you want them to grow up to be dull, humdrum, and timorous, with no hunger for adventure?"

"Everything you say makes me realize what a bad influence you'd be."

"What a good influence I'd be," he corrected sunnily.

The conversation was getting out of hand. "I wish you'd be serious," I said. "You've forgotten one deeply important thing. I could never love another man as I loved my husband."

He took both my hands in his. "I am serious, and I haven't forgotten it. But to give of that love won't lessen it, it will make it richer with the giving. For your own sake, as well as mine, will you try to think of it that way?"

"I have," I said honestly. "It's really late, we're both tired. Please go. And don't let's talk about it again."

"I won't," he promised. "Good night, my darling."

I knew that he would keep his promise, which was the reason that I let myself be persuaded to accept the Sheeans' invitation. I have little memory of that week-end, except that there were many Austrian servants wearing white gloves and hovering about a very small dining-room off a huge living-room. And Winnie wore a derby hat when he went to the village for a newspaper, and the guests were mostly men, and very important men. And of course I remember my first impression of Jeritza, who was the golden, buxom image of the way she'd looked on the stage of the Metropolitan. Warmth and kindness seemed to overflow from the very depths of her. She gathered me in a capacious embrace and said, "I want everyone to be as happy as I am."

When I next saw her, it was in New York, after Winnie's death, and I wished, then, that she could have been as happy as I was. Our friendship had endured, closer for the bond of sharing memories of a Hollywood before the giants had begun to topple, and because our hearts spoke the same language.

Summer passed imperceptibly into winter. "I miss the seasons," I complained that year.

"We'll fix that," Bill said with alacrity, and made good on our week-end at Arrowhead. It was necessary to put chains on the car to get through the snow, but it wasn't the same, it was picture snow, planted like scenery through the twelve months of the year. By Sunday morning, I had had enough of it, and so had the boys. "Let's start back before lunch," I said restlessly.

The telegram from my brother-in-law was waiting for me on the hall table. *"Florence had some abdominal pain and de Witt decided wise to operate. She is doing well. Will keep you informed. No need to worry. Love, Elmer."*

"I'm going home," I said.

Bill booked a seat on the next flight to New York. "Don't give a thought to anything here," he told me at the airport. "If it will make you feel easier about the boys, I'll sleep at the house."

"Thanks, but you're so near, anyway. Just keep an eye on them. I'll telephone as soon as I find out what it is."

When I walked into the hospital room, my sister didn't seem surprised. "I knew you'd come," she said. "De Witt says it's just a benign tumour," she added. "It's not serious."

"Pooh," I said. "Everybody has tumours."

She was mercifully drowsy from the heavy, post-operative sedation. "How are Bill and the children?" she murmured.

"Fine."

"Stay at the apartment——"

"Do you think I'm going to waste money on a hotel?"

She smiled, and fell asleep. I sat by her bed until de Witt came in. I followed him out to the corridor. It was difficult for him to speak, so I spoke first. "It isn't good, is it?"

He shook his head. "One of those things. Very little warning. Too much destruction of the liver to do anything but close her up again. And hope that the end will be merciful and quick."

I felt the old familiar sensation of my lips and throat turning numb with dryness. "How long do you think?"

"There's no telling. Weeks, perhaps, or it could be months. I wish, for her sake, that you could stay on a while. Or better still, come back when we get her home from the hospital. But I suppose you can't, with your work."

"Yes, I can. We were going to begin a new assignment after Christmas, but Bill can tackle it alone."

"Florence likes Bill. She thinks he's a wonderful person," de Witt mentioned, "And I like him, if that means anything."

"It does."

He cleared his throat. "This is pretty hard on you." Awkwardly, for he was schooled against emotion, he put his arm around me for the barest instant, and walked away abruptly, his white surgeon's coat flapping against his knees.

I telephoned Bill. He helped me crystallize the plans that were still nebulous in my mind. "It isn't urgent for me to be here while she's in the hospital, but after that I want to be free to come and go as often and as long at a time as she needs me. And with as little upset to the boys as possible. I don't like to uproot them, but Mademoiselle isn't the ideal person to assume responsibility, so do you think it would be advisable to enroll John and Peter as boarding pupils at 'Black Fox'? I've heard it is a good school, with not much stress on the military training for the younger pupils."

"Let me investigate and get back to you. If its scholastic rating is good, Paul might even bone up there for his college entrance exams."

"I hadn't thought of it, but it would simplify things to have them all under one roof."

"In which case," Bill carried it one step further, "you could give up Canon Drive and keep a couple of rooms at the Château Elysée for when you're here. I'd move back there too, it's a lot closer to 'Black Fox' than being at the other end of Beverly."

"None of this might be necessary," I faltered. "De Witt thinks—maybe weeks—but I have a feeling it's going to be much, much longer."

"Don't argue with your feelings," Bill told me.

I was glad that I hadn't. For the next five months, I literally commuted from New York to California. On one of my later trips, my sister surprised me by saying, "I wish Bill could manage to come with you, I'd love to see him again, but I suppose he can't get away from the studio."

"In a few weeks he can." I didn't tell her that Bill wasn't working at the studio, I didn't tell anyone what had really happened about the assignment we were scheduled to do for Metro. "I can't accept it," I'd told Rosalie. "My sister is ill."

"It sounds like the old gag. Is it?"

"No. It isn't."

"I'm sorry."

"Thank you.—But I'm sure that Bill can do just as good a job of it alone."

"Look," she said. "I won't pull my punches. There's not a

chance of his being able to get that assignment by himself."

"But you know by this time that he's as good as I am, and better!"

She shrugged. "Be that as it may—and I'm not denying that he's damn good—there isn't a studio in town that doesn't feel you're carrying him, and the only reason they're willing to take him on is because they know you don't want to work with anyone else."

"But it's so unfair, he's contributed tremendously to every script we've done together!"

"You can talk yourself blue in the face, but you'll never convince a producer of that."

"You tell the truth and no one believes you," I said angrily.

"In this town, the truth has nothing to do with it. You've got a name and you get three times his salary, so he's no good and you're great.—Do you want me to break it to him that the Metro assignment is off if you're not part of the package?"

"No," I said shortly. "I'll tell him."

It was another problem added to those that already pulled at me. How could I tell him without destroying his pride and his confidence? Should I broach it indignantly, sympathetically, or ironically? I wished I had never got him mixed up with me in that stupid dust storm story to begin with—he'd have either made his way with Winnie Sheean at Fox or gone back east to one of his numerous professions. Anything would have been preferable to my having unwittingly placed him in this humiliating position.

He spared me the indignity of any pussy-footing to avoid hurting him. "Of course Metro won't want me," he mentioned casually at dinner that evening. "I'm excess baggage as far as they're concerned."

The hot colour in my cheeks sufficed for answer.

"It's just as well, though, I wouldn't enjoy working on the script without you."

I was quick to grasp at the opening. "I know how it was after Phil Klein and I worked together. It's hard to break a team and take on a new collaborator. Also, I imagine Winnie will be delighted to have you back on the lot. You've got a natural camera sense. You ought to be a director, anyway, and not a pedestrian script-writer."

He covered my hand with his for an instant. "Don't worry about me, you have enough on your mind. I'm not even sure that I'll look for another job."

I hated to ask it, but I had to, struggling against the primness that edged my voice. "What will you do if you don't get another job?"

"I'll have plenty to keep me busy looking after your three brats," he returned lightly.

"But they're in school, you just can't fritter away your time——" I didn't say it. I had no right to say it.

He drove me to the airport the next morning. He said, "Keep me posted, and don't have the boys on your mind."

I tried not to think what he was going to do with the rest of his days—and all the days to follow. "Don't forget to check on the dogs a couple of times a week." It had been almost as hard to leave Pat and Freya in a kennel as to put the children in military school.

"This would be a pretty sorry business if I didn't have you to look after everything," I said, and lifted my lips to receive his kiss.

"It's a pretty sorry business, anyway. I wish I could be with you.—Did I ever tell you that I'm only half a person without you?"

"Yes, and didn't I ever tell you to go out and find some nice young girl to fall in love with?"

"I'll do that," he promised gravely. "I'll put it at the head of my list of 'things to do'."

He had plenty of opportunity to extricate himself completely from the encumbrances I had imposed on him, because I didn't return from that particular trip until the end of March. He met me at the plane. "You look so tired, darling. I'm glad you can tune out for a little while.—And everything's fine. Pups, kids—everything."

"And you?"

"Fine."

[233]

I didn't ask the question that was on the tip of my tongue. "I hope you've kept busy," I said instead, and casually.

"Oh, I have," he assured me. "I might sleep a little late, but I rarely turn in until three or four in the morning."

"Oh.—Do I know her?"

"Nope. But you will. And soon, I hope.—Wait here until I get your luggage."

"It's what you wanted," I told myself. And I told myself that I could never have made a go of carrying our relationship beyond a given point, because I was congenitally incapable of compromise.

In the car, he said, "Shall we call at the school on the way?"

"I'd like to. If I'm not holding you up from anything."

"For as long as you're here, my time is yours."

"I want to go back when the girls' Easter holiday is over. Donna knows now that it's hopeless, and she wants to stay at home but her father's against it. She's graduating from Smith in June, you know."

"No, I didn't, I thought next year. How are the girls taking it?"

"I think it's a little harder on Margot. Donna has a new love interest, which helps a little."

"I think I met him when we went east last time. A big blonde, handsome fellow?"

"No, this is another one, a completely different type, short and dark. I forget his last name, but his first name is Jonas, and Donna says he's brilliant in his particular field of research."

"What is it?"

"I can't remember.—My aunt is taking this terribly hard. After Mamma died, there was just the three of us—and with me living out here, she'll be so alone—I spoke to Missy before I left. She sounded very well. And she sent lovely flowers to the hospital."

He took his hand from the wheel to cover mine. "Don't talk. Just relax."

"I'm wound up, I guess. I never get a chance to cry. Everyone thinks I'm so damn strong.—It's heartbreaking to watch her grow weaker and more emaciated every day. And she's so sure she's going to get well, she's planning to come out to California this summer. Menas Gregory says that even doctors very often don't realize. I know that. It was like that with my husband."

"It's merciful," Bill said. "Be glad."

"They were both so young, with so much to live for. How can I be glad of anything?"

He gave me his handkerchief. "We'll drive straight to the Château, and go to the school later."

I nodded mutely. It would never do for the boys to catch me with red eyes.

It was the last week in April when my sister said, "I wish Bill were here. I'd love to see him."

"I think he'd love to come," I told her.

I called him that evening. "I'm all packed to leave," he said. "I was going to surprise you. I left Sonya's number at the school."

I was waiting for him at the hotel when he arrived. I didn't care about appearances, I sat in his room while he unpacked. "I didn't know I'd be so happy to have you here," I said. "You must be psychic, whether you admit it or not."

"I refuse to admit it." He laid a heavy oblong parcel in my lap. "A present for you."

"It feels like a manuscript."

"It is."

My heart lifted. "Then you took an assignment after all! Why didn't you tell me?"

"I didn't want you to know until I'd finished it."

"But for what studio?"

"For no studio. It was a different kind of assignment. You gave it to me a long time ago. It mayn't be any good, but it's the novel you told me I ought to write."

"Good or bad, you'll never know how happy I am about it."

"I do," he said. "You didn't fool me, you thought I was loafing."

"And I tried so hard to hide it. How could you finish it so quickly?"

"I told you I didn't get to bed until three or four in the morning."

"So you did."

"And it wasn't 'so quick' at that. Pretty nearly five months."

Pretty nearly five months. Five gruelling, endless months. . . . Please God, don't let her suffer much longer. . . .

"It's been a long time for you, too. If only you could tune out just for tonight," he said softly.

"I can't."

"Then I'll take you back to the apartment."

"I can go alone, you're tired from the trip."

"You're never going anywhere alone again," he said.

"Mrs. Lindsay is awake," the nurse greeted me. "She's been asking for you. You can go in before I give her a hypodermic."

I sat down beside the bed. "Bill is here. Would you like him to come in just for a moment?"

It was as if a skeleton smiled. And she was so beautiful. I wished that I could have spared Bill the shock of seeing her.

She had a bad night—the hypodermics were losing their effect. De Witt came early in the morning. I waited with Elmer in the living-room. We didn't talk, we just waited. De Witt's step sounded in the hall, and time stood still until he came to the door. "You'd better call Donna and Margot," he said.

My brother-in-law wet his lips, and so well I knew the ashen dryness of his throat. He turned to the window, his back towards us. "I'll telephone the girls," I told de Witt in a low voice, "but it'll be a while before they can get here."

"She's conscious at the moment," he answered my unspoken question. "She managed to ask me if Bill had gone back to California."

"Will it be all right for me to tell her that he hasn't?"

"Tell her anything that will make her happy. Even if you have to lie a little."

"I won't lie," I said.

Her eyes were closed, but she must have felt my presence because she pushed her hand towards me. I held it in mine, and bent over the bed. "Could you spare me for a couple of hours? I want to get married."

Her lips moved. "When?"

[236]

"Today."

"That's good," she whispered.

It was not yet eight o'clock, but I telephoned Bill at the hotel. "Will you marry me today?" I asked him.

At noon, in a small village called Wappinger Falls, where Bill knew the Justice of the Peace, we were pronounced man and wife. "I always get married like this," I said tremulously.

"Don't ever do it again."

My sister died that night. "I wanted to make her happy," I told Bill. "It wasn't fair to you, was it?"

"You'd have married me anyway," he said. "Perhaps not today, but you couldn't have stopped it happening."

In my secret heart I knew that it was true, and I felt at peace.

My brother-in-law went with us to Pawling, and we spread my sister's ashes in Missy's garden. Late April was a lovely time of year for gardens. "This is what she would have liked," he said.

We drove back to town with him so that we could spend that evening with the girls, and early the next morning we went out to try to find a place where we could bring the children home to live. It seemed strange not to have to consider being within commuting distance. "Somewhere between New York and Boston would be perfect," Bill said.

"But suppose Paul doesn't pass his entrance exams for Harvard?"

"He will," Bill said.

The whole of New England was ours for the choosing. We looked at an old salt-box house in Guildford—unspoiled, but cheerless. We almost liked a house in Saybrook, but not quite enough. We drove on to Old Lyme, but it was getting late, so we stayed at a pleasant inn, shaded by an immense weeping beech. "I'd love to have a tree like that," I said. "I don't know where I'd put it, but I'd love to have it."

Bill said, "It's the first thing I ever heard you say you really wanted."

We had dinner at the inn, took a walk down the wide main street, and then went to bed so that we could get an early start the next day. Such an awful smell came through the open windows that it wouldn't have had the nerve to be anything else but fertilizer on an adjoining field. "As long as I know what it is, I don't mind it," I said.

"Fertilizer's a wonderful smell," he defended.

I didn't trust the way he stood there, sniffing, and I remembered suddenly his preoccupation with all the ploughing and seeding that was going on in the countryside we'd passed through. I eyed him with growing suspicion. "You wouldn't by any chance have farming in your blood besides everything else?"

"I was hoping to keep it a secret. I'm a very good farmer," he admitted sheepishly.

"You're a writer now," I said sternly. "John Farrar agrees with me, he thinks *Rush to the Sun* is a magnificent novel."

"John's an old friend, he's prejudiced."

"Not too prejudiced to want to publish it at once."

"But I don't care for writers," he objected.

I knew what he meant, and I didn't care for them as a breed either. Sharing dislikes, I mused with satisfaction, was as sound a basis for marriage as many of the more advertised essentials. "Of course a writer could write and farm a little at the same time," I suggested tentatively.

"Or a farmer could farm and write a little," he amended.

So we found our farm in Lyme, and bought it without thinking twice about it. Why should we have? The house was a simple, eighteenth-century four-square clapboard, the old barns and silos were functional, and there were a couple of hundred rolling acres with enough meadow land to graze a sizeable herd of cows, and enough additional scrubland to pasture sheep and beef cattle.

Bill pointed out a lot of other things too, like the gravity spring, and the old stone fencing laid up to rotate the fields, and a section of soil that was good for alfalfa. It could have all sounded like gibberish to me, but oddly enough, it didn't. It looked as if I might have a trace of farming in my blood too.

Less than a week later, we were on our way to Los Angeles to bring the boys back and tie up loose ends. "I still feel guilty," I said on the plane, "when I think of all those tins of fruit and vegetables I left in the cellar of Canon Drive."

"People leave worse than that in cellars when they move," Bill set my conscience at ease. "You should know that now."

I knew it, all right. The cellar in Lyme was a nightmare of rubbish and filth, and the house was pretty much of a mess as well, but architecturally it had not been tampered with. No one had cared enough, which was all to the good. It was going to be fun to do over, there was no excitement in buying a place that you couldn't rebuild to make your own.

Bill's car was at the airport waiting for us like an old friend. "It won't be easy to tell the children," I said on the way into Los Angeles.

"About Florence?"

"And about us."

He pressed my hand. "No, it won't be easy. But don't let's underestimate them. They've done a lot of growing up these past years."

"I have too," I said.

I cannot pretend that it was a tranquil fortnight that preceded our final departure from the coast. "Stepfathers are mean," John said, a little white around the lips.

"Then don't think of him as a stepfather."

"But he's not my own father!"

"No one could ever be your own father."

"Then why is he your husband?"

"Oh, shut up, John," Paul answered for me.

Peter was less complicated—on the surface. (A month later, and for two fearful years thereafter, he suffered from asthma.) However, the immediacy of new adventures intrigued him, and he was full of questions about the farm that were simpler than John's to answer. "Can we have chickens too?"

"And pigs," Bill added. "Did you know that pigs are very clean if you give them a chance to be clean?"

Peter wasn't interested in the minor details of sanitation. "Can we have another cat?"

[239]

"Two," Bill promised rashly. (We began with two calicos, who are always female, and ended up with forty.)

My youngest made hay while the going was good. "I'd like a pony too." "Not right away," I called a halt. "Maybe next year we'll have horses. Bill likes to ride, and he'll teach you."

"I can ride by myself, boy," he swaggered. "I don't have to have anybody teach me."

"Don't be such a smart-aleck," Paul said.

I felt sorriest of all for Paul. He was mature enough to feel profoundly the loss of his aunt, to relive old memories, and to ponder, with conflict, the significance of my marriage. Moreover, he had his personal problems to contend with. He was in an agony of trepidation lest he failed his Harvard exams, but he was torn at the thought of leaving Bee Jay.

In the beginning, it wasn't easy for any of us. I tried not to show Bill that I was troubled to the very depths of my soul, but he sensed it. "You wouldn't be human if you weren't beset with doubts. Give the boys time. And, above all, be patient with yourself."

I was grateful to him for understanding. I almost said, "You sound so much like my husband," but wisdom came, unbidden, to stand at my shoulder, and I knew that I must consciously, as well as unconsciously, put widowhood for ever behind me. No two men are alike, and were I to rejoice in occasional similarities, I would be equally destroyed by the differences that exist in every human being. I had to reach beyond the strictures of my background and my upbringing. I had to learn that acceptance need not necessarily be the bedfellow of compromise.

Marriage, at best, is the rebirth of two souls. Second marriage is a very particular kind of rebirth.

4

SOME ACTORS ARE PEOPLE

All this happened a long while ago, and now Bill and I have been married for over a quarter of a century. I said at the beginning of this book that the farm remains one of our richest memories, but this doesn't mean that we didn't slave and struggle as proper farmers always have, since the beginning of time. The elements were against us from the start, for we had hardly finished our extensive alterations of house and out-buildings, when we ran smack into the big hurricane of 1938. We were in the area that suffered the heaviest damage and along with everything else that we lost, we almost lost John and Peter, who were on their way home from the rural school when the storm struck. They were marooned on a collapsing bridge that spanned the moiling Connecticut River, and Bill reached them not a moment too soon to swim to safety with them. Those were as hideous hours as I have ever lived through, for it wasn't until after midnight that they were able to make their way home through the mass of debris.

Our whole beautiful farm was a rubble of destruction, and no sooner had we restored it to a semblance of what it had been, than a fire started in the farmer's cottage, one bitter February day, and our barns burned to the ground.

We had already discovered that it takes a bottomless pit of money to run a farm under the most favourable conditions, but there's nothing like a brace of disasters to bring you into an uncomfortably close scraping acquaintance with that bottom. After we had tapped the last of our Hollywood savings, we had no alternative but to mortgage a space in our lives to turning out lucrative magazine serials under a flock of pseudonyms. I think they were considerably better than average, or John Farrar, Bill's publisher, wouldn't have wanted to bring them out in book form—which he did, under our final and permanent pen-name of "Franken Meloney."

We suffered neither pain nor shame in our literary prostitution. It was all in a good cause. *Women in White* cleaned up the shambles of huge fallen trees and replaced them with ones of approximate size (I had no patience to wait around for little trees to grow big). *Call Back Love* paid for the new barn unit; *Strange Victory* put us back in the poultry business; *Gus, the Magnificent* bought us the latest tractor model, and a couple of riding horses; and *American Bred*, a romance of the dogshow circuit, fittingly established our kennels, which housed, at a peak of fertility, twenty-six Great Danes, Freya's third litter of police puppies, an Irish wolf-hound, so chronically confused about the facts of life that we didn't bother to look around for a wife for him, and to balance him off, a working sheepdog, who raised our hopes periodically with false pregnancies. Last, but not least, we had intermittent doses of Missy's neurotic black poodle, but his disrupting influence was a small price to pay for her happy visits with us. She loved the farm almost as much as we did.

Our kennels were personal, and not commercial. We bred dogs and showed them, but we didn't sell them. Also, the glassed-in aviary, of which our parrot is the last living member, was an out-and-out hobby too, not to mention a small universe of cats that were housed and fed in separate quarters off the back-porch. But the farm itself was far from being a hobby. On the contrary, Longmeadow grew into a full-fledged productive enterprise, sufficiently outstanding and professional to be used as a model of diversified farming by the Agricultural College at Storrs. Our pedigreed pigs wallowed in a cement pool with a circulating system, our chickens fulfilled their functions under the most stimulating conditions and our handsome herd of Angus cattle wandered in and out of long, low sheds placed to advantage in the field that lay beyond the small fortress that enclosed our seven-star bull. It goes without saying that our sixty head of pure-bred

Jerseys were served, housed and grazed like royalty, while the white-tiled pasteurizing room could have answered the sanitary requirements of a hospital surgery. Small wonder that these pampered darlings should have acquitted themselves with premium milk, with the highest butter content in Connecticut.

We weren't successful with sheep, though. We loved the ram, who was a monster and a clown, with a particular yen for chasing Paul, but that was as far as it went. He was all front and no back, and the whole undertaking was hardly worth the endless dipping and shearing and tail-cropping, which always hurt me more than it hurt the lambs. Eventually the flock ended up as a pile of blankets, and our one income tax loss.

Income tax. Need I mention that the government finally took notice of those returns that I had filed in Hollywood. It was a dastardly trick after letting two full years elapse without so much as a peep out of Bill's precious Bureau of Internal Revenue. In all that time, how could I have resisted making smug jibes at his involved book-keeping system that isolated to the penny every dollar of income and outgo? He actually had three sets of books going—farm, literary, and investment, and as if that wasn't enough, he periodically handed them over to the expensive interpretation of a tax specialist in Bill Donovan's law office. "It's idiotic to make such a big production of every tiny expenditure," I scoffed impatiently. "Why don't you just do it the way I did it, in uncomplicated round figures?"

He told me why, but I didn't believe him until one day, out of the blue, the telephone rang and a very smooth voice asked me if I preferred to pay sixteen thousand dollars in back taxes or go to gaol. I thought it was Bill, trying to be funny, until I caught sight of him through the window, feeding the pigs. "I haven't got sixteen thousand dollars," I returned in a voice that matched my inquisitor's smoothness, "nor have I any intention of going to gaol." I had recently visited one of my agents in Sing-Sing, and had found prison life quite depressing, although rather congenial. In fact, my agent's closest cellmate was in the social register—or had been, up to the point of his defection—which suddenly made me realize that gaol wasn't only for murderers, anybody could land there, and for a variety of reasons. I covered my growing apprehension with bravado. "What is this all about and who are you?" I demanded of my inquisitor.

He said, "I'm from the Federal Bureau of Internal Revenue."

A small gasp must have escaped me, because he added softly, "I don't want to frighten you. I want to help you."

This came as a surprise, because according to Bill, the tax department was neither helpful nor co-operative. "How?" I asked guardedly.

He seemed to hesitate before he answered. "You understand, of course, that we can't make these adjustments in every case, but in your particular instance, an immediate payment of three thousand dollars would settle the claim to our mutual satisfaction."

I hadn't worked on dozens of bad movie scripts for nothing—I recognized what I thought was a bribe when I heard one. A few minutes later I was hot-footing it out to tell Bill what had happened. "And that's what goes on with your fine government," I accused him. "I'd rather pay the whole amount if I owe it, but I let him think I was sending the three thousand and that I was grateful to him for helping me out of a mess."

"For once," Bill complimented me grudgingly, "you told a lie without bungling it. It's a mess all right, but not anywhere near the mess it would have been if you'd played ball with him. I'd better get into town in the morning and find out if we're really into sixteen thousand back taxes."

"It's nice of you to use the editorial 'we'," I acknowledged in a meek voice. "Maybe you were right about round figures."

"I have carefully refrained from saying 'I told you so.'"

"I'd rather you said it and got it over with."

It was lucky for him that he didn't, because after he and his accountant spent a number of weeks reconstructing the years in question, I not only didn't owe the Government sixteen thousand dollars, but the Government owed me a hundred and twenty.

I think women ought to run the revenue department, and do away with all that ridiculous red tape. As a matter of fact I've got a lot of good ideas as to what I'd do, and wouldn't do, if I were President. But as I don't know much about politics, I keep them to myself.

Anyway, it was a pity that what with spending so much energy on meticulous records of income and outgo, writing serials, and running the farm, Bill had no desire to begin on a new novel, even though *Rush to the Sun* had attracted all the first-string adjectives like a magnet—powerful, commanding, impressive, illuminating, rugged and disturbing.

"Yes, and it didn't earn enough to build us another silo," he said.

"I want another book out of you, instead of another silo."

"Don't be an ass. A novel's only important to the person who writes it."

"Any novel that you write happens to be important to me, too."

"You're a slave driver. I get up at six every morning and put in a twelve hour day, what more do you want?"

"I told you. Another novel."

The issue didn't come to a head until Mr. Balmer of *Redbook* asked us to have lunch with him in town one day, and said that he would like us to write a three-part serial on a definite commitment. I didn't have to look at Bill to know that he had that damn silo in one eye and a hay-baler in the other, and good-bye novel. "A love story," Mr. Balmer went on, stammering a little in his eagerness, "something in the mood of the one-shot. Our readers liked it, we had a great deal of mail on it."

"But the one-shot wasn't a collaboration," I reminded him.

"True, true," he agreed, "but I understood that you and your husband preferred to write together, and you've certainly become a very successful team."

"I know we have," I got in ahead of Bill, "but you see, my husband's in the middle of a novel, so if you'd be willing just for me to write you three short stories instead, it might answer the same purpose."

I felt a kick under the table, and I knew that Bill was trying to nudge some sense into me—three short stories would bring in about one quarter the price that editors were willing to pay for a serial. But I was adamant and kicked him back. "I'd be willing to write the first story," I continued to address my remarks to Mr. Balmer, "without your feeling obliged to order the other two."

Mr. Balmer accepted the proposition with alacrity. "I'm delighted," he said. "Delighted."

"Well I'm not delighted," Bill exploded the minute we were alone. "What possessed you to do a thing like that!"

"Professional jealousy. *Redbook* is my bailiwick. Besides, I want to see if I've forgotten how to write a short story. And you'd better see if you've forgotten how to write a novel."

"Your tactics are showing," he said coldly. "We could have turned out a serial together in a few weeks, but no. Out of some misguided notion that it's for my good, you turn it down."

The next morning I almost did regret my noble gesture. I sat at the typewriter and my mind was a blank. Much as I hated to admit it, he was right—it was infinitely easier to pool our brains; indeed, so perfectly did we match our separate styles of writing that I could leave a half-finished page in the machine to go out to the barn for a whiff of air, and he'd come back from the barn, and pick up where I'd left off. Or vice versa. And if the editors happened to catch a slight shift of rhythm or phrasing, they invariably thought it was the other way around.

In the last serial, though, he went off the course for the first time. We were to end an instalment with a passionate love scene between our hero and heroine. I had brought them as far as dinner-for-two in the hero's country estate, and as I sat them down at the table, I left them there to go out to the kitchen for a bit of sustenance myself, and a few minutes later, I heard Bill clacking away with such speed and gusto that I decided it was a shame to interrupt the flow of his inspiration, and went upstairs to wash my hair. Sure enough, I returned to find a pile of freshly typed pages stacked neatly on my desk. Avidly, I started to read them. It was brilliant writing, vivid, and persuasive. My mouth watered. Left to my own devices, I could never have conceived such exotic food, such great wines. Six courses, and every course a literary and gustatory masterpiece.

I read the closing paragraph of the instalment, and then went back to the beginning of the meal. I carefully selected a soft blue pencil, and made a huge cross from the top to the bottom of each page and when I reached the bottom of the last page, I wrote in heavy script, *"They ate no dinner."—To be continued.*

I would have wrung my neck if I'd been he, but he generously conceded that the cut was justified, under the circumstances, they wouldn't have had much appetite. "That food is too good to waste, though," I said. "We'll save it and use it in the next serial."

Now there wasn't going to be a next serial, and judging by my growing frustration, there wasn't going to be a short story either. I'd said jokingly that I wanted to see if I'd forgotten how to write one, but it wasn't a joke any longer. The sheet of paper in the machine was as blank as my mind. "In a week, maybe less," I'd promised Mr. Balmer rashly. I'd be lucky to get it done in a month, and then it probably wouldn't be any good. Dejectedly, I went in search of Bill, but like a heartless wretch he'd gone off to the freight station to call for a tractor part. I looked in at the kennels to collect a couple of Danes, and brought them back to the house for company. They weren't completely trained, which took my mind off my mind, so to speak. With one eye cocked in their direction, I typed out a tentative title. *The Ultimate Passion.* I considered it. It was rather fitting for a story of young marriage, as it cleared the way for a baby. I put down the opening sentence. IT HAD BEEN A BEAUTIFUL NIGHT AND SHE LOVED HIM MORE THAN EVER IN THE MORNING.—Why not? It was the way a proper marriage always began and therefore it ought to be proper enough for *Redbook*, which was somewhat puritanical in its ideas.

I live or die by the first line of anything I write. It dictates the mood, the tempo, the quality of what follows, and it is difficult to go an octave above it or fall an octave below it. The long complete that Mr. Balmer had liked so much had been a chronicle of marital conflict, and although he had been dubious about the propriety of the opening line, he had resisted the temptation to change it. DENNY PICKED THEODORA UP AT A STREET CORNER, AND HIS MOTHER NEVER QUITE FORGOT IT. It

was the statement of the story in a single line; it didn't lend itself
to change.

I tried to remember the opening sentence of *Twice Born*, and
finally had to ferret out the book. BULAKOV WAS PLEASED. That,
too, had been a good springboard—Bulakov was pleased about
many things.

I went back to the typewriter, and re-read the words I'd just
written. They came to life for me, I was off to a running start.

"IF IT WEREN'T REAL LOVE," DAVID TOLD HER, "IF IT WERE
ONLY PHYSICAL, IT WOULDN'T BE THAT WAY."

David. I suppose I settled on the name because I'd always liked
it, limited to certain people. But the girl's name would have to be
a three-syllable one for rhythm. *Stephanie, Marjorie, Erica.* Those
we'd used in the serials, but even so they wouldn't have linked
happily with *David.* I tried my old alphabet system. *Allison.* Too
fussy. *Barbara.* Spoken normally, it boiled down to Bar'bra,
two syllables, not three. *Claudia.* That was better, slur it and you'd
get *Claudja,* which was silly, and no one would. *Claudia and David.*
It was tidy, I liked the sound of it.

And Mr. Balmer liked the story, and the characters. "They're
alive, keep on with them. When can you have the others ready?
I want to run them successively."

"Soon," I promised again, but not rashly, this time. The
second one, with the baby being born, was already as good as
finished and needed only to be put to paper. In the third story,
they'd moved from their small New York apartment into one of
the salt-box houses we had looked at in Guildford. The commuting was feasible for an architect—and David was an architect
because, with the making-over of Longmeadow, I discovered that
I'd definitely missed my vocation, and I could enjoy his profession
vicariously. I loved anything to do with building, steam-
shovels, and masonry. I loved the carpenters, the plumbers, the
painters—they were a wonderful lot of people in those days.
Cheerfully, and of their own volition, they thought nothing of
working from sun-up to sun-down, Saturdays included. Except,
of course, during fishing or hunting season, and then they'd
disappear for days at a time.

I had never been a late sleeper, and on a farm, where you literally go to bed with the chickens, the first crow of the cock is a welcome alarm clock. Bill was always up and out to the barn like a flash, and now I was up and down to my typewriter, with two hours' work under my belt by the time the boys were ready for breakfast. The three stories were in Mr. Balmer's hands before the end of the month. He was delighted, and ordered three more. It was no chore for me, because there were so many things that happened, naturally, to a young couple in love, but I must admit that I didn't bargain for still another group of three. "We've had an extraordinary response from our readers," Mr. Balmer told me generously. "The letters are pouring in, asking for more."

Thinking, at this point, in larger terms than an isolated short story, I planned to end the final trio on the fitting chord of a second baby for the young wife, combined with the loss of her mother. Had I the faintest inkling that I was to go on writing *Claudia* for Mr. Balmer over a period of twelve long years, I should never have been so shortsighted as to kill Mrs. Brown off at the very prime of her life, and mine. The act having been committed, however, her death had the virtue of rounding out the first nine stories into form and meaning, and John Farrar said he wanted to publish them in book form. To me, this so-called novel fell into the same category as the serials, so it didn't occur to me to submit the manuscript to Max Perkins. But after John had resigned from the firm of Farrar and Rinehart, Max told me that he had always loved *Claudia*, and asked for the next book, which happened to be the sixth of the series.

I'm getting ahead of myself. A lot happened before that happened.

We spent our first Christmas on the farm, but not the second one. One of my great reliefs was to discover that Bill wasn't Christmas-crazy. Missy was, though; she was like a little girl with her mound of unopened gifts beneath her tree, and a stocking in the fireplace. We made a fuss over the day for her sake, as well as for the children's, but for ourselves we were glad when the routine festivities of the holidays were over.

"How would you like to get out of this holly-bedecked rat-race?" he asked me on a bleak morning in mid-December. "With the boys, of course. We'll all pile in the station wagon and drive to Yucca Loma."

Yucca Loma was a sort of Château Elysée in the Mojave Desert, very different from Palm Springs, and we'd often gone there between picture assignments. Now with Peter slowly and manfully getting the better of his asthma, a few weeks of dry, hot sun was the very lift he needed, and it wouldn't hurt John, either, "But we can't leave Paul to shift for himself over the holidays." I demurred.

"Who said we should? He can fly out and meet us there."

"How soon do we start?"

"I guess we ought to wait until the boys get home for lunch."

"I guess," I acceded dryly.

We were gratified to see how handsomely they took it. They were getting used to us, and our way of doing things.

By the time the bus dropped them at the door at noon, we were packed and ready to leave for California. Not that there was much to pack. I literally didn't have a thing to wear other than jodhpurs and sweaters, which were fine for Yucca Loma and the farm, but hardly suitable for luncheon at the Vendôme, or dinner at the Trocadero in case we decided to spend a day or so in Hollywood. "Maybe to be on the safe side," I said, "we'd better stop on our way through New York so that I can pick up one half-way decent suit, at least."

"Maybe we'd better leave in the morning," Bill suggested pointedly. "I'd like to have the city behind us before dark."

"I won't hold you up more than a few minutes. We almost pass by Milgrim's anyway. I only hope Mrs. Vant is still there."

Mrs. Vant was my old standby when I was having troubles and babies, and she knew that anything that wasn't reduced and drastically, didn't get a second glance with me as Milgrim's was a very expensive and exclusive shop in those days. I suppose the only reason she bothered with me was because she'd read *Pattern* and when *Another Language* was produced, she became my personal press agent to customers and personnel alike. "Don't you think you ought to spend a little more money on yourself, considering you're a celebrity?" she'd try to wheedle me away from the sales rack. "I have some new things that have just come in——"

"Not if they're not reduced."

I don't think I ever bought anything that wasn't last season's.

Now, as I entered the shop, the years fell away. She recognized me the instant I stepped into the dress department, and regretfully, I had to cut short her surprise and pleasure; if Bill hadn't been waiting outside with a station wagon full of luggage and children, I'd have liked nothing better than to have answered her eager questions, and asked a few of my own. I remembered about her arthritis, and her sick husband, but I didn't dare waste time in unproductive chatter. "It's wonderful seeing you, too, you haven't changed a bit either," I got the amenities behind me in breathless haste. "I wish I wasn't in such a rush, but I'm on my way to the desert, and I need something that I can wear to go into Los Angeles if I have to." I was about to add that in this particular exigency, price was not my major concern, but her reflexes were so automatic that she immediately dashed off to some mysterious cubicle behind a velvet curtain and a moment later emerged with a soft swish of grey wool and fur across her arm. "Marked down to sixty-nine fifty," she announced. "Three pieces, dress hat and coat. Luckily you're still a model size, so you don't even have to try it on." She peered at a small tag dangling from the hem of the dress. "We copied this ensemble for three-eighty-five, and lost money on it and look what you're getting it for. It's a steal. An absolute steal. I'll have it packed in a box with plenty of tissue paper so that it won't crush or wrinkle on the trip, and wear it in good health!"

It was certainly a bargain, and I liked bargains, and I liked grey, but I eyed the coat dubiously. "Wait a minute before you pack it, it's imitation fur, isn't it?"

"Listen to her. Did you expect real chinchilla for twenty-five dollars? What am I talking about? It only comes to twenty-three for each garment."

"But doesn't it look cheap? Being imitation, I mean?"

"Cheap!" she threw back at me. "Two of the best dressed

women in New York ordered this ensemble, and you're getting the original and not just a copy. Grab it and enjoy it."

The whole transaction took less than ten minutes from start to finish. "That was pretty quick," Bill acknowledged grudgingly.

"I told you I'd be quick."

"Did you get something nice?" he asked with the perfunctory disinterest of the masculine male.

"The dress and the hat are, but the coat is rabbit."

I could see his nose go up the same as mine. "I can always wear it as a sport jacket with slacks, I don't have to use it as part of the ensemble. I can't get over how much it was reduced," I added gloatingly. "All three pieces for sixty-nine fifty."

"I wish you'd buy something at the proper price for once."

"If I'd had to pay the proper price for this, you'd be waiting out here for the rest of the day before I made up my mind."

"Well, let's get started," he said, and shoved the elegant box into the rear of the car.

It was a wonderful drive across the country except that the schoolmaster in Bill came out at every point of interest: Thus, the boys (and I) were exposed to a great wallop of education, meeting geography and history in the flesh, so to speak, instead of between the dry covers of a textbook. They, alas, did not fully appreciate their good fortune, and developed a sneaky tendency to read the comics whenever our backs were turned, which was practically always, as we were, of course, sitting in the front seat.

We took the southern route, by-passed Los Angeles, and headed straight through San Bernadino to Victorville, and on to the ranch. On the return trip, though, we took a different route, planning to spend a short time at the Beverly Hills Hotel. The boys wanted to re-visit their old haunts, and I was not averse to finally wearing the Milgrim ensemble.

The dress fitted perfectly, the soft grey beret was quite becoming and the only trouble with the coat was that it was rabbit pretending to be chinchilla. I carried it into the lobby over my arm, with the impressive label on the beautiful satin lining uppermost, and only a little of the fur peeping out from underneath. The hotel had undergone its first mammoth alteration since our departure from Hollywood, and we were a little taken aback by the mountains of incoming and outgoing luggage piled by the door, and the crowds of guests milling round the desk. "We should have telephoned," Bill said. "I just saw some people turned away, so they must be full up. Wait here, and I'll see if we have a chance."

I hadn't reckoned with California weather: a cold chill blew in from the constantly-opened doors, and it was either a question of getting pneumonia or putting on my coat, so I put it on. "Watch our suitcases," I adjured the boys, "and don't budge from this spot." I joined Bill at the desk, where he was chafing at the high-handed indifference of the two or three clerks in charge of reservations. "To hell with them," he muttered.

One of the older clerks—he introduced himself as the assistant manager—caught sight of us as we started to leave and asked solicitously if he could be of any service to us. "I'm afraid not," Bill said. "We have a couple of youngsters with us and I foolishly neglected to book rooms in advance."

"Don't give it another thought, sir. We can accommodate you in a very pleasant suite." He stepped from behind the desk and beckoned us to follow him. "I'll show you to your rooms," he said, "and if they aren't satisfactory, I'll arrange to give you one of the bungalows."

The suite was more than satisfactory. He whisked back the curtains, revealing a large patio for our exclusive use. "I'll have your luggage sent up at once," he said, as he bowed himself out, "and anything we can do to make you comfortable, you have only to pick up the telephone."

"Well, I'll be damned," said Bill, the minute we were alone. "How do you account for it?"

"I can't. Unless he recognized the name, and thought I was Missy."

"Missy never set foot in this hotel," Bill said. "Besides, if you were Missy, what would that make me?"

It didn't occur to either of us then that the little rabbits had already put their tails together and were starting on their self-appointed mission to bring me luck. On the contrary. I continued with callous ingratitude to be ashamed of them, which might sound as if I'd been brought up on ermines and sables, when actually I'd never owned anything more costly than a squirrel coat, and squirrel isn't such a lot better that rabbit, except that it doesn't try to pass for something it isn't.

I suppose it could have been my modest upbringing itself that contributed to my discomfort in sporting a mockery of chinchilla, and on a series of business meetings that developed shortly after our return from California, I again carried the coat over my arm, and deviously thrust it behind me out of sight, so that no one would offer to hang it up.

The meetings had to do with *Claudia*. The sponsor of "Grapenuts" wanted to buy it for the radio, and with what I did not then recognize to be an unwonted absence of contention, we entered quickly and painlessly into a most lucrative financial arrangement. However, listening to the programme when it reached the air, was not as painless. A pretty little girl interpreted *Claudia* in a reedy voice with no diction. I was happier with the casting of the husband, who had a beautiful voice, and a fine diction. His name was Richard Kolmar, and once in a while, when I hear him broadcast in the mornings with his wife, Dorothy Kilgallen, I wonder whether he remembers that he was the first of a long line of Davids. At any rate I am grateful to him for shepherding Claudia to her initial venture before a microphone.

I lived at too great a distance from the scene of operations, and was too occupied with other matters to be either a help or a hindrance to Claudia's weekly half-hour visit with her radio audience. Nevertheless, a certain amount of publicity splashed over on to me as her creator, and this, in conjunction with the constant appearance of my name on the cover of *Redbook*, evidently reminded John Golden of me. I remembered him as the veteran producer of *Turn to the Right*, and many other solid Broadway successes, but since I had never met him, I was surprised to receive a very friendly letter from him, asking me to lunch at Sardi's the following day, with or without my husband. It was such short notice that I wondered why he hadn't telephoned, but I had yet to discover that among his innumerable quirks—endearing and otherwise—was the fact that he never made a long-distance call, no matter how short a distance, if he could possibly avoid it. "What do you think he wants to see me about?" I asked Bill. "What do you think he wants? He wants you to write another play."

I shook my head. "I'm through with the theatre."

It was indicative of Mr. Golden's sheer compelling magnetism that he lured me back into it. Not immediately, of course. He disarmed me completely by talking about everything else under the sun before he got round to what was really on his mind, which, incidentally, was a starring vehicle for Gertrude Lawrence. I shall never forget his greeting when I walked into his huge, opulent office which lay down a narrow hall from the tiny, sordid space that served adequately enough as a working cubicle with two flat-topped tables—one for his secretary, Clarence, and the other for his manager, Captain Richard French—better known to his friends (which Bill and I were soon to be) as "Dixie."

Mr. Golden didn't rise from behind his mahogany desk—as big as any in Hollywood—as Clarence escorted me into his presence. He seemed a much larger man sitting, than he was when he stood up, having rather tapering legs against a substantial middle, topped by a generously-proportioned head. "Wait a minute," he stopped my progress across an oriental rug, "I have to put my tooth in!" He fished out a small denture from a stamp box, and popped it into his mouth. "Damn thing hurts. Only wear it for company," he explained. "Throw over your coat, I'll hang it up."

"Thanks, I'll keep it," I declined hastily.

"Chinchillas, eh?"

"No. Rabbit."

He grinned, and took out his tooth. "Okay, now you've seen it." He returned it to the stamp box, and opened the top drawer of his desk. "Catch. Here's a bar of chocolate."

I caught it and put it in my handbag. He scowled. "What are you doing that for?"

"I don't want to spoil my appetite, I'll save it for later."

"You're supposed to spoil your appetite. Throw it back!"

[255]

"I will not," I said.

He rose and strode over to a grand piano at the far side of the room, giving me a friendly whack as he passed behind me. "You're a nice girl, Rosie, I like you."

"My name is not 'Rosie.' It's Rosebud," I added.

With another broad grin, he sat down at the piano and played a lilting parody of "Sweet Rosie O'Grady," which, with less expert delivery, would have been neither funny nor captivating. On Mr. Golden, it was both, and I sat entranced at his vaudevillean antics, until suddenly he jumped up, slammed the lid of the piano shut, and said, "Let's eat.—Why didn't you bring your husband?"

"He's having lunch with his publisher."

"Oh. One of those."

I took umbrage. "What do you mean, 'one of those'?"

"I thought he was a farmer."

"He is."

"Rich?"

"Not from having money."

"That's the only kind of rich there is, my girl. And if he isn't, how did he buy you that coat? Or did somebody else?"

"No. He did. But it only cost twenty-three dollars."

Mr. Golden decided that he had met his match and I was pulling a few antics myself, so if he didn't believe me, there was nothing much that I could do about it. He swung into Sardi's with his arm around my shoulder, and on the way to his special table at the rear introduced me to half a dozen people as his long-lost daughter. By the end of lunch I felt as if I were. I had also begun to re-evaluate my reluctance to write another play. *Another Language*, with all its unhappy memories, was over and done with. The world of the theatre might be a very pleasant place to work in after all.

Adrienne Morrison was delighted to hear about my change of attitude. "High time," she said. "And a vehicle for Gertrude Lawrence? You're set!"

"I don't think I can write a 'vehicle'," I objected, "but I think *Claudia* might make a good play."

[256]

With BILL on the terrace at Sutton Square, New York

JOHN GOLDEN

There is a PS. on the back of this which reads "And on the other hand, since I took myself too seriously here's a poem:

To Willy & Nilly / Whose dramatic swilly /
Are filling my tilly / Yclept old Achilly /
Endorses this, silly / This daffy, down dilly /
Who gilds every lily. Nuts! / Love John."

"Don't even consider it," she flatly discouraged the idea. "You owe it to yourself to follow up *Another Language* with a much more important piece of work than a little domestic comedy."

Her advice didn't dissuade me, although I think that the radio programme was responsible for me going ahead with the idea, because suddenly I found myself wanting to interpret and project the characters as I envisioned them. Undaunted by the fact that the "e" on my typewriter was out of commission, the transition to play form was effortless, and again I wrote an act a day. "Dope, why didn't you use my machine?" Bill mumbled, as he struggled over the opening pages.

"I'm accustomed to mine," I said. "You'll get the knack of it once you get over expecting the 'e's'."

It was a temptation not to have the script retyped before I sent it on to Mr. Golden, but Bill said it was too good a play to use as a gag. I had the copy sent straight to the office from the typewriter agency, and, wonder of wonders, he telephoned me as soon as he finished reading it. "This is a long-distance call," he opened up without preamble, "so don't expect me to talk over three minutes, I've got my watch in front of me. Hop a train and I'll treat you to lunch. You can bring your husband. I'll treat him too."

"He's cutting the lambs' tails," I said, "and there's no train before noon, and I don't like the train anyway."

"He's cutting *what?*" Mr. Golden bellowed. "Never mind, don't tell me, it'll take too long, tell me tomorrow. I'll expect you in my office at twelve sharp."

"Did he like it?" Bill had rushed from the barn to hear the verdict.

"He didn't say. He's a lunatic. Our kind. Will you drive us in for lunch tomorrow with him?"

"I suppose I'll have to." Left to himself, Bill wouldn't have budged off the farm.

We had a vociferous session in Mr. Golden's office before we finally wandered over to Sardi's. "Hello, Willy and Nilly!" he greeted us jovially. "Hey, Rosie, why didn't you tell me he was such a good-looking devil?"

R [257]

"You didn't ask me. Let's talk about the play." I was already used to him, but I could feel that Bill had slight reservations about this congenial clown, and subtly Mr. Golden reacted similarly to Bill, and seemed relieved to take my hint and get down to the business in hand. He riffled through my manuscript which lay before him on the desk, and even at a distance, I saw that each page was marked with many darkly-pencilled circles, half-moons and question marks. "You didn't like it," I anticipated him.

"Hold your horses. I liked some of it, but it needs revision, and lots of it."

"I thought it was a pretty finished piece of work," Bill injected levelly.

"Construction-wise, it's great," Mr. Golden modified his overall criticism. "Perfect example of dramatic technique. But it won't last a week on Broadway as it stands now."

"Why not?" Bill asked.

It was evident that he was going to wage a bloodless battle for me, so I remained discreetly silent while Mr. Golden held forth on an almost total absence of action and suspense in the story, and the inconsistency of alternating "belly laughs" with tragedy. "Stick to one or the other, but you can't mix 'em," he declared, spanking the script with his hand. "After lunch, we'll go over my notes one by one, and by God, I think we can get a damn fine play of it!"

I nodded. "We could mortgage the farm so heavily that they almost lose it, and we could make a real threat of engaging Fritz and Bertha, without references, and most important of all, Claudia's mother wouldn't have to die. She could have a miraculous recovery at the last minute."

Mr. Golden's mouth fell open. "How'd you get hold of my notes, did you sneak in here while I was out of the room?"

"I didn't have to. I know exactly what changes you'd like me to make——"

"Rosie, you're a smart girl," he broke in, "a real professional. I was afraid I was going to have to put up a fight——"

It was my turn to break in. "You are," I said. "But it's not

[258]

going to do you any good because the play you want to produce isn't the play I want to write. It's just another radio script."

He deflated in stages like a large balloon with a slow leak. "Look here," he said belligerently, grabbing a piece of stationery from the top drawer of his desk, "you know what this emblem means on my letterhead? 'C-H-A-P'?"

"No. But I noticed it."

"Damn right you noticed it, I've had it there for as long as I've been in the theatre and that's as long as you're old!"

"Not quite," I said. "You're not that old and I'm not that young."

"Don't argue!" he yelled at me. "What I'm telling you is that you've got some mighty off-colour stuff in that simple-sounding script of yours——"

"Animals get pregnant just the same as humans," I reminded him mildly. "Only more so."

"Not in my productions! C-H-A-P stands for *Clean Holesome American Plays*—and that, by God, was before I knew that Holesome was spelled with a W!"

And I never did find out whether or not he was fooling or in earnest about his spelling.

Once more I found myself without an agent which, from one aspect, was fortuitous, because even if Adrienne had been in a position to function for me, I am sure she would have brought pressure upon me to make the changes that Mr. Golden insisted upon. She didn't have faith in the play, anyway, but apart from that, the sudden dissolution of her husband's firm had very nearly destroyed her. I was so terribly sorry and unhappy for her that I had no desire to affiliate with anyone else. Besides, I was glad that Mr. Golden seemed to have washed his hands of both me and Claudia. The hectic and demanding rhythm of the theatre was alien to the tempo of our lives; the farm remained an all-engrossing project, and the problems of a family did not lessen with their growing up. Paul was almost ready to graduate from Harvard when, all at once, war was in the air. It wasn't our war, but he waited only to finish his final term before he enlisted as a private.

For the first time in his twenty-one years, he became a stranger to me, but my Bill, along with Bill Donovan who had taken a great liking to Paul, understood the way he felt. And still I couldn't understand. I closed my heart from understanding. It was not right for my son, or any mother's son, to learn to kill, even though the need to do so might never arise. "It's not our war!" I kept protesting.

"Mother, if it ever gets to be our war," Paul told me, looking suddenly much older than he was, "I want to be ready."

"But it won't, it can't!" I denied passionately. "It's on the other side of the world!"

He grinned. "Okay, then you have nothing to worry about."

For a long while, I didn't worry. He was stationed at a training camp in Quincy, not so far from Lyme that we couldn't drive up to see him, or that he couldn't come down on leave to spend a day or two at the farm. I began to get used to the small shock of his handsomeness in uniform. I even admitted that the experience was good for him. "He's officer material," Bill Donovan told me. I was proud. Manhood became him vastly.

One night, about two months after he had been in training, the telephone rang, rousing me from a sound sleep. Blindly, and a little panicky, I reached for the instrument on the bedside table. "Miss Franken?"

"Yes! Who is it?"

"This is Lubitsch. Ernst Lubitsch. I would like to talk to you about one of your books——"

Relief that it was nothing about Paul, turned to anger on the same theory that had made me feel like slapping Peter that morning when he'd scared the wits out of me by tumbling down the stairs head first without hurting himself. "This is no time to wake anyone up by talking about *anything*," I rebuffed my inconsiderate caller, and banged the receiver.

"Who was it?" Bill mumbled drowsily.

"I don't know. Some idiot, at this hour."

I flounced back to sleep, upon which the telephone rang again.

"Miss Franken, we must have been disconnected, this is Ernst Lubitsch speaking——"

"Mr. Lubitsch," I told him icily, "we did not get disconnected, but if you insist on talking to me, please do so in the morning and stop disturbing the whole household at this ungodly hour. Good-bye."

Bill sat up in bed. "That wasn't Ernst Lubitsch, was it?"

"Yes, and what's the idea, why not *Ernest*, like other people? Who is he, anyway, to keep on waking us up like this? It must be after midnight."

Bill consulted his watch. "It's all of five minutes after nine," he finally announced. "And you bit a Hollywood director's head off twice in two minutes for calling you at—if I heard correctly —an 'ungodly hour'."

"Oh," I said. "*That* Lubitsch. No wonder he talked with an accent."

The telephone rang for the third time. I untwisted the cord and stretched the instrument across the bed. "You take it. Make some excuse that we thought it was later because we go to bed so early."

"Make your own excuses, and let the poor man finish what he wants to say, he probably wants to make a film of *Claudia*."

However, Mr. Lubitsch had given up, and a new voice greeted me. "Miss Franken, this is Sol Loesser, we're calling from the coast, and Ernst had difficulty getting through to you. How are you?"

"Very well, thank you." I knew who Mr. Loesser was—he had bought *Our Town*, and made a good picture of it.

"We've just finished reading *Strange Victory*," he went on rather quickly, as if fearing to be cut off, "and it's the sort of story that Ernst would like to direct, provided we could interest you and your husband in coming out here to write the script."

"Oh, dear," I said. "I don't think so. We just came back from California a couple of months ago."

"But you only stayed in Hollywood a day or so."

This was mystifying. "But we didn't see anyone, so how could you have known we were there?"

"It was in the press," Mr. Loesser returned matter-of-factly. "Anyway, maybe you'll change your mind. Talk it over with your husband, and let me call you again in the morning. I get to the office at ten—that would be one o'clock in Connecticut."

I was momentarily diverted by the three hours' difference in time that I had forgotten about—no wonder Mr. Lubitsch hadn't been able to grasp the idea that he had ruined our night's sleep. "We will," I promised Mr. Loesser contritely. "Good-bye."

"Will what?" Bill wanted to know, leaning on his elbow.

I yawned and turned off the lamp. "I'll tell you tomorrow, I don't want to wake myself up any more than I have to."

"Tell me now. Was it about *Claudia*?"

"No, *Strange Victory*."

Bill reached over to switch the lamp on again. "But that's a dead property, they can't want to buy it——"

"Only if we go out and write the script, which we won't."

"Why won't we? Of course we will. A couple of weeks' work out there, and we've got the new addition to the poultry unit!"

Suffice to say that we flew out to Hollywood a few days later. I was resigned but reluctant. Anything for the farm. "Bigger chickens for Loesser money," I quipped bleakly.

We were about to leave for the airport when the telephone rang. "It might be Paul," I said, and raced back to answer it. "Cut it short," Bill shouted after me, "or we'll miss the plane!"

It was John Golden who automatically cut it short. "No use wasting money on a long-distance call," he began as usual, "hop in your car and have lunch with me."

I explained that we were on our way to the coast. "We'll be back within a month though."

"Good," he said. "Have you done any rewriting on the play?"

"No."

"You're damn pig-headed, but never mind. Let's get on with it. Gertie Lawrence is crazy about the part, and with her in it you'll have a hit whether it's good or not."

"But she isn't right for Claudia!"

"Hurry up!" Bill yelled.

"What in blazes do you mean she isn't right?" Mr. Golden out-yelled him. "She's a great actress, she can play anything. I don't care what it is!"

"But I care. In the first place, she's English," I pointed out tactfully. "And Claudia's an eighteen-year-old American girl.— Look, we'll miss our plane, I'll call you tomorrow!"

"But you said you were going to Hollywood!"

"They happen to have telephones in California too! Good-bye!"

I had barely enough time to place the call before our meeting Mr. Loesser the next morning, but showman that he was, John refused to talk until he was ensconced at his table in Sardi's. I could hear the hubbub of voices and the clatter of dishes as the instrument was connected for his use, which meant that the conversation was a hit-and-miss affair. "Speak up!" he exhorted me.

"I'm shouting!"

"Who's your agent? I'll take a three months' option!" he gave up.

"I haven't any, and you don't need an option!"

He heard that one. "Good girl, Rosie!"

"Don't call me Rosie."

"All right, Rosebud, hurry back as fast as you can and we'll get this show on the road!"

"At least," I told Bill gloomily, as I returned the receiver to its hook, "he'll be fun to fight with." And fight we would! It was going to be a hard tussle to convince him that Miss Lawrence, skilled actress though she was, could not possibly play Claudia. However, there was no use worrying about it, literally and figuratively, before our chickens were hatched.

We found Sol Loesser to be quietly-mannered, and very agreeable, but we had no sooner sat down to our first conference than it became evident that he was thinking in terms of the script taking three and a half months to write rather than three and a half weeks. We should have expected it, knowing that it was the accepted procedure in motion pictures to like a story well enough to buy it, and then immediately throw it out and concoct a completely different story. "But we don't work that way." I protested against his opening gambit of changing the whole structure of the plot, and in the heat of my agitation I slipped off my coat and tossed it on to a chair some distance away, where it slithered over the wooden arm to the floor.

[263]

Instantly, Mr. Loesser leapt to his feet to retrieve it, and I could have kicked myself for wearing it, although it looked rather sporty with slacks, which were about the only things I had enough of to bring along with me on such short notice. "Please. It isn't worth bothering about," I murmured, embarrassed at the care with which he lifted the soft bundle of fur and arranged it over the back of the sofa. He gave it a little extra pat before he returned to the swivel chair behind his desk, and said, "Perhaps you're right about *Strange Victory* being a good story as it stands. Suppose you write the script as you see it, and I'll read it when you have it down on paper."

"Now, what do you think made him so tractable all of a sudden?" I asked Bill as we hurried back to our office to whip the opening sequence into shape before he could change his mind again.

"It beats me," said Bill. "That was the quickest switch I ever saw."

We quit work at five o'clock. We had accepted a dinner invitation for that evening, and my old black net, which I had hastily packed, had outlived its day so I hoped to pick up something to wear at Magnin's. We had to hurry to get there before closing time, for Magnin's was an elaborate emporium over on Wilshire Boulevard. Hollywood was changing fast. The Vendôme had been torn down, the Trocadero was boarded up, and secretaries weren't what they used to be. Grace was lost to us for ever in the passing of time and the anonymity of a typing pool.

The new shop was strange to me, with most of the old sales staff replaced by haughty and unfamiliar faces. The saleslady whom I diffidently accosted was sleekly plump, with big pearls in her ears and snowy-blue hair coiffed into a wig-like perfection. Instead of answering me, she simply stared, and I had to ask her again please to direct me to the dress department. I never did find out where it was. "Modom," she breathed, paying no attention to my question, "may I touch it?"

I hadn't the faintest idea what she wanted to touch, but I took a chance and said she could touch it, whereupon she extended a manicured hand and laid it reverently on the coat, slung as always across my arm. "Modom, I haven't seen chinchillas like these for years." I simply didn't have the heart to tell her that she was only touching rabbit. A couple of other sales-ladies drifted towards us, and I didn't have the heart to tell them either.

Five minutes later, I spotted our hired blue convertible in the crowded car park. "Well," Bill greeted me from behind the wheel, "you're certainly creating a record for speed when it comes to buying clothes."

"Except that I didn't buy anything."

"Why not?"

"Because," I told him loftily, "no one who wears a twenty-five thousand dollar chinchilla—especially with slacks—needs to spend any more money on clothes."

Back at the Beverly Hills Hotel, I hung the coat away in my wardrobe on a softly-padded hanger with the same solicitude and tenderness with which Mr. Sol Loesser had laid it across his sofa. I had scrunched, slung and generally abused that precious, delicate fur for the last time. It was not my conscious intention to go round fooling people, but if those wily little rabbits could fool Magnin's, they deserved infinitely more respect than I had hitherto accorded them.

We returned to the farm on schedule, although we could most advantageously have prolonged our stay. We had just about finished the *Strange Victory* script when Leland Heyward, then the most choosy and sought-after agent in Hollywood, approached us with an offer from Metro to write an original story for Claudette Colbert, and also an offer from another major studio to buy *Claudia* for fifty thousand dollars. I liked Leland at once, and so did Bill, but we explained that we had hatched all the chickens we needed for the moment, and as for *Claudia*, I had written a play based on episodes in the first book that I had as good as promised to Mr. Golden, if he wished to produce it.

I might have known that something was in the air when I discovered that John had telephoned Lyme twice in anticipation of our homecoming. "You're late getting back!" he accused me when

I returned his urgent message to phone him at once. "I wasted a couple of phones trying to reach you."

"The plane was late, not us," I apologized.

"Never mind that now," he said. "Gertie wants to prove to you that she can play Claudia so she's all set for an hour's radio show on the 'Pursuit of Happiness' programme three weeks from Sunday, with Burgess Meredith playing David."

It was as unlikely a bit of casting as I could imagine, but I was so sure that "Grapenuts" would never sanction a competing radio performance that I made no issue of the choice. I can only say that it was a tribute to Miss Lawrence's combination of charm and persuasion that both agency and sponsor actually did permit the property to be broadcast on two separate programmes simultaneously.

Although it was good entertainment, even Mr. Golden grudgingly conceded that the characterizations did not exactly portray a vulnerable love story between an unsophisticated teen-age bride and her more mature and understanding husband. "You win, Rosie. How about Katherine Hepburn or Frances Farmer?"

Maybe I should have been grateful that I had a producer who was willing to cushion box-office success with the costly insurance of a star, but I held obdurately to my theory that, since I had never described Claudia in any of the stories, I wanted an unknown actress with no previous identity to an audience.

"You won't *have* an audience with an unknown!" Mr. Golden shouted, and added that an expensive director he was "dickering" with agreed that, if Hepburn was not available, Farmer would be great. Great.

"I don't care how 'expensive' he is," I argued, "he's not the right director for this play if he wants that sort of casting."

Mr. Golden glared at me. "Okay. You have the right to veto, but if we don't get this show off the ground pretty soon, we'll miss the season. And what's worse than that, the Dramatist Guild will be after me to renew my option and that will cost me more money."

"It would absolutely bankrupt you," I sympathized. He really was fun to fight with. I was developing a great affection for him,

SOME ACTORS ARE PEOPLE

and I resolved to try to be less stubborn and not to block his efforts with fruitless arguments. He hadn't held out for Gertrude Lawrence once he realized he'd been wrong, so the best thing to do was to go back to the farm and give him a free hand without my interference.

I hadn't stayed away more than a couple of days when he telephoned. "Okay, Rosie, we've got it licked, no time to talk, be at my office as near noon as you can make it, I have a big surprise for you——"

"What?" I broke in cagily.

"Never mind what, I guarantee you'll like it. In fact I'm so sure of it, I've got Wilmington and Washington pencilled in for the try-out, and the Booth Theatre reserved for New York. Now get the hell on a train as fast as you damn well can."

I'd already missed the train that would get me to New York around noon. "You'd better drive me in anyway. I have a feeling I'm going to need your moral support," I told Bill dubiously.

It turned out that I needed him even more than I thought I might. Straight off it wasn't a good sign for John to be so full of beams when we walked into his office. "Well, if it isn't my old friends Willy and Nilly!" he greeted us ebulliently. "Hey, did I invite you, Willy?"

"No, I just came along for the ride," Bill returned amiably. "My treat for lunch."

John gave a large wave of his hand on the way to reaching for his tooth. "Nonsense, man, I don't pay for my food, I sign for it. Sit down, sit down. And let me tell you that for once I'm not afraid of you two ganging up on me." He rang for Clarence, who appeared instantaneously with his thin, serious face wreathed in smiles. "He's outside, Mr. Golden, he just arrived."

"Have him wait a minute. Don't send him in until I buzz."

"Yes, sir." Clarence whisked off. John rose from behind his desk to give me a paternal squeeze. "Rosie, I might yell at you, but I admire your judgment. Hate to admit it, but I do. And that, by God, is why I turned this town upside down to find you the director you'd be satisfied with." He paused to heighten the effect of his crowning revelation. "At this moment, in my

[267]

waiting-room, sits the man who did such a magnificent job for you on *Another Language*. And if he did it once, he'll do it again. So now you know what my surprise is, and don't you ever say your Uncle John doesn't love you."

Bill's eyes met mine, and as I had not the ghost of an intention of repeating my experience with Arthur Beckhard, I grasped at the only alternative that was open to me.

"John, it was awfully nice of you to have gone to all that trouble for me, but now I have a surprise for you. I've decided to direct *Claudia* myself."

"You're joking," he said flatly.

"I'm not."

"But you've never directed a play in your life! I'm investing a lot of money in this show, and I'm not going to let some damn fool whim of yours jeopardize its success!"

"It's no damn fool whim," Bill said, as if my ultimatum had come as no astonishment to him. "Let her do it, John. You won't regret it."

John's face sagged. "I might have known the pair of you would gang up on me after all. But I'll tell you one thing. If I do let her do it, you'll be the ones to regret it. So I'm advising you right now to grab that fifty-thousand dollar film offer and skip the stage production because once this play's a flop, and it will be, she won't be able to sell it to Hollywood at any price. Mind you, this is against my own interests, there won't be a penny in it for me, and I stand to lose what I've already put into the show."

It was true, and I recall appreciatively that John was being honest and generous to a degree, as, in his strangely contradictory fashion, he often was. "Now, understand this," he warned me in dead earnest, when he eventually accepted the fact that I was willing to take the gamble of the play being a flop, "if you bungle it, and I have to call in a professional director, his salary comes out of your royalties. Is that clear?"

I nodded, too scared, suddenly, to speak. He put his arm around me. "And I'm going to see to it that you won't lose out on the deal: I'm going to give you a straight fifteen per cent on everything over fourteen thousand a week."

Remembering my minimum royalties from *Another Language*, a considerable portion of which I never received, I was more than ever speechless at his generosity, and later nothing could convince me that he simply failed to realize at the time that the Booth Theatre played, at full capacity, to slightly under fourteen thousand. Bill, gentleman that he was, allowed me to keep my illusions, but when, several years later, *Claudia* enjoyed a return engagement at the St. James' Theatre, he blandly assumed that the original agreement carried on. John literally tore his hair out. "That damned house grosses somewhere in the neighbourhood of twenty-two thousand!" he yelled. "You can't do this to me!"

"I'm not doing anything to you," Bill said innocently. "A contract is a contract."

It was a funny thing how Bill functioned like a hard-headed businessman only when it came to protecting my interests.

I had some pretty tough sledding, though, before *Claudia* was properly launched as a Broadway success. Having committed myself, I was, at the very start, beset by the problem of trying to divide my life between New York and Lyme. Too many hours and too much energy had to be expended in travelling backwards and forwards, especially since I was under the additional pressure of having to turn out a monthly Claudia story for *Redbook*. "We'd better rent an apartment in town," Bill said.

"You mean you'd leave the farm to stay with me?" I asked incredulously.

"We can get back for week-ends."

It was more than I'd expected of him, and it undoubtedly simplified matters to an extent, but I still had reservations about leaving the boys so constantly. John had a habit of breaking up dogfights barehanded (Freya was getting to be crotchety and demanding in her old age), and Peter had a lurking desire to see if he couldn't "hypnotize" the bull into a state of docile obedience. To add to my worries they were both itching to take a hand at ploughing, and I could not overcome the lingering horror of Sydney Howard having been crushed to death by his own tractor.

The upshot of it was that we popped them into a good boarding school halfway between Lyme and New York, where we could pick them up on Saturday mornings and drop them on our way back to town Sunday evenings. As for Paul, he was on manoeuvres at Fort Bragg, and the busier I kept the less apt I was to worry about him.

My mind finally at ease, I lost no time in preparing for an uninterrupted routine of work. I found a wonderfully spacious place to live on Washington Square, furnished it quickly with large strokes of dramatic black and white, finished up a Claudia story, and was ready to start casting the play all within a period of less than a month. Then my troubles really began, for I was still adamant about finding an unknown, which proved to be a self-defeating task, in so far as she had to have the experience and the equipment to carry one of the longest parts ever written. I think I must have looked at, read, and rejected nearly five hundred eager young applicants, many of whom were later to become successful stars. At the time, however, they were just nice little girls like Nancy Kelly, Dorothy Malone, Ann Baxter, Marge Champion, Betsy Drake, Maureen Stapleton, and innumerable others. I keep running into them to this day, and I often wonder how I escaped being stabbed with a knife every time I walked into Sardi's for lunch. There were, of source, dozens of youthful aspirants with ambitions that did not centre exclusively on a stage career, but to all of them I tried to be gentle and tactful, relying frequently on the valid excuse that they were "too pretty" or "too glamorous". "Claudia is just a plain, American girl," I explained truthfully.

Bill aided and abetted me in the long, arduous search, but John was becoming increasingly impatient. "I'll give you one more week," he finally announced his ultimatum, "and then we're going ahead with Frances Farmer."

I had nothing against Frances Farmer, except that everything about her, including her beauty, was alien to the character. "Will you take a gamble with me?" I asked Bill at the end of a particularly gruelling and fruitless day.

"I always have," he replied mildly.

"All right. Then the first girl who comes in tomorrow morning without red toe-nails, red finger-nails, yellow hair and a mink coat is going to play Claudia. Regardless."

"Irregardless," he amended, and I knew that he was with me. That is how Dorothy Maguire happened to get the part. She was the first girl to walk into the small filing-room at the end of the hall that John had turned over to me for casting purposes. She wore a nutria coat, slightly curly from having weathered some rainy days, but her hair made up for it by being perfectly straight, and of a pale, childish texture, with half of it looped up into a flat pompadour, and the other half hanging down her back. I hadn't figured on earrings, but her nails more than met my requirements. Not only were they guiltless of crimson lacquer, but they bore the clean and rather uneven testimony of home-made manicures. I could have taken an oath on it that her quite large, but modestly shod, feet had likewise never seen the inside of a beauty parlour.

I avoided meeting Bill's eyes, and I also avoided the usual procedure of asking her to read a few lines of the script, because no matter how she read them, it wouldn't have changed my mind. We escorted her into Mr. Golden's office. He was seated behind his desk, talking to his sister.

When not within hearing distance, I alluded to her as Aunt God-damn Nellie, for in order to justify her indubitable status as a tax-deduction, she always had a little say about everything, and sometimes a lot to say about nothing. Now I acknowledged her presence with a civil nod, and addressed myself pleasantly, but firmly, to her brother. "John, this is Claudia."

"You're kidding," John grinned, but it takes a woman to know a woman and Aunt Nellie somehow knew that I wasn't "kidding," and she made no effort to disguise her horrified disapproval. Whereupon Dorothy burst into tears. My heart ached for the poor child until I finally discovered what she was blubbering about. "I wanted the part of 'Miss Liberty Jones', " she wept, "but Nancy Coleman got it instead!"

It was ironic. Hundreds of aspiring young actresses drooling for the part of Claudia, and here I was, going out on a limb for a girl who had her heart set on being Miss Liberty Jones! I

[271]

doubt if Dorothy ever put the disappointment behind her even though the Barry play choked to an early death because of its intellectual earnestness. But hankering as she did for the part, I could understand why she felt that her close identification with Claudia for so many years ruined her reputation.

John, on the other hand, was firmly convinced that she was going to "ruin" Claudia along with his investment, and from the sizzling tension in his office it wasn't too soon to start proving him wrong. We took her home with us for lunch, and began working with her on the script that afternoon.

"But she has truly beautiful eyes and she doesn't drop her 'g's'," I told Bill as I climbed wearily into bed at eight o'clock.

"Yes, Miss Franken."

I threw a pillow at him.

Dorothy's salary was only fifty-seven fifty a week but even so John Golden couldn't get over not liking her. He said she had the biggest hands and feet he ever saw, and what was worse, she didn't know what to do with them. He was right, but I found it all to the good to capitalize her liabilities into assets. Although she was, I believe, twenty-six or seven, she'd kept all the gaucheries of extreme youth, as well as the round, full face of a child, so I wrote a line into the script that endeared her to the audience, if not to the producer. "David, I have a face like a baked potato."—When little Phyllis Thaxter played the part in the Chicago company, I changed the line to, "David, I have a face like a banana."—One of the advantages of writing and directing one's own play is that you never have to ask permission of anybody to do anything. Nor is there any trick to directing, when, with a slight change of word or movement, you can tailor a part to an actor like a comfortable old suit of clothes, which was the way the part was tailored to Dorothy during the preliminary hours that we spent together at Washington Square, and over the weekends, at the farm. The characterization needed constant vigilance against "cuteness" and to avoid it I redistributed lines and reactions so that Claudia never had to wrestle laughs for herself, and the fact that it appeared as if she carried the comedy is an ovation

Rehearsal of *Soldier's Wife* at the farm. LILY DARVAS, TITO VUOLO, FRIEDA INNESCOURT, MARTHA SCOTT, MYRON McCORRMICK, myself and GLENN ANDERS

Doctors Disagree: JOHN IRELAND and DOLLY HAAS

Outrageous Fortune:
MARGARET WILLIAMS and
ELSIE FERGUSON

to the tender and able cast that surrounded her. Donald Cook, who had just finished a season with Gertrude Lawrence, was not my physical image of David, but he supplied what was far more important—the most expert timing of any actor I've ever worked with. Frances Starr had not been on the stage for many years, but she hadn't lost the solid rudiments of her Belasco training. I had met her briefly at Yucca Loma during my Hollywood days, and even then I was drawn to her because she looked so much as my mother used to—the same clear blue eyes and flaxen hair, tied into a fragrant package of honest middle-age. It didn't take me long to sign her up as Claudia's mother, and for once, John Golden was in wholehearted accord. She was a "name." He also approved John Williams as the Englishman, but the casting of Bertha found us at odds again. "You want a big fat comfortable character woman. Someone the audience is going to recognize as a servant in the house," John instructed me.

"I want Adrienne Gessner," I said. Adrienne was small, even dainty, with chiselled features, a soft Austrian accent, imbued with the aristocracy of the European stage. I was aware that this group of competent and knowing performers could have undermined an inexperienced young actress at every point, indeed Mr. Golden prophesied glumly that they were going to "make her look like a monkey," but it is one of the happier stories of the theatre that they supported her unstintingly, and lent her validity and confidence.

Trusting them as I did, I was obsessed by none of the worries that contribute to the traditional first-night jitters, and polished off a large lobster before the curtain went up at Wilmington. I remember "Dixie" staring at me with a sickly yellow expression on his face as he struggled to down a bowl of crackers and milk. Even Bill couldn't bring himself to join me in the lobster, and settled on scrambled eggs, and as for John Golden, he elected to hear the disastrous outcome of the opening at his home in Long Island. Everyone but me—and a little bit of Bill—seemed morbidly convinced that the play was doomed to failure.

"If it doesn't go over," I gave the cast a last-minute talk, "you've done the best you could, and we've all had a good time

s

doing it, so just relax, and if you fluff or forget your lines, don't worry. That's why I've put a bowl of chocolates on the desk, so that you can eat your way out of it, if you do."

Nobody had to eat the sweets, so I guess everything went off better than anyone expected. John Golden gathered his courage and promised to meet us in Washington. We played only a split week in Wilmington, and on Sunday afternoon, Bill and I started off on what should have been a relatively short drive to the capital. It was then, and only then, that I began to get stage-fright. We had been invited, with Missy, to stay at the White House during the try-out, and now that the visit was imminent, it loomed up more as an ordeal than a pleasurable experience. Missy had had to bow out because of ill health, but she'd told us before we'd left New York that Mrs. Roosevelt expected us just the same.

I'd never met Mrs. Roosevelt, so I didn't fool myself that the invitation was anything but a courtesy to Missy, who was always a great favourite at the White House, no matter who was President. "If only we could get out of it," I kept moaning to Bill, and sure enough, halfway to Washington, it looked for a while as if my prayer was to be granted. Out of what was actually a clear sky, we slid into one of the worst sleet storms that had ever hit that area. To say that the road was a sheet of ice is an understatement. The wheels of the car skidded drunkenly from side to side, as if controlled by some mindless demon. Traffic blocked into a solid mass for as far as we could see ahead, and February roared its bitter venom against the setting sun, adding darkness to the peril that inched along beside us.

"We've gone six-tenths of a mile in an hour and forty minutes," Bill remarked tightly. "Keep your eye out for any place that looks as if it might have a phone and I'll try to steer over to it so that you can tell Mrs. Roosevelt we can't make it."

I responded with appropriate if hypocritical regret and finally spied the flickering lights of a wayside diner. A couple of other cars slid towards it, too, and I had to wait my turn at a slot machine on a wall beside the cash register. There was a lot of noise so that I couldn't keep my end of the conversation as discreetly lowered as I would have liked. The cashier snickered when I asked the operator to connect me with the White House, and then a couple of other people snickered as I ran out of nickels and dimes waiting for the proper intermediary to deliver my message to the First Lady. At long last, a feminine voice, wavy but pleasant, greeted me by name, and assuming the courtesy to be that of a well-trained secretary, I tendered my explanation and apologies for our absence.

"But you must come right along, my dear, whenever you can," the voice enjoined me. "We're not dining for another hour, and it doesn't matter in the least how late you are. It's really a dreadful storm, so don't hurry. I was sorry to hear about Missy not being well enough to come, but Franklin and I are so looking forward to having you and your husband. . . ."

Bill reached over to open the car door for me. "What's the matter?" he was quick to notice my dejection. "Telephone lines down?"

"The telephone line is working perfectly," I told him bitingly, "and Franklin is looking forward to meeting us. She answered the phone herself."

I was yet to realize that whenever she was within earshot of it, Eleanor Roosevelt always answered the telephone herself. It was one of the immediate bonds between us.

It was after ten o'clock when we drove up to the White House gates, past the guard who nodded us on our way. I don't thrill easily, but I think if I hadn't been so dishevelled and cold, I would have experienced a very real flutter of excitement as we walked up the wide steps of the loveliest mansion in the world. "Here comes 'Mr. Crim' to welcome us," Bill said in an undertone. Bill had been a frequent visitor at the White House when Calvin Coolidge was President, so I wasn't surprised when the stately old usher recognized him and greeted him by name. I loved "Mr. Crim" at once—he reminded me of James, but my panic mounted as I saw our luggage being lifted from the car. "You've got to get us out of staying overnight," I whispered to Bill in agitation. "I want to take a bath and relax and go to sleep

in a hotel room, or I'll never get through the opening tomorrow."
Mrs. Roosevelt, however, had other plans for me. I remember
her saying, "This is the best hotel in Washington. You're staying
right here where you can have quiet and privacy."

The only other thing that I remember about that evening was
that we arrived in the middle of some sort of a large supper party—
I forget what the occasion was—but Marian Anderson sang, and I
was seated at a small table opposite Jane Cowl. We recognized
each other from the casting days of *Fortnight*, but Miss Cowl,
famous for her gentle glamour and the incessant, graceful swishing
of her handkerchief, had not fancied herself in a mother rôle, and
I agreed at the time that she would not have been right for the
part. Now, with a gracious smile that bore no malice, she leaned
across the expanse of white damask. "And how," she asked me,
"did your little play go over in Wilmington?"

Diminutives set my teeth on edge, except in permissible
application to puppies, kittens and babies. Applied to a play, the
inference carries a stiletto edged with poison, and in my already
jaundiced state of mind, Miss Cowl, with everyone else, had
sweetly relegated *Claudia* to the doom of theatrical inconsequence.
"We got good reviews, but you can't tell on a try-out," I
replied, with neither distinction nor assurance, and wished I was
back on the farm where I had known more peace and happiness
than I had ever thought to find again in my life. Oddly enough,
though, Bill's attitude repeated a familiar pattern. I couldn't say
he was stage-struck, exactly, yet he'd devoted his entire time to
being with me during all the various phases of my renewed fling
at the theatre. John Golden had remarked upon it—pleasantly,
because he liked Bill, but pointedly, because he was puzzled.
"Say, hasn't that guy of yours got a job of his own to do in
Lyme?" Yes, he did have a job to do both on his new novel and
the management of what had now grown into a flourishing dairy
and poultry enterprise, but I didn't admit to John that I was
almost as disturbed as he was at my husband's willingness to
spend his days quietly watching rehearsals from the front, or
being a passive participant in all the many business discussions
that took place during the launching of the play. Out of fairness

to him, I'd hesitantly mentioned John's reaction the evening before we left for Wilmington. "I think you ought to know . . ." I'd ended rather falteringly.

"I know."

"And you don't mind what anyone thinks?" I'd stared at him in wonder.

"Why should I?"

"You shouldn't," I admitted, with an incredulous admiration for his indifference as to how he might appear to others. I had already learned from this second marriage that trust, however blind, is the foundation of a sound relationship, and although I was baffled at his sanguine acceptance of the rôle of the "author's husband," I felt an implicit confidence that he would not violate my respect for his manhood, any more than he had let me down during the months of my sister's illness when he had remained in Hollywood and made no effort to find another film assignment on his own. It was only when he had presented to me the finished manuscript of *Rush to the Sun*, that I realized that the limitation was mine in having expected him to adhere to my particular conception of male functioning. . . .

"And is that handsome young man you came in with, your new husband?"

The question was not so much an interruption of my thoughts as an exaggeration of the subtle problems that nagged at bits and corners of my mind when vigilance gave way to vulnerability. I knew that I was over-sensitive in feeling that Miss Cowl was being less innocent than arch, so I let the "young" and the "handsome" go unchallenged, since neither attribute could be denied. "He's not so terribly new, we've been married several years," I said, and immediately wished that I could have risen above this childish defence.

"Dear me, how time does fly," Miss Cowl remarked. "I remember your darling little boys the afternoon I came to that nice apartment on Central Park West. They must be quite grown up."

"Yes. Paul's in the Army."

"It was never produced, was it?"

"*Fortnight*?—No."

"Well, that's the theatre, my dear." She waved her handkerchief. "I do hope you have better luck with this one. And if I weren't leaving for New York on the midnight train, I wouldn't miss your opening for all the tea in China. I shall have to dash back to my hotel to pack directly the party is over. Can I give you a lift in my taxi? Where are you staying?"

"Thank you, we have the car," I almost told her that from the way things looked, we'd probably have to be staying at the White House. But I didn't. You didn't use that kind of hospitality to serve your own ends. When the cast discovered the next morning that we hadn't checked in at the hotel, we merely said that we were stopping with friends at 1600 Pennsylvania Avenue, and only John Golden, who kept his word about coming to Washington, pulled us up short. "What do you mean, '1600 Pennsylvania Avenue'?" he bellowed. "That's the White House! Bring me some stationery from there, or better yet, get me invited to dinner!"

We weren't stationery stealers, and to the best of my recollection, he got himself invited, and I think his shameless persistence was the beginning of his long friendship with Mrs. Roosevelt.

Our first visit to the White House was when mine started, too. I couldn't help but respond to this warm and gracious woman—too warm, too gracious, sometimes for her own good. I learned much about her from Malvina Thompson, who very nearly worshipped her. We had long talks together in her small, cluttered office off the big, wide family hall, where Mrs. Roosevelt had breakfast with us every morning. I remember one thing about those breakfasts—the President's wife automatically bending to pick up my napkin every time it slipped from my lap to the floor, which happened with embarrassing frequency inasmuch as I'm a napkin dropper from way back.

At dinner, I always sat next to the President himself, and I was greatly impressed by his being so genuinely interested in how the play was going. In my ignorance, I thought it was going fine, but I didn't know until long afterwards, how near we'd come to closing down at the end of our two weeks in Washington, and I recount, without malice, exactly what happened, simply because I think it's a funny story. We were rehearsing *Outrageous Fortune* when our company manager happened to ask me, one day, if I knew that John Golden had tried to bribe the critics in Wilmington to give bad notices to the play and Dorothy Maguire, so that he could induce me to do some rewriting and open in New York with Frances Farmer. I said I not only hadn't heard of it, but I didn't believe it, and nothing would ever make me believe it of John. However, my faith, if not my affection, might have needed a little bolstering, because I repeated the unlikely bit of gossip to an associate in John's office. "Bribe the critics in Wilmington? Ridiculous! Why, John didn't even go to Wilmington," he denied vociferously, "there's not a word of truth in that story!"

I was about to say, with contrition not unmixed with relief, that I was sure there wasn't a word of truth in it, when he added reflectively, "In Washington, yes. But not in Wilmington."

And still I loved John Golden, even though I couldn't like him. I despised the shabby way he'd treat an actor who desperately needed work. "We'll take him. He's got wrinkles in his belly, we can get him for peanuts."—The Toronto road company was full of just those wrinkles, yet he showed me a diamond-studded gold box he'd ordered for Gertrude Lawrence's birthday. "Damn piece of junk cost me over a thousand dollars," he announced proudly, and I didn't doubt that it cost every penny of it. I thought, "If only he'd give Clarence that five dollar raise he's been asking for. . . ."

A strange man, John Golden. The most delightful, horrible, lovable rascal I've ever known.

The play began to jell with its first matinée audience, and by the end of the try-out, the performances were smooth and easy, and we had successfully weathered a small intermediary crisis of plugging for laughs. Olga Baclonova was the worst offender, with the flashing part of the opera singer offering too much temptation to resist. "If you don't bring the house down every time you open your mouth," I promised her, "I'll see if I can't wheedle Mr. Golden into letting you have a mink coat if we go over in New York." Olga was mad about furs, and the meagre silver fox stole she had to wear was destroying her—John was not a spendthrift when it came to dressing his shows. And he got away easy with this one, a maid's uniform, and only a single change of street-suit for Frances Starr, who didn't appear in the second act on account of having X-rays at the doctor's, and the same costume for Claudia's sister-in-law, first act and last. Dorothy wore an inexpensive, but entirely appropriate skirt and sweater throughout most of the play, but since a fifty-seven fifty actress didn't rate a maid to keep her pressed and tidy, she was soon bagging out in a most unbecoming fashion.

"For Chrissake," John stormed, "get her out of that knitted stuff! What am I paying good money for to have this show dressed! Look at her!"

"I'll buy her another outfit myself," I smoothed him down.

Dorothy was delighted at the idea of a new dress, and on the morning of our opening night in New York (we'd returned from the tour only the previous day, which was Sunday) we started off on a shopping expedition. She skipped along beside me, giving vent, every so often, to her pleasure in the tub of butter into which she finally realized that she had tumbled—Miss Liberty Jones having already gasped her last breath. "Oh, Miss Franken, what a glory day!" Miss Dorothy Maguire kept chirping. "What a glory day!"

I had not been aware, until the sudden collapse of my patience, that I might have been germinating a mild case of nerves.

"Dorothy if you don't say 'glorious' I'll swat you one!" I protested hoarsely, and over an ice-cream soda repented my outburst. "I have a sudden feeling," I said soberly, "that even if the play flops, *Claudia* is going to make a star out of you, and I don't want to be responsible for a success that might stand between you and happiness. If you let it."

She opened her blue eyes wide. "Whatever do you mean, Miss Franken?"

"Promise me you won't get a swell-head, or lose your sense of values," I phrased my sentiments in more explicit terms. "Being a star will never keep you warm nights. Get married, have children, and if the stage gets in the way, forget it."

Her lovely eyes grew wider, if possible, and it was one of those things you're sorry you began the minute you've begun. I paid for the sodas, and we finished our shopping. Having studied Dorothy's figure behind the footlights, I decided that one of those full-skirted crisp little peasant dresses with straps coming up over a frilly white blouse might answer the more obvious of John's objections. It did. Indeed the new frock became part of the Maguire legend, and if there was a little too much of an Alice-in-Wonderland look in her get-up, I firmly made up my mind to keep my mouth shut about it.

Our dress-rehearsal was scheduled for three o'clock, but on account of setting up the stage and the lights, we had to start the first act in the lobby below—a usual, but highly unsatisfactory procedure. By five o'clock, however, we were on set and well on to the end of the third act, with everyone in high good humour and no one complaining of butterflies in the stomach. Bill and I sat in the front watching the smooth meshing of the play uneasily. There were a lot of theatre adages you could laugh at, but not quite ignore, such as moving scenery in the rain, and a bad dress-rehearsal auguring a good opening performance. So far there wasn't a hitch. "We'll be lucky if it goes half as well tonight," I whispered at the closing curtain. And then, all at once, it happened. Or could I be sure that it happened? I leaned over to whisper to Bill again. "Did you see what I saw?"

His voice came out of the darkness in sepulchral gloom. "I saw. What are you going to do about it?"

"Take it out of course."

The lights went up. I climbed the small ladder to the stage. Frances Starr, who had never caused me a moment's pain, hurried towards me, her sweet face aglow. "Did you notice the little bit of business that suddenly came to me? Isn't it the perfect touch? And so natural, just that tiny stagger across the stage as I say good-bye and go upstairs. It tells the audience the whole tragic story that Mrs. Brown is never going to come down those stairs again."

I started to explain to her that I didn't want the play to end on a note of tragedy, but I simply couldn't command the brutality to deprive her of a heartbreaking exit that she'd thought up all by herself. She had my mother's blue eyes and flaxen hair. How could I hurt her?

I telephoned John after the rehearsal. He was at his home in Long Island and intended to stay there, as he was too cowardly ever to attend his Broadway openings.

"How'd it go, Rosie?"

"We have a stagger, Johnnie."

I didn't have to say another word—John's lively comprehension was one of his most endearing attributes. He merely said, "Tough luck, Rosie, it's the old Belasco touch coming out at the last minute and I'm afraid you're stuck with it."

"I will not bring the final curtain down on a stagger," I told him firmly.

"Look. Take the advice of an old man and leave it be. It's too late to try to change it now, you'd only upset her."

"I won't upset her, but that stagger is going to come out."

"How?"

"I don't know yet."

He didn't argue the point. "Rosie, I'm warning you," he said seriously, "don't try to fight Belasco's ghost."

"You'd better listen to him," Bill added his warning after I'd hung up.

"And be a sitting target for the critics to damn my little play as soap-opera? A soupy exit isn't going to do Frances any good as an actress, either."

At seven-thirty that evening, I still hadn't hit upon a painless removal of the stagger. We dressed early, allowing overselves time to stop off at the Waldorf to see Missy, who was laid up again with a return of the low-grade fever that had kept her from going to Washington with us. To our anxious eyes, she seemed to be slowly losing ground, but now, as always, her indomitable will refused to acknowledge the handicaps of a fragile body, and she continued to carry on a full work programme from her bed.

Her face brightened when she saw us. She lifted my hand to her lips. "How I wish I could be there tonight," she said wistfully. "I'm so proud of my beautiful daughter."

It was one of her tender exaggerations, for beautiful I wasn't, with my broken nose unfixed. "I only look as if I look beautiful," I explained. "I'm wearing my chinchillas for luck, and I dug up this old Hollywood dinner gown that's so out of fashion it gives the impression of being ahead of fashion."

"No matter, you look just grand anyway," Geraldine spoke up from the other side of the room. Geraldine was God's gift to Missy—personal maid, cook, and nurse, combined into a single package of Irish devotion. "But one thing is missing, if you don't mind my mentioning it," she ventured diffidently. "You must have forgotten your pearls in the excitement."

"I didn't forget them, I haven't any," I told her cheerfully.

"Then wear mine," she offered on an impulse of pure generosity. "A person's neck seems sort of naked without beads I always say. Especially with bare shoulders and all."

Before I could convince her that I rarely wore jewellery of any kind, she had removed a string of large, uniform globules from her own neck. "Here. Put them on and see the difference they make," she urged.

I drew back instinctively. "No, please, I couldn't. I mean I might lose them," I amended in haste.

"Small loss if you did, a dollar ninety-eight is all I paid for them. Here, let me do the fastening then you won't have to lift your arms."

Like Frances, I couldn't bear to hurt her. "Thank you," I murmured. "I'll be very careful of them."

I intended to take them off in the taxi on the way to the theatre, but I suppose I was thinking about that stagger and it completely slipped my mind both then and afterwards. We'd overstayed our time with Missy and first-night crowds were thronging the lobby and the pavement when we got there. Bill loitered to give the policeman's horse a lump of sugar, but I raced on ahead through the stage entrance. "I've just had an idea!" I yelled to him. "Dixie has a couple of seats saved for us in the last row, I'll meet you there!"

[283]

Don, Frances and Dorothy had already taken their places on the set. They greeted my dressy appearance with an astonishment that wasn't entirely flattering. Don gave one of his famous double-takes accompanied by a low whistle, Frances exclaimed, "Rose, what a magnificent coat!" and Dorothy crooned over my gorgeous pearls. "We didn't recognize you at first," she confided.

"Thanks," I said, "but save your compliments until later, and give me one minute to re-stage the last scene of the last act. . . ."

From the way they recoiled in horror, I might just as well have thrown a hand-grenade into their midst, and indeed I knew I was committing a cardinal sin in ringing in any sort of a change, no matter how minor, a scant fifteen minutes before a Broadway opening.

"Miss Franken, it would upset me!" Dorothy wailed.

"I'd be willing to try anything *tomorrow*," Frances protested in agitation, "but not now!"

Only Don maintained a semblance of equilibrium in the face of my unorthodox request. "If you two would shut up, I'd like to hear what it is," he said.

"I want to play the closing scene at the foot of the stairs instead of in the middle of the stage."

"Good." His eye caught mine, and I could see that he'd got the point, and that I could count on him as an ally. "I like it," he said. "I felt embarrassed while Frances took that long walk across to the steps."

"It didn't feel long to me," Frances demurred.

"And I didn't feel embarrassed," Dorothy objected mutinously. (Young actresses learn fast to covet centre-stage.)

"Take my word for it, this is better," Don said firmly, and put an end to the argument by pushing them to the new position.

"I believe I do feel more comfortable having the balustrade to put my hand on," Frances acknowledged. "How does it look?"

"Let's see how it plays," I deferred cagily.

Time was running out. I could hear a mounting rumble behind the asbestos curtain as I watched her mount the bottom stair to deliver her farewell line. Then she started up the remaining steps, faltering into the first indication of a stagger a hair's breadth out of sight-line of the audience. It played exactly as I'd intended it should.

Ignominiously, I hurried from the stage, avoiding the wicked grin on Don's face, and I only hope, if Frances ever reads this, that she will forgive us our conspiracy. If she weren't such a nice person I wouldn't have tried to let her have her cake and eat it, too.

The house lights had dimmed to half, but Olga Baclonova was lying in wait for me in the wings. She didn't make her entrance until the second act, and I'd been aware of her, standing in bathrobe and curlers, watching the proceedings avidly. "Miss Franken!" she hissed, clutching at me, "could I ask you something a minute?"

I concluded that she wanted to make hay and with some last-minute change in her own part, but instead, she imprisoned my arm and ran her fingers over my sleeve with the glint of the fur maniac in her eyes. "It isn't real chinchilla, is it, Miss Franken?"

Oh, dear, I thought, could it be that my poor little bunnies had finally met their Waterloo? I hesitated, torn between loyalty and my ineptitude as a liar. "Real chinchilla?" I echoed with an enigmatic smile. "Oh come now, Olga, what do *you* think?"

I disengaged myself from her grasp, and for all I know, she's still thinking about it.

I realized one thing, though. I had lived contentedly for half my life without hankering for a string of pearls, but the time had come when I could no longer afford to wear priceless furs with a naked neck, as Geraldine put it. After I read the reviews the next morning, I headed for a jewellery shop on Fifth Avenue, and selected a lovely double necklace, reposing in a velvet box. I tried them on.

"They suit you perfectly, madam," the salesman assured me. "And you say they're only cultured?"

"Madam, if these were real they'd be worth a king's ransom, and you can believe me, madam, to the average person, it's virtually impossible to tell the difference."

"I do believe you," I murmured. "How soon can you make a delivery?"

"In town?"

"Yes. The Waldorf."

"Immediately, madam. By special messenger."

I couldn't remember Geraldine's last name, so I sent the pearls care of Missy, hoping that the velvet box would atone for their not being quite as large as the ones she'd bought for herself.

With the first week's box-office receipts, John hired a mink coat to replace Olga's silver-fox and told me to engage a special understudy for Dorothy, instead of relying on the general understudy, who was geared to jump from wig to wig in case of emergency. "And while you're at it," he added, in sheepish admission that the play was a success, "you might as well get busy on a Chicago company."

I had been hoping to return to a normal existence on the farm, but instead I began a new search for another Claudia. I came up with two very young actresses—both unknown, and both named Phyllis. Phyllis Thaxter was as cleanly fragrant as a bar of good, unscented soap, and Phyllis Walker was downright beautiful. "At least you've picked yourself some glamour this time," John complimented me. But he was so loath to admit that critics and public alike had fallen in love with Dorothy, that I took a perverse pleasure in telling him that it was the little Thaxter girl whom I had chosen as Dorothy's successor.

"Good God, Rosie, you mean to say you're wasting the other one's looks on an understudy part?"

"It's a pity, but I have to."

"Damn it, why do you have to?"

"Because Phyllis Walker happens to be married, and has two children."

"And since when are you against marriage?"

"I'm all for it, but Claudia doesn't grow up into being a wife until the last line of the play, and Phyllis Walker is too emotionally complete to make all that wide-eyed immaturity convincing."

"So you're going to use a girl who hasn't got a goddam thing in her favour except innocence?"

"Stop hollering, that's a lot in her favour."

"What good does it do me to holler?" he subsided glumly.
"You're as stubborn as they come. But I haven't forgotten that
you pulled the goddamdest trick in show business with that
stagger——"

"I'm not proud of it, and I'd like to forget it," I interrupted.

"Well, I'm proud of it, and I'm going to give you a chance to
pull another one. This is Saturday. If you're so set on Thaxter, I'll
go along with you. Put her in the matinée next Wednesday, and
let's see what we've got in her—if anything."

I couldn't believe at first that he was serious, that he actually
expected a child whose major stage experience consisted of a walk-
on part of the maid in *There Shall Be No Night* to appear before a
Broadway audience without the weeks of indoctrination and
rehearsals that Dorothy had enjoyed. "If you weren't the veteran
producer of 'Clean, Holesome American Plays'," I replied
scathingly, "I would tell you exactly what I think of you and your
sadistic proposal. But I'll call your bluff. I'll take her to the farm
with us tonight and work with her up there until Wednesday
morning."

"It's a deal, Mrs. Svengali. If she falls on her face, it'll save us
a lot of pain, and it won't hurt business for one matinée."

"She won't fall on her face," I asserted with more bravado
than I felt. I didn't dare warn Phyllis about the ordeal that lay
ahead of her until she'd had a good night's rest, and a nourishing
breakfast. Then I wooed her outdoors into a warm, sunny
morning, and pointed across the lawn with a bright, cheery smile,
full of mesmerism. "Look over there."

She looked. "My goodness, you've got the whole set laid out
on the grass, furniture and all!"

"That's so that you'll be accustomed to the real stage set by
Wednesday."

"Wednesday?"

"Yes, Mr. Golden wants you to play Claudia on the matinée,"
I mentioned casually.

"I couldn't!" she gasped. "I don't even know the lines."

"You're a quick study, there's nothing to it," I bolstered her
against collapse. "You can wear the sweater and skirt you have on,

[287]

and I've got a negligée we can drape round you for your sexy scene."

"I'd just die!" she quavered. "I couldn't get through it, I know I couldn't."

"Nonsense!" I said.

By Tuesday evening she was letter-perfect in the part, and she had mastered the moves and the handling of props. "You're going to be wonderful," I promised her. "The cast has a call for one o'clock tomorrow, and all you need is a quick run-through with them to get used to their voices. Don't worry about anything, put everything out of your mind, and go to bed."

"You'd better get to bed yourself," Bill advised me.

"I will," I said wearily.

I was almost asleep when John telephoned that the whole project was off. "Maguire just told Dixie during the last intermission that she has talked to her agent and there's nothing in her contract that says she has to let anybody else play her part as long as she's able to perform. And Equity will back her up."

The unworthy thought occurred to me that John had been aware of this situation all along, and now, at the last moment, he was using it as an excuse to back out of having started something he didn't want to finish. "To hell with her contract, she damn well ought to give another young actress the same break she had," he added with such ferocity that I knew I had misjudged him. "Why don't you call her yourself, and see if you can talk her into it?"

I gave Dorothy time to return to her apartment. It wasn't difficult to persuade her. "I'll do it, but I'll only do it because you're asking me to, Miss Franken," she gave in magnanimously.

I thanked her for her unselfish gesture, but my feelings were mixed. Her refusal might have been a good way out to save all our faces.

To the few of us who knew the facts, little Phyllis Thaxter made theatrical history that Wednesday matinée. At the end of the first act John said excitedly, "I'm going back-stage with a contract before anyone else grabs her, she's a great little trouper!"

At the end of the second act he had corralled a couple of photographers and reporters, and the next day the newspapers carried Phyllis's picture and the story that John Golden had discovered another unknown young actress to launch into stardom.

I'm not minimizing John's inordinate flair for publicity. For all his noisy barking, he had the bite of a highly skilled producer, and if it weren't for his canny business management and exploitation, I doubt that *Claudia* would have enjoyed a long Broadway run with a return engagement and two flourishing road companies. His ingenuity was boundless, although occasionally embarrassing. I winced at the spectacle of Elsie the Cow (rented from Borden's Milk Company), holding court in Shubert Alley, but it was the kind of blatant promotion that stimulated a lively interest among the picture companies. We had any number of offers, yet I voted to sell the property to David Selznick for twenty thousand dollars less than Warner Brothers bid for it, not only because Mr. Selznick had distinguished himself with *Gone with the Wind*, but also because he was willing to cast Dorothy Maguire as Claudia, whereas other studios preferred an established star.

"It's my money you're throwing out as well as your own, but it's your play, Rosie," John gave in resignedly.

After the contract was signed, Mr. Selznick asked me to make film tests of Dorothy and Phyllis Thaxter. Poor little Phyllis Walker looked so wistful at not being included that I made one of her too, and sent it on to the coast with the others. All three tests were fruitful. Dorothy's marked the beginning of her film career, Phyllis Thaxter was immediately signed up by Metro-Goldwyn-Mayer, but Phyllis Walker outdid them both. She became Mrs. David Selznick.

Often, in the years that followed, I wondered about her, and the rôle that Claudia had played in her destiny. Then, at the theatre several months ago, one of our guests whispered, "Don't look now, but isn't that Jennifer Jones a few rows behind us?"

It was, and it wasn't, for to me the girl who waved and smiled back at me was just the old Phyllis Walker, as lovely and unspoiled as ever, though perhaps a little sadder and wiser. During

T   [289]

the interval, when we met in the aisle, I knew that I was right, success and fame had not too greatly changed her.

The next day I received a lovely sheaf of flowers. The card read, With love and thanks, Jennifer.

It was one of the more rewarding moments that occasionally happen in that alien world behind the footlights.

With three American companies of *Claudia* in full swing and also English and Australian productions in preparation, I finally felt free to go back to Lyme with Bill. December 7th had come and passed, war had been declared, and we could no longer afford to run the place on an absentee basis. We had already lost two farmhands to the draft.

Early in November, Paul had taken a convoy down to Fort Bragg for manœuvres, but now he had returned to Quincy, with a ten-day leave in store for him. On the morning before his arrival, while I was getting his room ready for him, Bill came to the door. "I'm going over to Storrs, so don't count on me for lunch."

I always liked to be in on those periodic trips to the agricultural college. "It's snowing," I said. "Can't you put it off?"

"Come along with me now, why not?" he read my motive. "You can finish what you're doing this afternoon."

I returned a box of civilian odds and ends to the top shelf of the cupboard and closed the door. I said, without meaning or wanting to say it, "I won't be here this afternoon. If I hurry, I can catch the eleven o'clock train to Quincy."

"Quincy?" he echoed blankly. "What for?"

"I have to see Paul."

He gave me a friendly whack. "Cut out the fooling, and let's get started while the roads are clear."

"Bill, I'm not fooling. I'm not going with you, I'm going to Quincy."

He stared at me. "I think you actually mean it!"

"I do."

"Look, darling, Paul will be here tomorrow for two whole weeks. Remember?" He spoke slowly, patiently, as if reasoning with a child. I felt like a child, obedient to an impulse beyond my comprehension. "I remember," I said. "But I have to go anyway, and don't ask me why, because I don't know why. All I know is that I suddenly want to go to Quincy."

His patience gave out. "I'm leaving." He turned at the door.

"You're too young and too old to behave like this," he said in a cold voice. "If you don't snap out of this insane whim, and if you're not here when I come back, there's going to be trouble."

I didn't have to ask him what kind of trouble. I had an idea it would be bad trouble, but it didn't matter. I began packing my overnight bag.

I heard the savage skitter of gravel as his car circled the driveway, and a short while later I heard the car drive in again. He stalked back into the room. In ominous silence, his lips set in a grim line, he stripped off his lumberjack and yanked a suit from its hanger. "Why are you changing your clothes?" I asked meekly.

"Because I'm a jackass married to an idiot," he ground out between his teeth. "Rather than worry about you, I'll use a week's quota of petrol to drive you up on the assumption that you're not mentally capable of getting there by yourself."

I was both touched and appalled. "You'd better let me go alone on the train," I begged him. "If you take me, you'll only get madder and madder at me on the way."

"You can say that again," he promised with relish.

It was a ghastly trip over icy roads and through high mounds of drifting snow. When we reached Quincy it was after seven. The Army base looked lonely, with dim lights from the barracks flickering eerily through the darkness. Bill rolled down the window of the car to call to a young private who was hurrying towards the gates. "Could you tell me where we can find Lieutenant Paul Franken?"

"Yes, sir, I'm in his platoon, sir, but I'm afraid he's off on leave."

"He can't be, he wasn't supposed to go until tomorrow morning!" I protested on a gasp of horror.

"I'll see, ma'am, if he's still here. Who shall I tell him if he is?"

"His mother," I said faintly.

Bill couldn't resist the obvious. "It'll serve you bloody well right," he said, "if we're stuck up here in this blizzard while he's down at the farm waiting for us."

Miserably I agreed that it would, but just the same I couldn't bear to think of it. I huddled back into the cold leather seat, and nearly prayed.

"It's your dumb luck he hasn't gone yet."

Relief and thankfulness welled within me as I leaned forward to peer out at a familiar figure hurrying towards us. Humility vanished like sleet in the sun. "See?" I triumphed. "Now I know why I wanted to come, the three of us can drive back and if we're stuck, we'll all be stuck together."

Paul put a quick end to any such idea. "Mother, for God's sake, this isn't a kindergarten, this is the United States Army. I go on leave when I'm scheduled to go on leave and that's tomorrow morning and not a minute earlier!" He turned his fury on Bill. "Why in hell did you bring her, when you knew I was coming home—you're as much to blame as she is!"

"Being married to her is contagious," Bill acknowledged bitterly.

I tried to keep my teeth from chattering in a combination of chill and chagrin, so that I could remind them that I was older than they were and entitled to a degree of respect, when suddenly the same young private reappeared.

"Lieutenant Franken, Captain Griswold wants to see you right away."

"Be back in a minute," Paul growled at us.

It was a great deal longer than a minute before he came back. He didn't say anything, he just opened the door of the car and climbed in beside us. In the small radius of light from the dashboard, I saw that his face was pale and strained with a new kind of tension and when he finally spoke the anger had drained from his voice. "There's a coffee shop nearby," he said. "Captain Griswold's given me fifteen minutes to have a bite of supper with you." He cleared his throat. "Sort of a good thing you came after all, because my leave has been cancelled."

Disappointment crowded my throat. "But they can't do that!"

In answer, I felt the fleeting pressure of his hand on mine. "They can, mother. The order just came through that we're shipping out at midnight."

Shipping out! The words echoed back a hollow finality. "Where?"

"Destination unknown, but nothing to worry about. Tell Mother, Bill, that there's nothing to worry about."

Nothing to worry about. His regiment was the first to go overseas, and weeks passed before a cable reached us from "Somewhere-in-Australia." *All well. Arrived safely. Love. Paul.*

That night in Quincy was the last time I saw him for nearly four long years.

It was only a short while after the cable came that I was called to Washington with a group of journalists to be apprised of certain grim facts that were, for the present, being kept from the American people. Within the four walls of General Arnold's private office, he told us bluntly that our troops in Australia were lacking ammunition and equipment, and their plight was desperate. The Japanese were sinking our hospital ships at Darwin, and massing for an attack behind the Coral Reefs off the opposite coast of Townsville.

I remember the terrible quietness of my body, and having to stay quiet so as not to unleash the agony inside of me. I believe it was Russel Crouse who finally whispered to the General that I had a son in the South Pacific. I recall that he was a very kind man, for he was deeply concerned at having spoken so freely in my presence. "I'd rather know than not know," I told him.

It was a hard day to live through, but hard days lay ahead for many American women. We hadn't learned to accept the ruthless slaughter of our sons and husbands as the British and the French had learned. Nor were we forced to live with the horror of war lurking in our skies and at our shores. We remained civilians to the very end, safe from the threat of bombings and destruction.

Not that anyone was safe, anywhere. Grief played no favourites.

Carole Lombard perished on a mission of mercy, and a circus tent collapsed one sunny afternoon in Hartford. Some of the men in Paul's battery lost wives and children in that tragedy, and others sweated out an eternity of hours, waiting for the final casualty lists to reach them in a far-off land. Darkness seemed to have descended upon the whole earth.

Paul had sailed in February and it wasn't until the beginning of April that his first letter arrived. It was so heavily censored that we could only read between the few short lines that he was stationed in a small village on the northern coast of Australia. "I'm feeling fine, and everything is very quiet." How could he have guessed that I knew from that session in General Arnold's office that the "quiet little village" was Townsville, base headquarters for reconnaissance flights into Port Moresby, and strategic target for a Japanese attack?

"Townsville is protected by the Coral Reefs," Bill showed me on the map.

I wanted desperately to believe him, but fear stayed with me and haunted me every waking moment. I tried to find forgetfulness in work, sandwiching farm and household chores with intensive hours at the typewriter until I was tired enough to fall into bed at night and sleep from sheer exhaustion. I suppose it was evasion, in a way, but sometimes creation is accomplished in escape, and I realize, in retrospect, that the war years, and those directly following the war, were the most consistently productive of my haphazard writing career. I realize also that I might have made more of a splash in the literary world had I strait-jacketed my efforts into excelling as a dramatist, or a novelist, or even a short-story writer, but either I had too much ego or not enough ego to aim for prominence in any one medium. Bill was guilty of much the same philosophy. We tackled anything and everything that challenged our interest, including radio, films, and later, television. Between us we earned an incredible amount of money, most of which the government took. For once, I held no grudge against that much maligned Bureau of Internal Revenue. The more we paid over to it, the happier I was to think that we were helping to meet the needs of our fighting men. (I feel obliged to add that once the war had been paid for, I got mad at taxes all over again.)

Neither of us, in these days, entertained the slightest snootiness towards Hollywood, although no amount of money could induce us, at this stage of our lives, to accept a screen assignment. (Again honesty compels me to admit that our services have not been wildly in demand in recent years.) However, at the time that David Selznick bought *Claudia*, he was anxious to pin us down to conferring with him during the following winter, when he expected to begin work on the picture. But suddenly he revised his schedule, and urgently requested our presence on the coast early in April.

"He can't release the film version while the play is running, so what's his rush?" I objected.

Bill said he didn't know, but that a change of scene would do me good. He wasn't in the mood for a holiday any more than I was, but nevertheless we tried to make the best of it.

"Take along your chinchilla coat, it might save arguments at a story conference," he said.

"And my pearls," I added heavily.

It was our last feeble attempt at humour. The second day on the train news of the Coral Sea Battle broke over the radio. For the remainder of that endless nightmare across the country, we scarcely ate or slept. We sat in the lounge car listening in frozen silence to Drew Pearson's unremitting broadcasts that finally prepared the American people for the annihilation of our troops stationed at Townsville behind the ineffectual barrier of the Coral Reefs. General Arnold's dire prophecy had come to pass, and for the first time since Paul's departure Bill could offer me no words of comfort.

And then the miracle happened, like the other miracles that happened later on at Oro Bay, and the Kadota Trail and the Bismarck Islands. *Coral Sea Disaster Averted. United States Air Force Destroys Japanese Fleet Massing for Invasion of Townsville. Army Casualties Light.* Those were the headlines that greeted us as we stepped off the train into the hazy sunlight of a Los Angeles morning. The relief was so shattering that for a while I couldn't speak. I felt Bill's arm around me, giving me once more the strength to hope, and the dignity of acceptance.

"Even if Paul is among those casualties, think of all the mothers' sons who have been saved," I said with difficulty. "How long before we'll know anything?"

His arm tightened. "Not long. But he's all right.—I'm entitled to feelings too."

The telephone was ringing as we entered the hotel suite. It was David Selznick, saying how sorry he was that he'd been unable to meet us. "I sent my car and chauffeur, I hope he wasn't late——"

"No, he was at the station. Thank you."

"Is your accommodation comfortable? If not, don't hesitate to say so, and I'll have it changed."

I glanced at the large elegant drawing-room, glimpsing the sumptuous bedroom beyond. "I'm sure we'll be very comfortable."

A short silence fell between us. Finally, he said, clearing his throat a little, "Have you seen the morning papers?"

"Yes. It's wonderful," I said, too choked to say anything more.

He cleared his throat again. "Does Bill feel the same way?"

"I guess he set me the example," I said tremulously.

"Well I'm certainly relieved that you're both taking it like this. I was afraid you'd be terribly upset."

"I didn't realize that you even knew Paul was in Townsville. How did you find out?"

"What on earth are you talking about?"

"The Coral Sea battle, of course."

"Oh," he said, a little vacantly, as if he'd never heard of the Coral Sea. "I thought you were talking about *Claudia*. I gave the release to the papers this morning that I'd sold out to Twentieth Century Fox. We're meeting at the studio at eleven. I'll send my chauffeur for you both." He rang off before I could recover my wits and indeed it wasn't until we were in the middle of the conference that the impact of the transaction dawned on me. The room was full of expensive smoke and important men, unfamiliar to me because they had long since succeeded the old régime of Winfield

Sheean. They couldn't have been more deferential, assuring me that no one was better equipped to write and direct the property than the creator of *Claudia*, and everything would be done to make my stay in Hollywood comfortable and happy. Perhaps my husband and I would prefer a house in Beverly Hills or Bel-Air rather than living in a hotel?

I rose to my feet, and looked round this circle of faces, affluent without impressiveness, and attractive without charm. "I appreciate your generosity and your kindness," I said, "but there is one thing that you have overlooked. Had I wished to sell *Claudia* to Twentieth Century Fox I would have sold her to Warner Brothers." I turned to Mr. Selznick. "Would you be good enough to telephone your secretary to get us seats back to New York this evening?"

"You can't seriously mean that!" he expostulated.

I wondered if I would have been more co-operative if it hadn't been for the Coral Sea Battle, inasmuch as I had no quarrel with Mr. Selznick's personal motive; it was possible that he hadn't known that he was going to dispose of the property when he'd purchased the *Claudia* rights for twenty thousand dollars less than Warner's had offered. It didn't matter though. It wasn't my business, or my problem. "I'm afraid I do mean it," I said.

He appealed to Bill. "She's throwing away a great opportunity, can't you make her realize that this is an extremely advantageous deal I've worked out for her?"

"I doubt that I could be very persuasive," Bill replied courteously, "since I'm in full agreement with her decision." We always put on a united front in public, but this time I could tell that he meant what he said.

We were both glad, disgracefully glad, to get back to the farm. Neither of us felt that we had walked out on *Claudia* because the contract stipulated that the picture adhere faithfully to the story of the play. Nor did we have any idea that we had insulted the studio irrevocably. Hollywood might have changed, but not that much.

No word from Paul, or about Paul, awaited our homecoming. "We'd have heard by now," Bill said elliptically.

A few days after our return, a wire came over the telephone for Charlie, one of our farmhands. I went in search of Bill. "It's from the War Department," I told him, feeling drained of energy and colour.

"Charlie's out in the fields, I'll take the message," Bill said.

I stood beside him fearing to look at what he wrote. "Bob?" I whispered.

Bill nodded.

"But he hasn't even gone overseas yet?"

"He was killed in manœuvres."

The following day, a cable arrived from "Somewhere-in-New Guinea." "All well. Love, Paul."

I wept anew for Charlie. All sons were my son. The war was doing that to parents.

Geography has never been one of my strong points—rivers, mountains, states and countries sift out of my brain as if through a sieve; but an island thousands of miles away became more real to me than the town I lived in, and I came to know every inch of the jungles of New Guinea from the tip end of Oro Bay to the far reaches of Lae and Salamaua. Death and destruction raged throughout the world, but the South Pacific was my private war. Significance stalked every muted headline in the newspapers, every veiled communiqué over the radio. I continued to work like a labourer on the farm and like a demon at my typewriter, but I lived only for the sound of the mail car clattering up the road.

There was a day when two letters came at once—and then there were no letters at all.

I woke up one cold bleak morning, and I said to Bill, "I have a good feeling." I was so sure that at last I was going to get a letter that my heart turned into a sick lump in my chest when the mail-lady dug into her canvas bag and vouchsafed the information that the first of the month was mostly bills. "Looks like some fan letters too. Must be real exciting being an important author."

My lips moved woodenly. "Nothing is important except the letter you didn't bring me."

"I guess it's near three weeks now. . . ."

"Five weeks, yesterday."

"Ayah." She leaned down to put the battered old sedan into gear. "Those teensy-weensy little Victory notes don't say much anyhow."

Much? How could she know what even a few words could mean? I turned and walked back towards the house, thinking how lucky she was in her spinsterhood. The price of loving came high.

Bill came hurrying from the barn. "Nothing," I answered his unspoken question. The strained lines around his mouth hurt me. He and Paul had become very close, a relationship that was to endure and strengthen throughout the years. I managed to force some lightness into my voice. "I'll save you the trouble of saying it: 'No news is good news'."

Like an awkwardly devised cue, the telephone rang. His arm swept me back. "I'll get it. I'm expecting a call from the plumber," he lied. I died a little as he lifted the receiver.

For long and intermittent periods in my life I had lived with my heart in my throat, but this raging massacre of loved ones was different from anything I had ever experienced. My mother must have known just such anguished waiting when my brother went to war, but I had been as insentient as the mail-lady. You had to go through it for yourself.

I was aware that Bill was shoving the instrument into my numb hands. "Here, talk to him, it's only Mr. Balmer."

I couldn't imagine what the editor of *Redbook* could want, and even after I hung up I wasn't any the wiser. All he said was "Could I possibly come into town right away to see him," I relayed to Bill.

"What about?"

"I don't know. He said it was something he'd have to discuss with me in private.—Maybe that's the good feeling I woke up with. I won't have to write any more Claudia stories, he's had enough, and he's too nice to tell me over the phone.—Anything you have to do in New York?"

"No. And I think he'd rather I wasn't there."

It occurred to me later that he must have had an idea of what it was all about, but for myself I was so overwhelmed with the incredibleness of it, that I simply couldn't believe that I was hearing Mr. Balmer correctly. Everything he told me was tinged with unreality, and shrouded in secrecy, like the meeting in General Arnold's office. Only it wasn't terrifying. It was like a wonderful dream, and I didn't want to wake up from it before I'd given my answer.

"You don't know, you can't know what it means to me, Mr. Balmer. Of course I'll go."

"If you still feel that way tomorrow, my dear, I'll accept your decision," he said, "but it wouldn't be right to hold you to it before you've carefully considered every aspect of the mission. You must recognize that we're in the middle of a war, and that you'll be the first woman to be flown into New Guinea. It goes without saying that you'll be given every possible government security, but you can't interview our soldiers without having to come pretty close to the fighting. I'm not at all certain that your husband is going to be willing for you to be exposed to the risks that are inherent in this trip."

I hadn't thought that far. In my joy at the very thought of seeing Paul, I'd forgotten about Bill. In the train going back to Lyme, I feverishly rehearsed arguments and persuasions to break down his resistance, borrowing bits and pieces from his periodic bolstering of my own morale. How often he tried to make me swallow the philosophy that Paul was as safe in the jungles as crossing Fifth Avenue; or that we could have burned to death in our beds when the barns caught fire; and what about Carole Lombard, and the collapse of the circus tent in Hartford? And now I could add Bob to my cause. Bob had been killed before he even had a chance to go overseas. . . . It all sounded so convincing, and yet I didn't dare to hope that Bill would be convinced, chiefly because I knew how I would feel if our positions were reversed. I couldn't stop him from courting danger, but with a deep and secret passion I'd want to stop him. I didn't have the courage or the selflessness willingly to let go of the people I loved.

The train clanked and slowed. I lifted my coat and gloves down from the rack. My mind was made up. I had felt that something wonderful was going to happen when I'd awakened this morning, and it had happened.

Bill was waiting for me at the station in the pick-up, with huge bags of grain sitting in the back like dumpy old ladies. I climbed in the front seat with him. "You smell nice," I said, holding him close for an extra moment, as if already I were tasting separation. "As if you'd been pitching silage. Everything all right? Boys? Dogs? Cows?"

"You've only been gone a few hours. Stop making conversation. What did Mr. Balmer want to talk to you about?"

I told him. "All this secrecy," I finished with calculated nonchalance, "is just routine security measures. You can see how careful the government is being if even John and Peter aren't supposed to know about it."

Bill said, "There's no need for them to know. I'll tell them where you are after you get there."

I couldn't be sure that he realized what he had just said. His eyes were fixed on the road ahead, and his face told no tales. Only his hands, usually so relaxed on the wheel, looked knuckle-bound and rigid. "I expected an argument," I faltered. "I thought you'd raise all sorts of objections."

"How could I?" He pulled over to avoid the inexpert weaving of an oncoming car without berating the driver for her sex. "Of course you must go," he said. "You'll do a good job."

My heart was too full to speak. After a moment, he put his hand on my knee. "I'll get a few little gadgets that you can stick in your bag, for Paul."

I couldn't demean the moment with my gratitude. I knew him well enough to know that he wasn't trying to be noble. If he were, he wouldn't have been.

For the first time in months, I didn't hide the radio beneath my pillow to catch the last news bulletin at night, and the earliest morning broadcast. For me, the darkness that had fallen on the world had lifted. I sent up a formless prayer that whatever small talent had been given me for putting words on paper would not fail me on this mission.

It was scarcely dawn when I awakened. Bill, lying very still, was awake, too. It was as if I could hear him, staring up at the ceiling. I didn't move, or speak, feeling his need to be alone.

Through the windows, I could see a light in the barn—days began early on the farm now, what with three milkings instead of two. Soon the kitchen door opened, and closed, and I knew that John was on his way to the poultry house. He loved all animals, but how he hated chickens! I didn't blame him. There was no in-between to chickens. One minute they were sweet little yellow fluffs in the brooder, and then all at once they were beady-eyed hens, untidy and smelly. I was glad that Peter, home on holiday, was old enough to take over the candling of the eggs, an ignominious chore somewhat like shelling peas. It was more to my taste to work the manure spreader and help with the pasteurizing. I was getting to be passable at both of these highly diversified but obscurely related tasks.

I was aware, through the feathery drift of my reflections, that Bill was no longer beside me. He had risen cautiously, avoiding the temperamental floorboard near the bathroom so as not to wake me. Farmer-wise, he dressed quickly, without shaving, and tiptoed down the stairs. Once more the kitchen door opened, and closed. He was on his way to the barn. In a little while Peter would be getting up, vague as a poet in assembling his clothes and putting on his shoes. Already the intangibles that were to shape his destiny were crowding into his young brain.

I wondered how Bill was going to break the news of my whereabouts to the boys, and how they would react. I remembered their attitude when Paul had gone overseas. Over and above the emotional wrench, they had pretended envy, delivering themselves of the flat opinion that "some fellows had all the luck," and Bill had added, "I'd change places with him like a shot." Of course I knew—or thought I knew—that the three of them were in cahoots to minimize the hardships of war for my especial benefit.

It was disturbing that the incident, long past, should without warning relive itself so vividly that I hid my head under the covers as if to ward off the doubt that suddenly assailed me. What self-appointed prerogative had entitled me to diminish their maleness in order to serve my weakness? What right had I to assume that their envy was mere pretence? It was incomprehensible that it should be otherwise, but until this moment in the vast solitude of dawn, my soul had not stretched to comprehension. I had not even tried to understand Paul's impulse to enlist, and yet it had suited my sentimental purpose to glorify the normalcy of his functioning, and to negate the fact that these three who had to stay behind were no less soldiers than if they were beneath a shatter of gunfire in New Guinea. It was simply that the battlefield couldn't use them. Bill was over-age for active service. Peter was scarcely in his teens, and John, seething with rebellion, was frozen to the farm. I didn't want to face it, but perhaps I was needed on the farm, too, for reasons material and otherwise. We were all in this war, one way or another, and who was to say which way was the easiest?

My lips tasted of salt. I, who so seldom cried, was learning the humility of tears. I had also found the courage to cry openly and honestly, for myself.

Sacrifice parades under strange guises, and although it is not too often constructive, and very rarely selfless, I recognized this to be the supreme renunciation of my life when I telephoned Mr. Balmer later that morning to tell him my final and considered decision.

I had a feeling that he had expected me to change my mind. Either he thought that I was scared to go, or that Bill was scared to let me go. I don't know which. I didn't explain. I just thanked him, and said I was sorry.

But Bill would expect an explanation, and how could I accuse him of emotions he had not revealed to me? Also, how could I make him believe that I was afraid, when he knew that I was prey to every kind of fear except the fear of danger to my physical being? I couldn't even make the legitimate excuse of saying that there were any number of writers who could do the job in New Guinea, and there was only one of me to do the peculiarly complicated job at home. Martyrs were not his dish of tea.

He caught me off guard when he came in from the fields an

hour too early for lunch. "It's nowhere near ready," I greeted him inhospitably.

"I'm not hungry. You were supposed to telephone Mr. Balmer not later than eleven."

"I did."

"Did he say when you'd be leaving?"

"I'm not leaving."

"What do you mean? Is it off?"

I was into it now, and I had no alternative but to feel my way as I went along. "I don't know whether 'it's off,' but I'm off," I said with a stab of flippancy.

He grabbed my shoulder and yanked me round so that I couldn't evade his eyes. "Let me get this straight. Are you trying to tell me you've decided to turn the assignment down?"

"That's right."

"Why?"

"I changed my mind, that's all."

"Then change it back again if you've any mistaken idea that you're doing it for my sake," he said harshly. "Or because you think John and Peter might worry about you. Tough luck if they do," he added, only he used another word instead of luck, with a tonic intent to offend.

I let it pass. "It would be very tough," I said slowly, for the thought had only just occurred to me, "if Paul happened to be the one who might do the worrying."

"Nonsense. Paul wouldn't know you were coming until you got there."

"But it's after I got there that I mean. He's fighting a war in the jungle, and I think the mother of a soldier has no business being in the jungle at the same time that her son is fighting a war. I don't deny that I want to go, and that I want to see him more than anything in the world, but I don't think he'd want to see me. I think it would take his mind off what he has to do. I think he'd worry, and that's more important than the boys' worrying. I'm not sure that I have the right to put myself or my wishes ahead of his peace of mind."

It was a long speech for either of us to make to the other, but even after I finished, he didn't say anything, and I couldn't tell what he was thinking. He just stood there looking at me, his eyes puzzled, and a little troubled.

"I'm rationalizing again," I finally said it for him.

I felt his hand on my shoulder, but this time the roughness was gone. "If you are, it's a man's way of rationalizing." He smiled faintly. "So don't expect me to tell you that you're wrong. I'll only say that you surprise me."

I didn't surprise him as much as I surprised myself.

It's one thing to make a decision, and another not to brood about it or to regret it. I ruled the episode from my mind as if it had never happened, but I continued to feel a gnawing emptiness, like a cherished pregnancy come to nothing. Many of my friends sought short-cuts to serenity by submerging themselves in cults, or defence work, or canteen service, and I wished that I could do the same. But group functioning was not for me, nor could I find solace in spiritual sedation. Instead, I tried to keep my values straight and my hope secure in watching the eternal cycle of life, and the mystery of the seasons. As far back as my early childhood, I used to experience an awe that was very near a sense of holiness, as, with each new spring, the snows melted, and the lilacs in the back-yard in Harlem began to put out delicate rosettes of green leaves along the dark empty branches that had seemed so dead.

I was ashamed to tell anyone about the way I felt, even my mother, and yet that secret reverence remained strong within me, and over the years I drew upon it to nourish my spirit and refresh my faith. Now, whenever I knelt before a new-born calf, or looked up at an apple tree in blossom, or a dog-wood promised with clusters of red berries against its withering foliage, I felt as if I were before an altar. If a heathen can be a deeply religious person, I am that heathen.

It is perhaps a little late in this chronicle to mention that we are a family of heathens. Neither the boys, nor their father, nor I, ever attended, formally, a House of Worship, and I am blessed indeed that Bill shares our creed that God is not to be sought, found, or appeased in separate cubicles on special days. We believe simply, and without controversy or discussion, that religion is a state of being, free of intolerance, avarice and hate, and that the colour of one's skin or the shape of one's nose is a mere accident of birth. There must be thousands upon thousands who feel as we do, but even as I put these words to paper prejudice continues to permeate the farthest corners of the universe, and mad men are roaming the continents threatening to commit, again, every unholy violation against the human race. Surely it is the unalienable right of all wives, mothers and sweethearts on the face of this earth to scream in protest against a generation resigned to bloodshed.

Unhappily, however, women by and large do not scream well or becomingly. Emotionalism too often traps us into ineffectiveness, and occasionally, as the cream of us wade through the slime of politics, and battle our way into high places with our hair-ribbons on, we become a little absurd. Perhaps it's an acute case of sour grapes that provokes this caustic criticism of my sex, for I acknowledge that I am not equipped by education, or fired sufficiently by ambition, to attempt to accede my limitations. Whatever small screaming I managed to accomplish, I addressed in private to my typewriter, and because I had something to say that I felt needed to be said, I wrote *Outrageous Fortune.* Or rather it seemed to write itself, effortlessly and objectively, for within a week from the day I started the first act, I gave Bill the manuscript to read.

"It's the best thing you've done," he said.

"I think so," I agreed, "but I don't think John Golden's going to think so."

He didn't. "Good God, Rosie, how does a nice girl like you know about such things, this is censorable stuff, by God!"

"I've been censored before."

"The hell you have."

"One of my novels was not only censored, it was suppressed."

He stared at me. "No kidding."

"I'll send it to you."

"I don't want to read it." He removed his false tooth, and placed it thoughtfully in its small case. "You know something,

Rosie? I think we could save this play; it's got humour and good tight construction. Change your characters into nice people like Claudia, and we're in business again."

"These are nice people."

"Not in my book they're not. Matter of fact, I don't even understand them."

He didn't want to understand them. John lived very comfortably with himself. "You poor, silly old bastard," I said. We parted with the deepest affection and regret.

A few days later I was surprised to receive a letter from John Wilson saying that he'd heard I'd written a new play (the underground of the theatre works in mysterious ways), and he would be grateful if I would let him read it.

I had never met Mr. Wilson, but I knew that he was responsible, or partially responsible, for bringing Noel Coward's plays to America, which was to me sufficient token of his sophistication and good taste. It was also an indication that he might like *Outrageous Fortune*.

He did. "I'm terribly excited about it," he told me over the telephone. "I'm leaving for San Francisco this evening for ten days, but I'm frightfully anxious to sit down with you the very moment I get back."

I was pleased at his enthusiasm, and the postponement of our meeting suited me perfectly. I'd have wanted Bill to be there, which would have been difficult for the next week or so, for he had his hands full breaking in two new men on the farm. And mighty lucky we were to get them, because in addition to having the highest references, they were both disbarred from military service. Vernon had lost two fingers on his right hand in a buzz-saw accident, and Al had a chronic cardiac condition which didn't interfere with his being a first-rate herdsman. "I think our troubles are over," Bill reported after the first few days. "They're competent, they like working with the 'boss's son', and John seems to like working with them."

That was important, for John had been anything but a happy boy these past months. One after another his friends had either enlisted or become of draft age, and he felt he was stuck on the farm with a degrading succession of incompetent 4Fs in search of short hours and easy jobs.

"You're glad I'm not in the Army!" he accused me bitterly.

"I'm glad for my sake," I admitted, "and for Bill's. He couldn't possibly run the place without you at this moment."

"Then sell the damned animals, and get rid of the place!"

My temper flared, as it seldom did with the boys. "You selfish brat! A productive farm like this is an important contribution in wartime and you know it!"

He knew it, but he refused to acknowledge it, and we could only hope that the respect of decent, capable men like Vernon and Al would help to restore his own self-esteem.

On the Saturday morning following their arrival, an expensive looking car drove up to the door, and I recognized Gilbert Miller, of all people, backing out of the front seat on to our gravel path. I hadn't laid eyes on him since the opening of *Another Language* in London, and I couldn't imagine what had occasioned this unannounced visit. "Hello," he beamed, "I was just passing by and I thought I'd come in to buy a pig. A lady pig," he stipulated.

"What on earth do you want a sow for?" I asked him distrustfully. We were extremely particular about the people to whom we sold our breeding-stock, and the only thing I could imagine Mr. Miller doing with one of our fine pigs was to have it slaughtered for an unrationed supply of hams and bacon. But no. He said he wanted it for a pet at his country place near Bridgeport, and the reason he preferred a female was because he thought he might name it after one of his favourite actresses.

Impishly, he waited for me to ask him who she was, but I didn't have to—there weren't too many dark-haired actresses with slightly porcine features currently appearing in one of Mr. Miller's productions. She was quite attractive, anyway, inasmuch as most people resemble a certain kind of dog, or feline, or rodent, or even an underwear button or a poached egg. However, I had never credited Mr. Miller with any particular perspicacity, kindly or otherwise, and I must say I was reluctantly conditioned in his favour. I was immediately unconditioned, though, when, having asked him into the house out of the hot sun, he made a beeline for an eighteenth-century Adam chair which crumbled beneath his weight like a box of matches. I helped him up off the floor and steered him into a sturdy Chippendale, quickly rescuing a lamp as it teetered in nervous reaction to his proximity. Then I hurried to get him a glass of cold rich milk and some cookies in order to keep him occupied, so that he wouldn't move about the room from chair to chair.

"Where's Bill?" I asked John, who was just coming into the kitchen with a basket of fresh eggs.

"I don't know. I don't keep tabs on him."

He strode off, back to the poultry house, his heavy boots clumping over the stone path. I bit my lips, restraining my anger and frustration. Through the window I saw Bill come out of the barn. He stopped John briefly and I saw John brush past him. I felt suddenly bereaved. Would his own father have known how to break through this barrier of resentment?

"Another one of his moods?" Bill inquired from the doorway. "Yes."

"Look. There are plenty of kids who'd be glad to escape the draft. You wouldn't like that either."

"I know."

"And if you're getting that milk for me, don't."

"I'm not."

"What car is that outside?"

"It's what I'm getting the milk for. He came to buy a pig."

"It doesn't look like a car that wants a pig. Who is it?"

"You'll never guess. Gilbert Miller."

"The hell he came to buy a pig, he came to buy *Outrageous Fortune*."

I arrayed a tidy circle of cookies on a plate. "Not Gilbert. He doesn't produce new plays, he re-produces successes. So he's hardly apt to be interested in something that John Golden's turned down."

"On the other hand he's probably heard that John Wilson is very keen on it."

It was a possibility that hadn't occurred to me. "In that case,"

I said firmly, "we'll teach him a lesson. He says he came to buy a pig, so a pig is what he's going to get. And at a handsome price. He busted our Adam chair."

"How?"

"Just sitting in it."

So those were the contributing factors of Gilbert Miller ending up with a black sow and *Outrageous Fortune*, which I agreed to sell to him on the assumption that he would co-produce it with Mr. Wilson, with whom I had had several conferences on his return from San Francisco. I liked his approach to the play, as I expected I would, but for some reason or other the partnership did not eventuate, leaving Gilbert free to follow an all too familiar pattern.

He closed *Outrageous Fortune* the morning after it opened in Boston.

From the start, he wasn't so much fun to fight with as John Golden. For one thing, he never yelled or hollered at me. We had restrained discussions in his impeccably decorated office in Rockefeller Center, or at luncheon in his favourite restaurant, where a short, long-haired violinist bent over the table and played at me during the whole meal with melting eyes, which took the edge off my appetite. I'd always looked forward to lunch with John, responding happily to old Mr. Sardi's smiling welcome as he invariably escorted us to our special table as if we didn't know where it was or how to find it. Nor was Renee a mere hat-check girl, she was, rather, the warm human barometer of the theatre world, and I missed our snatches of gossip and her sweetly acid commentaries on the passing parade.

There was no such happy attunement in the costly surroundings of the Gilbert Miller organization. Unlike John, Gilbert liked spending money. He preferred to engage only the highest salaried actors, and that was where we had our first serious dispute. "I have good news for you. Gertrude Lawrence loves the part and wants to play it," he announced at the very outset of our association. *Oh, dear,* I thought in dismay, *here we go again,* and once more it fell to my lot to explain to Miss Lawrence that much as I admired her, I didn't feel that she was right for the character of Crystal.

But now I could say, with complete honesty, "You're too young."

Without the faintest trace of animosity, she agreed with me, but Mr. Miller was not so readily persuaded. "Have you any better suggestion than Gertie?" he inquired with admirable restraint.

"Yes. Elsie Ferguson."

His restraint vanished. "Elsie Ferguson!" he echoed, his whole face literally wobbling with horror. "Impossible. She hasn't been on the stage for years; in fact, I doubt if any agent in town would know where to find her."

"I've found her. She lives a few miles from us in Lyme. And because she hasn't been on the stage for years, audiences won't identify her with any recent rôles. She'll bring an air of mystery to the part, which is what I want."

His lips set into his cheeks like soft granite. "Elsie Ferguson is bad news," he said with finality. "There isn't a producer in his right senses who would take the gamble with her."

"Oh," I said. I was in no position to dispute the statement, since I had had little contact with Miss Ferguson other than a neighbourly wave as Bill and I occasionally rode past her house to exercise our horses, or encountered her on one of her solitary walks. Even in country sweaters and skirts, she was an arresting figure, no longer slim, or flawlessly beautiful, but still emanating stardom in the regal lift of her head and the rich, vital timbre of her voice. I'd often wondered why she'd given up the stage, and now I gathered that it was the stage that had given her up. She "spelled trouble." On the other hand, John Golden had warned me that Donald Cook "spelled trouble," too, and he hadn't missed a single performance of *Claudia* in almost two years, or given me less that the utmost loyalty and respect. "Every relationship generates a different chemical," I said to Bill, loath to relinquish Miss Ferguson as perfect casting.

"Go ahead, give her the script," he encouraged me. "See what you get when you read with her."

She read the lines slowly, gropingly, as if unsure of herself, but she brought a deference to the characterization, and a knowledge-able recognition of the values in the play. I knew that with hard

[311]

work, and unremitting patience, she would supply the magic that would ultimately mould Crystal into a shimmering reality. However, I judiciously withheld my decision until I had a frank talk with her concerning her past misdemeanours, which I had since learned included a crisis of ringing down the curtain halfway through an opening night, never to ring it up again. She didn't deny it. She said, in her throaty, glorious voice, "Why those goddam small potato miserable sons of bitches."

It was scarcely the chastened attitude that I'd expected, and I concluded that it was expedient to clarify the basis of any future association between us. "I'm directing this play, but Mr. Miller is producing it," I told her. "If I can persuade him to give you the part, we must have it understood clearly that there is going to be one star in the production, but that star will not be Elsie Ferguson: it will be Rose Franken."

This blatant exercise of my authority was alien and obnoxious to me, but it was a dose of preventive medicine that both of us had to swallow. I was prepared for her to throw the script in my face and tell me to go blazes, and I dare say she would have done just that if the long-forgotten smell of grease-paint had not already intoxicated her into repentance and submission. With the terms of our relationship firmly established, I felt that it was quite safe to inform Gilbert that I was ready to assume the full responsibility of giving Elsie Ferguson a run-of-the-play contract.

John Golden would have flown at me in a rage, but Gilbert just walked into the beautiful toilet that adjoined his office, and closed the door. He didn't come out again, so I caught the three-ten express back to Lyme, taking the precaution to notify his secretary of his whereabouts.

In turn, his secretary notified me, a day or so later, that Mr. Miller was confined to his bed with some obscure but debilitating malady that the doctor was as yet unable to diagnose.

"I'm afraid it's me," I told Bill contritely.

Gilbert was laid up for several weeks at his country place, and when he was better, Bill and I called on him one day on our

way to Pawling to see Missy. I was glad that he seemed to harbour
no ill will towards me. On the contrary he apologized for being
incapacitated, and having to delay production of the play.
"But I'm thinking about it," he assured me in a weak voice.
"I'd like to get Ethel Waters for the part of Cynthia. What do
you think of the idea?"

I thought that Ethel Waters was a fine actress of stellar pro-
portions, but not at all suited for the part of Crystal's little
coloured maid. I had an entirely different idea for that small but
important bit of casting, but I evaded a direct answer with a
truthful question. "Ethel Waters is pretty expensive for a
supporting rôle, isn't she?"

"Of course she is. But I prefer to have expensive actors in my
productions."

Because he'd been ill, I refrained from telling him that I had
already cast the whole play in my mind for peanuts. John
Golden thrived on peanuts. He would have kissed me on both
cheeks for saving him money, but poor Gilbert would have had
a relapse. I glanced at my watch. Bill read the signal. "We'd
better start if we want to get to Missy's."

"I understand your mother has a home in Pawling," Gilbert
said.

"Yes. She's lived there for years."

"Very famous woman," he approved vaguely. "Tribune,
foreign decorations, Madame Curie and all that. Good friend of
the Duke and Duchess, too, they speak of her quite often. I hear
she's always suffered more or less from poor health."

It was my turn to say "Yes." Neither of us wanted to talk
about Missy. It was as if to voice our concern for her would lend
substance to the slow encroachment of the disease that she had
held at bay since she was seventeen. I doubt that anyone outside
of ourselves and a few close friends knew that it was only her
unvanquished spirit that still kept her small frail body alive.

She had moved back to Pawling with the warm weather, so that
she could lie in the sun and watch her garden reach its peak of
bloom. Today when we arrived, the air was soft and fragrant, the
roses were a riot of colour, and the tiny brook babbled gaily between

banks of iris and early annuals. But the long chair on the terrace was empty, with her favourite Afghan folded mutely across the foot of it. Geraldine met us at the door. "The doctor's been and gone. She wanted a hypodermic for the pain in her chest so as she'd be able to sit up and talk to you, without you worrying over her.—You'll be staying for supper, won't you? I have a chicken on. Maybe between the two of you, you can coax her to take a bit of the broth."

We didn't coax her. Missy shuddered at the sight of food, and we felt that the human body was entitled to the dignity of election. "If you're not hungry, you don't have to," I said.

"Thanks, darlin'."

We didn't go back to the farm that night. Geraldine made up the beds in the little guest room on the floor above. We stayed for many nights, until there was no longer any need to stay, and even then we didn't want to leave her. Nor could I bear the thought of her being all alone in a funeral parlour.

"Not the farm," Bill answered my unspoken wish. "It wouldn't be fair to John or Peter."

"Then Washington Square." Missy had always enjoyed the big high-ceilinged living-room, and she would like to rest among the masses of flowers that were already pouring in.

"Thank you for me, and thank you for her," Bill said.

I thought of my sister's ashes, scattered in Missy's garden, and I thought of all the other warm, generous things that she had done for me, and for the boys. This small gesture of love was so pitifully little to give her in return.

She was buried from St. Patrick's Cathedral. People, great and small, came from far and wide in tribute. I don't like funerals, and I don't intend to have even a modest one. But Missy would have loved her wonderfully rewarding send-off. She was a child about gifts, and this was like one last, beautiful Christmas present.

Eve Curie was in the car with Bill and me going out to the cemetery. It seemed right and fitting that she should be with us.

Strange. Much as I loved Missy, I did not weep for her until a few days later when Sandy, our oldest Dane, was found in her kennel choked to death, with her collar caught on the rail of her pen. I couldn't stop crying for the needlessness of it, and the loss. "This is silly," I blubbered.

"No, it isn't," Bill said. "You remember how you cried when Pansy was run over. It wasn't just Pansy you were crying for, it was everything that little cat stood for." He gave me his handkerchief. "Sandy was the first Dane we bought when we bought the farm. Paul loved that pup, and he was devoted to Missy. You wanted him to find his world intact when he comes home from the war."

I blew my nose. "And now I keep wondering what else is going to happen."

"That's really being silly," he said.

"I know. Why don't you give me a good kick in the pants and tell me to grow up."

"Because I'm not taking it a hell of a lot better myself."

"At least you're not bawling your head off like a fool."

"What do you think I was doing when I walked over to the alfalfa field by myself?"

At lunch Peter tried to hide one of his tell-tale wheezes, and John's eyes were red and he was gentle. Somehow I felt that the family was united again in spite of Paul being thousands of miles away.

Lucky for the world around us, however, people eventually emerge from the rarefied climate of any profound experience, even the lurking shadow of war, tinged with only a sediment of sweetness to dilute the salt and acid of the normal bloodstream. Life on the farm went on as usual. Gilbert's recovery was slow, and in the meantime I began lining up the remainder of the cast for his doubtful approval—an obscure but solid actor for the lead, and two completely unknown young actors for the supporting male rôles. But the hardest hurdle for him to meet would surely be my choice for Cynthia. Slight and irregular in build, with gold caps on her teeth and silver loops in her ears, she was the embodiment of Crystal's faithful little bodyguard. She had never been on the stage before, so I arranged for a leave of absence for her (I didn't want her to lose her job in the beauty shop which paid fifteen good steady dollars a week), and took her up to the farm where I taught her the rudiments of acting. With that instinctive rhythm and mimicry that springs so naturally from the Negro heritage, her scenes with Miss Ferguson were moving and spontaneous, and I experienced once again the pleasure and satisfaction of discovering and moulding a new talent. I was pretty certain though, that when Gilbert was able to return to his office, he would promptly drop his option, and John Wilson would promptly pick it up. He, too, might feel it unwise to rely on Miss Ferguson to carry the play, but I had a feeling that he would be willing to take the gamble and go along with me on my other off-beat ideas. I was ready to settle on Margalo Gilmore, with her turned-up nose, for the part of the young Jewess; Margaret Hamilton, with her turned-down nose, to portray the Catholic wife, and an ex-prizefighter to play the sensitive homosexual. The only conventional and safe bit of casting was my choice of Maria Ouspenskaya for the old mother.

While I awaited Gilbert's full recovery (and possible relapse), I got ready the third *Claudia* novel for publication, and wrote a couple of more stories for *Redbook*. With Vernon, Al and John managing the farm to his satisfaction, Bill also went back to his typewriter. One afternoon, his agent came up from New York on a belated condolence call. He had sold Missy a great deal of material during her editorial career, and her death was a professional as well as a personal loss to him, but being of French descent he was not averse to bringing a little business into his visit on the side. He wheedled Bill into discussing the general concept of his new novel, pronounced it a very important piece of work (it was magnificent), and urged him to finish it for Christmas publication. "Maybe," Bill said noncommittally.

"I've given up trying to get him to realize that his writing is important," I said.

"Look who's talking!" Bill retorted.

"By the way." The little agent carefully set down his cocktail glass, and turned his attention in my direction. "While I am here, would you mind if I took a look in your trunk?"

It was, to say the least, a quite unconventional overture. "He only means that writers usually have a trunkful of old manuscripts somewhere around," Bill explained with a grin.

"Well, I haven't," I said, and then suddenly I remembered that my sister had stored a steamer trunk full of papers and photographs when I'd moved to California, and Donna had sent it on to me after we'd bought the farm. I'd immediately relegated it to the attic, and forgotten all about it. Now I decided that it was high time that I opened it up and pitched out most of the contents. Missy had taught me a lesson. She'd been a squirrel, she'd actually had to have an annexe built into the house in Pawling to hold all the things she couldn't bear to part with, from her great-grandmother's wedding dress to Bill's first pair of baby-shoes. Paradoxically, a single metal file in her study contained the precious heritage of the Curie papers, original manuscripts of famous authors, and portfolios of invaluable autographs and letters dating as far back as the days of General Lee. "Since I have nothing of any importance to leave you and the boys," I promised Bill, "I will do you the favour of seeing that my effects fit into a five-pound tin candy-box, plus, of course, my chinchillas and my pearls. On second thoughts, I think I'd like to be cremated in them, so that takes care of that."

"Pretty swanky corpse you'll make," Bill commented.

"I suppose you can't wait to see me."

In spite of my flippancy, I was in earnest about not leaving a mess of stuff behind me. "I might as well go over that trunk myself," I told Bill's agent, "so if you want to see what's in it, you can come to the attic with me, but I can tell you in advance there's nothing you'd be interested in."

From my point of view there wasn't—just memories tied up in some family pictures and the thin yellowed pages of a pile of old short stories. The little agent was quick to rescue them from being tossed into a large wastepaper basket that I had efficiently brought up from the back porch. "These I would like to read," he said, riffling through them, and deftly discarding a couple of play folders, much as the Danes would daintily remove from a bowl of meat an offending carrot or pea. "I am not a theatrical agent," he said. "I am interested in the stories only."

"You might think you are, but the youngest of them is about twenty years old and they've all been rejected at least a dozen times."

"I would like to read them, anyway, if I may." He tucked them into his capacious briefcase. "I will let you know what I think."

After he left, Bill picked up the two remaining manuscripts. "This is a carbon of *Fortnight*," he discovered. "But you never told me you wrote *Doctors Disagree* as a play before it was a serial."

"It was right after we got back from London—I thought it would amuse him if I showed off what I knew about medicine," I said haltingly. "I remember that he thought it was awfully good, but there wasn't time to do anything about it. Later on it seemed silly not to use the material when the *Ladies' Home Journal* wanted a story centred round a hospital."

Curiously, Bill started to glance through the manuscript standing up, and then he sat down at his desk and read it straight through. He's one of those fast new-fangled readers, and so are the boys—they could gobble up a whole book, a page at a glance, while I plodded through it word by word. I hated them for it, especially if I happened to write what they were so nonchalantly skimming through.

"Say, this is a damn good piece of work!" Bill greeted me as I came down from putting out the lights in the attic.

"It must be terribly dated, isn't it?"

"It isn't. That's what surprises me. I bet John Golden would produce it without changing a line of it."

"Even if you're telling me the truth, I can't very well submit it to John while I'm still tied up with Gilbert."

"All right, let him read it first."

John never got the chance to even consider the play because Gilbert telephoned me from his sick bed, and I clearly recall the peculiar phrasing of his reaction. "I hope I'm not going to insult you," he said, "if I'm perfectly honest and tell you that I like *Doctors Disagree* much better than *Claudia*."

"Not at all," I said. "I much prefer the Claudia stories myself to the play."

"Really? I'll have to read them some day," he promised vaguely. "And we'll discuss this new play of yours as soon as I'm up and about again."

"He didn't so much as mention *Outrageous Fortune,*" I relayed the gist of the conversation to Bill.

"That means he's not going to drop his option until he gets a few more opinions on *Doctors Disagree.* He might want a financial stake in it."

Bill came pretty close to discerning what was in Gilbert's mind. He wasn't happy about *Outrageous Fortune,* but he made casual references to out-of-town bookings for a November production. I felt under no particular pressure. I had chosen my cast and everyone was willing to postpone the signing of contracts until Gilbert returned to his office.

Meanwhile, Metro had been asking us to go out to Hollywood to write an original screenplay, but neither Bill nor I welcomed the idea of making the trip again. "Let them buy *Fortnight,*" Bill suggested.

"They don't want it, Adrienne Morrison tried to sell it to them years ago," I said.

"That was years ago. You have a name now."

"If I have, it must have sneaked up on me while I wasn't looking," I said. "Anyway I don't subscribe to this cock-eyed theory that success breeds success. If something is good, it's good, and if it isn't, it isn't."

I ate my words. Metro bought *Fortnight* as a vehicle for Claudette Colbert, Walter Pidgeon and June Allyson, and Bill's agent sold every last story in that dilapidated old trunk. "I am very pleased," he said, with justifiable pride in his salesmanship, "that *Harper's Bazaar* accepted 'Little Cakes' in spite of its controversial subject matter, and I am also very pleased that Mr. Herbert Mayes of *Good Housekeeping* offered such a handsome price for the story about the two old ladies and the toy shop."

I had never heard of Mr. Herbert Mayes at that time, my magazine contacts being largely limited to *Redbook,* but I immediately concluded that the current editor of *Good Housekeeping* was a blithering idiot to pay so much for a story that I would have joyfully sold to his predecessor, Mr. Bigelow, for twenty-five dollars—or less.

When Mr. Mayes asked Bill and me to dinner at his apartment, however, I was bound to admit that he didn't look like an idiot, which confused me. "I can't understand your being so silly as to buy a story for five thousand dollars that I literally couldn't give away to your magazine twenty-something years ago," I chided him, as he pulled out my chair at the table.

Mr Mayes had an arrestingly alert face, and an outgiving manner that had perhaps put me a little too much at my ease with him, for he suddenly stiffened, and the set of his pleasantly flat lips wasn't quite as pleasant as it had been a moment before. "I haven't the remotest idea what you're talking about," he said. "The story I bought from you was the last one you'd written, and your agent assured me that he had submitted it to no other editor."

"He hadn't. He wasn't in business when I wrote that story. It suddenly dawns on me that he had it retyped, redated, and then sold it to you under false pretences. He hasn't sent me your cheque yet, and I'll certainly see that he returns it to you."

It was at once evident that Mr. Mayes was neither grateful for my honesty nor pleased at the prospect of getting his money back. "You do not know me well enough yet," he replied, "to know that I am never swayed by anyone else's judgment."

"I must admire your respect for your own opinion, because most people are sheep," I told him cosily, "but I still think you're an ass to be taken in by that unprincipled little Frenchman."

My intentions were decent, but I should have had the sense to have made my point and quit before calling Mr. Mayes, however endearingly, an ass. He raised his voice slightly so that everyone at the table who had been surreptitiously listening to our conversation could plainly hear his firm and final dismissal of the discussion. "I consider the story I have just bought from you," he said loudly and clearly, "to be one of the best short stories I have ever read."

The longer I live, the less sure I am that I know anything about anything. I was wrong about that story, and Mr. Mayes was right.

He must have been right, since I have no other explanation as to how those two old ladies who had been withering away in the dark bottom of my trunk for nearly a quarter of a century, could have ended up in an anthology.

To my surprise, I wasn't ashamed of the remaining stories; in fact, I thought they were as good as if not better than anything I had written since, with the exception of *Outrageous Fortune*, which I hoped would be in rehearsal by the end of August. When Gilbert returned to his office he spoke sketchily of an autumn production, but made no move to sign up the actors.

In the meantime, John Golden had taken advantage of the summer lull at the box-office to send the Broadway company of *Claudia* on a tour of major cities across the country, with a contemplated return engagement at reduced prices. Fortunately, Dorothy Maguire was the only one of the cast who was reluctant to appear in New York at "cut rate," but as she wanted to leave the play anyway to rest up before the start of the picture, John decided to replace her with Phyllis Thaxter in Washington. "Then she'll be set in the part before we open in San Francisco. And you can stay at the White House again and save me your expenses," he added with a verbal poke in my ribs.

"I wish you'd stop holding that visit against me," I said. "I told you that I was only invited as a courtesy to Bill's mother."

With his childlike mixture of envy and awe, it was hard to convince him that I was invited for the second time also because of Missy, for about ten days later, Bill and I met Mrs. Roosevelt in Baltimore at the launching of a government ship named in Missy's honour. As I broke the bottle across the hull and watched the S.S. *Marie M. Meloney* glide majestically into the water, I felt the tears well into my eyes—it was like a second funeral.

"My dear——" Even before I turned, there was no mistaking the voice, and I accepted humbly, as homage to Missy, the quick sympathy of Eleanor Roosevelt's lips against my cheek. Then immediately, the toothy, familiar smile restored us to the casual. "I was so interested to read in the newspapers that *Claudia* will be coming back to Washington. Do you expect to be there too?"

"Yes, I'm rehearsing our Chicago girl, and I want to put in some new bits of business, it keeps the performance fresh and alive."

"That sounds as if you might be working quite hard," Mrs. Roosevelt said, "and as the White House will be more comfortable for you than a hotel, Franklin and I would so enjoy having you and you husband stay with us again."

"We'd love to," I heard myself say.

Bill regarded me quizzically when we were alone. "I suppose you feel in that cock-eyed way of yours, that Pennsylvania Avenue is as close to New Guinea as you can get."

"You could be right," I admitted. "I wondered why I accepted without thinking twice about it. Especially since I know she only asked me for Missy's sake."

"This time I think she asked you for yourself," Bill said.

"Really?"

"Really."

I hoped he was right. But I still had my peace to make with John Golden. "I'm sorry, but we'll be staying at the White House after all," I apologized.

We reached Washington on a balmy Sunday evening. A hint of Indian summer lingered in the air, and yet the cold chill of war was more to be felt in this great mansion than in the homes of ordinary citizens. Mrs. Roosevelt greeted us in the entrance hall, and herself escorted us to the Lincoln Room. I looked up at the vast bed and I wondered whether she had, in full awareness, known that to sleep in this bed could not fail to replenish my faith in the ultimate triumph of good over evil and right over wrong. She was no longer the First Lady, and I was no longer a visiting playwright. We were simply two mothers, suffering the silent bloodshed of war. "More than anywhere else in the White House," she said merely, "I feel a sense of peace when I walk into this room." She turned at the door. "We'll join Franklin in the library for cocktails at seven-thirty." Then she added, happily, "We're having steak for dinner tonight as a special treat."

I thought guiltily of our unavoidable surplus of meat on the farm. "The least we can do is to eat up as little of their precious steak as possible," I called to Bill from the mammoth depths of the old-fashioned tub in our bathroom.

"You'd better hurry or you'll keep the President waiting," he called back.

Hurry as I did, he was dressed before I was, and he made me nervous by not saying anything. "Just standing and looking at me like a wounded deer isn't helping," I told him irritably. "You don't have to wait for me, go on ahead."

"Can you find your way?"

"I'm not a complete idiot."

If not complete, I was pretty much of a one, because I kept pressing the wrong buttons in the automatic lift, and I had to keep sticking my head out at each floor, hoping to discover some familiar landmark to lead me to the President's private quarters.

My third try carried me all the way down to the basement, where I noticed two men flattened against the wall as if they were hiding from something or somebody, and maybe I imagined it, but I could have sworn that the same two men confronted me on the landing above. I felt horribly confused by this time, especially when a series of deafening alarms suddenly began to sound off, one after another. I scurried back into the cage, stabbing blindly at yet another button on the panel, and to my great relief I finally emerged into what I recognized to be the proper corridor. I made a dash for the library, stalked by a disturbing feeling that I was being watched by unseen eyes, and followed by noiseless steps.

The President had already been wheeled in, a light blanket folded across his knees—he was always the first to enter and the last to leave a room, as if to minimize, for others, his physical incapacity. In many small ways, he was one of the most deeply thoughtful people I have ever known. He said now, allaying what must have been my obvious state of agitation, "There seems to be a little excitement going on with the secret service. Nothing to be alarmed about, my dear, probably some innocent intruder, but this is wartime, and we have to take precautions."

"Yes, I know," I quavered.

I avoided meeting the wicked glint in Bill's eyes. I also knew that he knew exactly who that innocent intruder was.

I had never found meals at the White House to be in any way extravagant or outstanding, but the steak that night was downright pitiful, paper-thin, stringy and tough. Notwithstanding, the President consumed his portion with gusto, and reluctantly but appreciatively accepted half of mine. "Please, take it, we get all we want on the farm. And we have butter and cream," I confessed, for there was no butter on the bread-and-butter plates, and only bluish hot milk for the coffee that had been sent to our room when we arrived.

"Tell me about the farm," he said, ungrudging of our plenty.

He listened attentively to my judiciously curtailed resumé of our agricultural activities, and then he said, "Now tell me about Paul. When did you last hear from him?"

"Almost six weeks ago."

"We'll try to get some later news of him for you."

"Thank you." My throat choked with the gratitude that filled me. It was not an idle promise. I had learned by this time that he was a man who never forgot (or forgave) either the big things or the little things.

I carry no banner of defence for Franklin Delano Roosevelt, and any partisan views that I might voice would merely be a parrot-like reflection of our life and times. I only know that I loved and admired him for many reasons, and when he died it was as if I had lost a dear, close friend.

Our stay in Washington entailed a more strenuous stretch of rehearsals than I had anticipated. There is nothing as destructive to a performance as disharmony behind the footlights, and it was my first experience in watching a subtle distortion of the basic values of the play. "Those two females ought to have their tails kicked," Bill muttered halfway through the opening night.

"It's my fault," I admitted. "I should have done something about it when Don Cook telephoned me from Boston——"

"Why didn't you?"

"I thought he said they were looking at his tie and I told him just to ignore it, it wasn't worth getting so upset about."

It wasn't until I actually perceived what was going on that I realized that poor Don had fallen victim to one of the age-old bitcheries of the stage. It wasn't the sort of thing you could catch anyone red-handed at, either.

"But I'm not doing a thing, Miss Franken!"

"Oh, yes you are, and stop it!"

While I was at it, I got out the drawl that had crept into Dorothy's speech, a trick that young actresses were beginning to adopt as a substitute for competence. And why not, if it fooled audiences and critics alike? But Dorothy was a good sport about it. She not only submitted to my last directorial injunctions, but when we parted at the close of her final performance, she begged me to believe that in spite of a long and tiring Broadway run and all the hardships of the road, she was actually glad of the experience, and didn't regret a moment of it.—I thanked her.

With Phyllis effortlessly taking over the role the following night, Bill and I could hardly wait to get back to the farm. The air was so fresh, and all the cows and pups and geese and pigs such thoroughly nice creatures to live amongst that I felt that here, on these rich green acres, was everything I could ask of life, except for the war to be over and Paul to return home safe and well. But how could I forget that Eleanor Roosevelt's three sons were fighting the cause of peace? I had observed and learned much during this last stay in the White House, and again, as in *Outrageous Fortune*, I felt that there were things that needed to be said, not in defence of the President and his wife, but more simply about two human beings who were compounded of flesh and blood, and therefore vulnerable to the cruel criticism of an unthinking and embittered democracy. There had been an evening, towards the end of our visit, when young Franklin was expected on the briefest of leaves from the European theatre, and I shared, vicariously, the joy of his parents, the excitement of his wife who had come up from Texas to meet him, and the festive preparations for a welcoming dinner of—not steak—but lobster. Bill and I both felt loath to intrude upon the intimacy of the short reunion, but

Mrs. Roosevelt would not hear of our dining at a restaurant. "The war has made us into one big family," she said.

Nevertheless, we used the excuse of a late rehearsal to absent ourselves from cocktails, but when we walked into the dining-room we saw at once that a young lieutenant was seated between Mrs. Roosevelt and her daughter-in-law. Franklin had sent his second-in-command in his place.

Afterwards, Malvina Thompson told me grimly what had happened. "At the last minute he decided not to come, because he wanted to protect his father from the lash of public opinion. Damn the public," she added, with that forthrightness that I so admired in her. "All three boys told me before they went over-seas that they hoped that one of them would be killed in battle. And their mother knows that they feel that way. Shocking, isn't it?"

It was more than shocking that our American democracy should be so served. Nor had I been guiltless in this crucifixion. I remembered that long before I met Eleanor Roosevelt, I had been prejudiced by the unfortunate chemistry of her voice, her photographs, and an almost stupidly honest avowal of her convictions. "You're right, she's stupid to lay herself open to criticism the way she does," Malvina agreed in one of our many talks together, "but she's the nearest to the Christ spirit that we're likely to encounter in our time."

I couldn't put Malvina's words out of my mind, and I felt impelled to put into my own words the truth about this gloriously stupid woman whose undevious soul made her the easy target of political as well as personal venom. There was nothing undevious about my soul, though. If indeed I had won some small name for myself in the literary world, now was the time to trade on it. I telephoned Edwin Balmer as soon as I got back to Lyme, and nearly startled him out of his gentle wits. "I'm going to write an article," I informed him. "I'm calling it 'Second Thoughts on the First Lady,' and I want ten thousand dollars for it which I will divide equally in contributions to the Red Cross and the March of Dimes."

I heard him gasp as audibly as if he were standing beside me. I gasped a little too. Price had never been an issue between us, and here I was demanding twice the amount of money that Herbert Mayes had bought the two old ladies for. "It isn't as if I were keeping any of it for myself," I broke the heavy silence on the other end of the wire.

"But it isn't the money," Mr. Balmer finally managed to convey to me. "In fact, I've been meaning to talk to you about the Claudia stories. They've been doubling our news-stand circulation, and I think we ought to double what we're paying you——"

"You're paying me enough for them," I interrupted crisply. "It's just the article I want more for."

"Miss Franken, I can't publish the article," he said starkly.

"But you haven't read it yet, so how do you know?"

"Because it would be against our editorial policy."

Bill had prepared me for this political issue, and I was ready for it. "In that case, Mr. Balmer, I don't think that *Redbook* ought to publish *Claudia*."

"I don't understand. What do you mean?" he stammered.

"I mean that I come from a long line of Republicans too, Mr. Balmer. And if I can write that article, your readers can read it, and they're exactly the readers I would like to have read it. I'm sorry to make this ultimatum, but it's something I feel very strongly about, and if *Redbook* will not publish the article, they will never publish anything else of mine."

"Perhaps if you change the title of the article. . . ." he wavered.

"The title stays, and I want the article printed word for word."

He surrendered to my terms, and I felt awful about it. In excuse for my piratical tactics, however, Mr. Balmer did not suffer from having a literary gun held to his head. The article met with a reception that justified the magazine bringing out a reprint edition in pamphlet form, and I remember Vernon racing across the lawn one evening to tell us to turn on the radio quickly and listen to Walter Winchell. I was much gratified. Mr. Winchell hadn't talked about me on the air since he had broadcast the fact that I had lost three fingers in the dining-room door.

The success of the piece further cemented my affiliation with

Redbook, and I turned out another batch of Claudia stories, and found that I enjoyed writing them after my intensive stint of Washington rehearsals. I always gagged a little at having to listen to my own lines *ad nauseam*, and this particular overdose of Claudia was more than ever an ordeal, for she had long since progressed beyond the wide-eyed innocence of the young bride in the play. It was somewhat of an intellectual challenge, at this stage of her development, to shepherd her through a miscarriage, a so-called nervous breakdown, and a mature and knowledgeable approach to a tenuous crisis in her marital relationship. I was, in truth, frequently astonished that Mr. Balmer, the most moral of editorial guardians, condoned the increasing sophistication of the stories.

I was in the middle of manipulating a delicate episode between Claudia and her trained nurse, when Gilbert Miller decided to go ahead with the production of *Outrageous Fortune*.

"I hope your husband will be able to stay in town with you," he said anxiously. He had none of John Golden's niggling reservations about Bill. On the contrary, he had the greatest respect for him, addressed him affectionately as "old boy," and introduced him to his tailor. But apart from that I suspected that he was counting on a close marital influence in the matter of casting.

However, once he resigned himself to the fact that he couldn't turn to Bill for support, he listlessly signed up the actors I had chosen, and looked ill again. His interest revived with the designing and décor of the play's single set, since the scene was laid in a sumptuous home on the Jersey shore, and offered a suitable background for expensive furnishings, and a painting from his father-in-law's great art collection. Similarly, the costuming swelled the budget to a respectable figure. Kitty, Gilbert's wife, always "dressed" his shows, and although I insisted on Margaret wearing her own shabby little blouse-and-skirt, loop earrings, and no porcelain jackets on her front teeth, I was pleased to have Elsie, especially, decked out in the costliest of creations from Kitty's favourite couturière. Looking back on what was, for us, three easy-moving and serene weeks of rehearsal, I realize, with compunction, that the set and the clothes probably constituted for Gilbert and Kitty the only rewarding aspects of the whole production.

Mistakenly, on the opening night of the Boston try-out, I felt that I had atoned to them for whatever stubbornness I had shown. My judgment was vindicated. The entire cast turned in flawless performances, and the play (I thought) held together, and the confluence of its theme emerged with lucidity. Bill stood with me at the back of the theatre, and confessed to a lump in his throat during the last act, which was all I needed to sustain my idiotic conviction, especially when I saw Gilbert and Kitty rise from their seats, and hurry up the aisle as the curtain fell on the final scene. "They're racing backstage to congratulate the cast," I whispered happily.

I was wrong on more than one count. They weren't headed for back-stage, and immediately upon reading the first two bad reviews in the morning papers, Gilbert closed the play.

Like a fool, I'd telephoned home when we returned to the hotel that night—primarily to find out if any post had come from Paul—but also to report to John that both the play and the cast had come through magnificently. He was up and waiting for the call, being the only one of the boys with a lively, but thank heaven, healthy affinity for the theatre; his interest in the smallest detail of the opening was gratifying.

"How about Elsie Ferguson. Did she forget her lines?"

"She was superb!" Bill exulted from the extension in the bedroom.

"Gosh, that's great! Are you going to wait up for the reviews?"

"No need to," I assured him confidently, "but we'll call you in the morning after we've seen them."

"Tell Vernon to hold off with the feed order," Bill added. "I'll be back on Wednesday."

A lot we knew what was going to be happening by Wednesday.

"Look, John," Bill broke the news the next day, "do you think you and Vernon and Al could run the farm without me for a while?"

"Sure, but why? Anything wrong?"

"A little," I admitted from the extension in the other room. "The morning papers were brutal."

"What'd they say, the stupid bums?"

"They praised *Another Language* and *Claudia* all over again." This softened the verdict of those particular Boston intellects who, in vitriolic summation, agreed with John Golden that they didn't know what I was talking about in my latest play, and why wasn't I content to let my talents serve the cause of normal, happy people? It is ironic to reflect that there was as yet no precedence for the violence, filth and depravity in the dramatic output that was later to merit the plaudits of these same custodians of public sentiment, and in comparison to which, *Outrageous Fortune* paled into a gentle story of gentle people in conflict with themselves and the world outside of themselves. On the morning of October 19, 1943, however, I seemed to have committed the unforgivable sin of transgressing beyond the palatable verities of life, and the conventional craftsmanship of my previous plays.

"Don't worry about the farm, it's running fine, but what's happening now, are you staying on with Mother while she rewrites?" John reverted to Bill's query.

"I'm not rewriting," I injected. "My new producer doesn't want a word of the play changed, he's going to bring it into New York exactly as it is."

"Gosh, Mother, that's great, who is he?"

"Me," Bill said.

"But gosh, Bill," John stammered, "don't you have to know something about producing to be a producer?"

"He does," I said. "Why do you think he was hanging around the theatre all the time we were doing *Claudia*?"

"I just thought he wanted to," John gave himself away.

"I wanted to," Bill amended, "on the theory that it's always a good thing to learn everything you can learn about something you don't know anything about."

"Gosh," John said again, as if it were the only word he could think of, "it's sure coming in handy, and I sure am with you, Bill. Good luck."

"Thank you, old boy."

"That yellow-bellied son of a bitch," John said, and I didn't reprove him for what I recognized to be an overt accolade to Bill. "You should be pleased," Bill returned the accolade after we'd hung up. "A brat one minute and a man the next. It takes a load off my mind with the farm." He glanced at his watch. "I can walk over with you to talk to the cast, and still catch the noon plane to New York."

I had to say it. I said, "I think you ought to wait and see if the afternoon papers crucify us too."

"It won't change my mind, no matter what they say. Unless you're afraid to trust me with as good a play as this is."

I was touched at his way of putting it. "Don't be silly. You weren't picking John Golden's brains behind his back all those weeks for fun."

"I hope not," he said.

His first big test came a short while later when he faced the cast. The stage manager had sent out a ten-thirty call on the assumption that actors are always up early on the morning after an opening, either to gloat or gloom over their individual reviews. Bill had never worked closely with actors, and I wondered whether I ought to prepare him for what I knew was going to be a subtle switch in an erstwhile eager and co-operative relationship, and then I decided, somewhat like a brooding mother, that it was wiser not to try to run interference for him in this heart-over-head undertaking that he was apparently bent on going through with.

What few notes I had jotted down during the performance the previous evening were fortunately unimportant, for the entire cast had come off so well in the reviews that they could not help but feel that they were not only above criticism, but had lent their talents to promoting an utter and dismal failure. So obvious was their attitude of mingled sympathy and patronage, that we both realized that Gilbert must have already posted the closing notice. It shouldn't have surprised us, because while he was still in his bathrobe that morning he had summoned us to his room to announce that he had already cancelled the Royale Theatre in New York, along with a substantial advance sale, and a large subscription of benefit performances that would have at least given us some sort of insurance against financial disaster. "You work fast, Gilbert," Bill had remarked quietly.

"It's my business to work fast and cut my losses, old boy. No hard feelings, I hope."

"None," Bill agreed, "but as I intend to assume complete responsibility for the production—excluding of course your father-in-law's painting—I shall ask you to take no further steps in closing the play."

Gilbert waggled a warning finger. "You mustn't do it, old boy. Really. With those reviews you don't stand a chance, you'll lose your shirt."

"It's my shirt," Bill returned with a pleasant smile that was a little white round the edges.

His lips were less white than straight-set as he formally apprised the cast of his decision to bring the play into New York. "I am glad to be able to give you the opportunity of being seen on Broadway, which is understandably the primary aim of every actor, but in the capacity of your future producer, I would like to leave one thought with you: gratifying though it is that your performances last night justified Miss Franken's faith in you, I must remind you that few critics are astute enough to realize that actors are as good as the lines they are given to read, and the direction that teaches them how to read those lines."

A hard fast silence fell upon the despondent but complacent group that were gathered before us on the stage. Then Maria Ouspenskaya stepped forth, with all the tradition of the European artist housed in her small, gnarled body. "I have been a teacher of acting for many years," she said, "and I can say that Mr. Meloney is speaking the truth. I am proud to be in this play."

Bill said, "Thank you, Madame. Thank you very much."

Elsie Ferguson moved forward from the suddenly humbled company. "Would you mind if I gave the new producer a kiss?" she asked me.

Bill looked uncomfortable. He hadn't bargained for kissing, but I generously granted Elsie permission to go right ahead. I was vastly relieved. He had made his first big hurdle in winning the respect of his actors.

I drove out to the airport with him. While we waited for the plane, he stepped over to the news-stand, and returned with a single paper.

"This just came in, the afternoon editions aren't out yet," he vouchsafed briefly. As he riffled through to the theatre columns and spanked the page into a neat oblong, my heart took a sick lurch. I could face up to any review except a review in the *Christian Science Monitor*. The dramatic editor, who signed himself L. A. Sloper, enjoyed a wide and justifiable reputation of being a critic of unbiased perception, and having been exceedingly kind to *Another Language* and *Claudia* I didn't have the courage to hear what he had to say about *Outrageous Fortune*, except that whatever he did have to say would be said with an objective intelligence, worthy of an author's consideration. "He's bound to hate it even worse than the ordinary critics," I hazarded faintly.

Bill's face was noncommittal. He sat down beside me on the bench, sharing the page so that I could read the review for myself.

After the first paragraph, I said shakily, "I think I'm going to cry."

Bill said, "I think I'll join you."

If it hadn't been for the stormy and highly controversial reception of *Outrageous Fortune*, I might still be slave to a clipping bureau, but as I recall, it was Mr. Kronenberger's review in a New York paper called *PM* that was the final indignity that caused me to cancel my subscription for all time. I would be at a loss, therefore, to quote from the critical reactions to any plays or novels subsequent to *Outrageous Fortune*, but it so happens that in going over a lot of ancient photographs (I am not emancipated when it comes to tearing up old pictures) I unearthed a thick, expandable black album, very musty and partially mildewed, into which my Aunt Jane had fatuously pasted the duplicate clippings of all of my literary endeavours from *Pattern* up to—and including—*Outrageous Fortune*. Which turns out to be a good thing, because it's going to save time and space to copy, verbatim, certain extracts of the press that will best give a capsule account of Bill's and my first joint venture into the theatre. I will start off with Mr. Sloper's review, which came as such an emotional astonishment to our lacerated spirits. Sitting on that hard bench in the Boston airport, we read as follows:

> *"Rose Franken has written in* Outrageous Fortune *a brilliant, subtle, moving drama, leagues beyond* Claudia *and* Another Language. *Daring greatly, she has presented a social study based on three main motifs, the race problem, homosexuality and marital maladjustment. Usually, when a playwright attempts to handle so many themes in one play, the result is confusion. Miss Franken has managed her material with a contrapuntal mastery which achieves a fundamental unity."*

That was the opening paragraph, and in re-reading the *Monitor* clipping, I can honestly report that in the whole of two long columns, Mr. Sloper did not qualify or temper his unstinting admiration for the play, the direction, and the actors who performed in it.

I need not add that his opinion was like a benediction to us, but nevertheless I felt a deep satisfaction in knowing that Bill had not waited for Mr. Sloper's acclaim to bolster his faith in the play, or confirm his intention to produce it. However, it needed Mr. Sloper's enthusiastic endorsement to give several of the local critics pause for belated thought. For example, Mr. Elliot Norton's tempering of his initial review in a Sunday editorial, notified his readers in big headlines that *"OUTRAGEOUS FORTUNE* MIGHT HAVE BEEN A GOOD PLAY," after which he went on to say that "ROSE FRANKEN'S LATEST OFFERING CLOSED FOR GOOD LAST NIGHT AFTER A LONE, LEAN WEEK AT THE WILBUR THEATRE."

It is an accurate report of our try-out in Boston, except for one small detail. Either Mr. Norton was unaware that the play was not closing "for good," or he could not believe that any producer in his right mind would throw good money after bad. And maybe he was right. We'd already thrown in the equivalent of a sizable herd of pedigreed Jerseys and it looked as if we were going to be mortgaging the whole farm before we were finished. Everything was against us. We had no advance sale, adverse publicity, and the Forty-eighth Street Theatre, which was disadvantageous both in its location and state of disrepair, but it was the only house available to us on any terms. In the five days that Bill had spent alone in New York, he had tried to reclaim the Royale, and salvage at least some fraction of the benefit performances to couch our losses, but he'd soon discovered that Broadway was quick to sniff out the aura of failure. "I'm afraid I'm not going to be able to give you a very glamorous opening-night audience," he prepared me. "We'll have to paper the house to fill it."

I swallowed my premonitions of utter disaster. "That's the only thing to do," I said.

A lot of things have happened to me in my life that I can't explain, and the New York opening of *Outrageous Fortune* is one of them. It sounds fantastic—and I can count the times that I have used the word—to say that when our taxi drew up in front of the Forty-Eighth Street Theatre on the cold, rainy afternoon we returned from Boston, we saw a long line of people waiting patiently outside of the deserted box office.

"Get busy," Bill hissed in my ear, as he unlocked the cage. "Take the money, use these note-pads for receipts, and tell everyone to come back tomorrow for their tickets."

I was too dazed to do anything but blindly follow his instructions. If I had had a white apron, I'd have felt like a delicatessen-store wife waiting on crowds of hungry customers.

Bill and I worked at it until dark. In the morning, the box-office men took over. By evening we were sold out to standing room for its first night, and very nearly sold out for the remainder of the week.

If I were reading this, I wouldn't believe me, but according to my scrapbook, *Variety* the bible of show business verifies the fact: "FORTUNE" FINE $9000 IN 1ST FIVE TIMES."

And below in more intelligible phrasing:

"Gilbert Miller appears to have guessed wrong when he abandoned Outrageous Fortune *by Rose Franken, whose husband, William Brown Meloney, is presenting the drama at the Forty-Eighth Street Theatre. It is another play that drew mostly adverse notices this season but appears to be clicking at the box-office regardless. After première,* Fortune *jumped close to capacity, and surprised even Broadway."*

[335]

It would be reasonable to conclude after the preceding notation that the miracle that resulted from that rainy afternoon in the box office marked the end of our troubles. But it was only the beginning of them.

At eleven o'clock on the morning of the opening, we were having a run-through on the stage to test out lighting and acoustics, and everything was working so smoothly, and my actors were so exhilarated by the constant buzz of activity round the box office, that I thought I had nothing more to worry about. Elsie Ferguson was sitting alone out front, watching the rehearsal. I moved down the aisle and said cheerily, "It's almost time for your entrance, Elsie."

Her voice came at me out of the darkness. "Time for my entrance," she repeated in a melodramatic crescendo, "What entrance? I have no intention of performing in this wretched theatre tonight! Nobody can give Elsie Ferguson a dressing-room that isn't fit for a dog! I'm going back to my home in the country, and to hell with a stinking stage career, and to hell with your miserable play!"

She had to be joking, it was unthinkable that it could be otherwise. And then something in the set of her jaw, and the way she sat with her shoulders glued against the back of the seat signalled a warning that she was in deadly earnest. She had done it before, and she was about to do it again, only this time the curtain would not be rung down halfway through an opening night, the curtain wasn't going to go up. Elsie Ferguson was walking out on us.

My knees knocked together and my heart hammered, but I had to say something, anything, in response to this staggering ultimatum. "Elsie, I can't begin to tell you how much I admire you," I propounded with a fervency that I prayed would cover the quavering of my voice.

She squared round to stare at me. "What do you mean, you 'admire me', " she demanded from the very depths of her larynx. "What are you trying to pull?"

Her astonishment fed my courage. "I'm not trying to pull

anything," I assured her earnestly. "I admire you because I can't imagine any other ageing actress who would have the sheer guts to stage a come-back, and then admit at the very last moment that she couldn't go through with it."

"Who said I couldn't go through with it!" Fury thundered through her sonorous, pear-shaped enunciation. "I can damn well go through with it, but I don't choose to. Your little act doesn't fool me one bit. You're scared pink, my girl. You know as well as I do that you can't open your play tonight, because you haven't even got an understudy who could walk on in my place!"

She'd come so close to the truth that my knees stopped shaking only because they had turned to rubber beneath me. But she'd showed me, unwittingly, how and where to aim my last blow, and if it didn't work, *Outrageous Fortune* was finished, Bill was finished, and our bank account was finished. "We haven't got a special understudy for Ouspenskaya either," I admitted, "because it isn't necessary. Maria would give a performance if she had to be carried on to the stage." (Which actually happened when she came down with an influenza and a hundred and four temperature several weeks later). "And I certainly don't need an understudy for you, Elsie. Didn't you ever guess that I was a frustrated actress?"

"You! This is to laugh. Really, to laugh!"

"Why is it to laugh? Who do you think taught you your every line, your every move? Why, I've been aching to play the part of Crystal, so if you're worried about our not opening tonight, you run along back to Lyme and don't give it a thought. Of course," I added regretfully, "I wish there were time to refit your clothes for me, but there isn't, so the wardrobe woman will have to sort of wind and drape me into everything with pins. It'll make a good news story, anyway. I can just see the headlines in Variety: *Author Director Nabs Fat Ferguson Role. Wins Plaudits Swimming in Star's Costumes.*"

It was at that precise instant that my play, Bill's reputation, and our joint savings hung in the balance. Elsie rose to her feet, smacked up the adjoining seat and stepped majestically into the aisle. "You bitch!" she ground out between her teeth. "Out of my way!"

x [337]

I felt the imperious swing of her arm as she pushed me aside and strode—not up the aisle towards the exit door, but down the aisle towards the stage. I groped for the seat that she had vacated and very nearly collapsed at the shuddering possibility that this last bluff might not have come off. I wasn't a frustrated actress, I would sooner have cut both wrists with my throat thrown in for good measure, rather than have died a slow death behind the foot-lights in front of an audience.

I was aware that Bill had moved in beside me, and in silence we watched the rehearsal together.

"It's going fine, isn't it?" he whispered.

"Fine."

"Elsie's great, isn't she?"

"Great."

"Pretty good thing we didn't listen to all that vicious gossip about her."

"Pretty," I agreed.

We passed the Waldorf on the way to the theatre. "You're the one Missy would be proud of this evening," I told Bill.

A pile of telegrams awaited us back-stage. And there was a beautiful basket of yellow roses for me. The card read simply, "Elsie."

I handed it to Bill, and in return he handed me a wire addressed to him. "You son of a gun. John Golden."

Our press agent rushed up to us. "We've got a real carriage trade opening, believe it or not, black ties, dowagers with dog-collars and lots of mink and sables. But only one chinchilla," he added respectfully, as he eyed me up and down.

I hadn't taken the coat along to Boston, but I wasn't running any chances in New York. We could tell the next morning how those little rabbits had worked hard for me, but still the reviews were mixed. "You were right when you said I had a name," I told Bill grimly. "I have. But it's turned out to be Claudia."

He couldn't deny it. As sound and impartial a critic as Richard Cooke, of the *Wall Street Journal*, dragged her into his evaluation of *Outrageous Fortune*. He wrote:

"Rose Franken's inclination toward delineating unusual and slightly obscure relationships between human beings was given its head in her new play, which made its bow last night at the Forty-Eighth Street Theatre. The result is a play which is more cause for thought than excitement; its values are debatable but interesting. . . . Not everyone will like it, but I believe that people who are seriously interested in the theatre will find it worth seeing. . . . She succeeds in treating problems which most people discuss in whispers—if at all—with good taste and aplomb. . . . Miss Franken, as in *Claudia*, has succeeded in impregnating them with her own unmistakable and distinctive touch, which is at once literary and emotional. . . . *Outrageous Fortune* evidently will not have the success of Claudia, and does not deserve to have. But it nevertheless is a mature, skillful and sincere effort and one which it must have taken a good bit of courage to write. Personally, I wish Miss Franken well."

Mr. Sherburne, editor of the drama section of the New York *Monitor*, was, like his Boston colleague Mr. Sloper, one of the few exceptions who ignored the starry-eyed young bride clinging to my literary coat-tails, and wrote a most thoughtful and commendatory appraisal of *Outrageous Fortune* purely on its own merits. And it was additionally gratifying to me that he did not ignore Bill as my producer:

"William Brown Meloney presented *Outrageous Fortune* at the Forty-Eighth Street Theatre on Wednesday evening. In writing the play, Miss Franken has manifested the sort of daring that derives only from deep feeling. Seeing human beings as individuals, she could not bring herself to cast them into stock stage patterns. . . ."

It is an interesting commentary on critical perspicacity to mention at this point that a number of reviewers accused me of using not only stock characters, but stock actors. Why, for example, was I so unimaginative a director as to cast a coloured actress who had been appearing on the stage for years on end, playing maids' parts?. . . . Even Margaret herself took umbrage at that one, pleased though she was at being mistaken for a professional. All in all, George Jean Nathan was perhaps our staunchest champion, for he too extended his high regard to Bill. In one of his many allusions to *Outrageous Fortune*, he wrote:

"... And there is something else to be said for the rookies (producers). It took one of them, Meloney, to give New York the best new play of the season after one of the veterans, Gilbert Miller, who had previously been the producer, withdrew from its sponsorship, fearful of losing money and position after it had received some idiotically bad notices in its out-of-town showing. . . ."

These excerpts may convey an impression that we received a predominantly favourable press. Unfortunately that is not the case, for a number of critics resented my impudent excursion into the realm of serious drama, although Mr. Kronenberger was a little more vociferous in voicing his opinion. His caption declared *Outrageous Fortune* to be "*Very Fancy BUT VERY Foolish*," after which he summed up my talents in one blistering sentence:

"... Such as they are, Miss Franken's real gifts lie in a far more housefrauish direction; when, for example, she talks about food, she makes sense."

It is just as well that I cancelled my clipping service at that point. Thereby I have avoided a possible ulcer, along with mountains of scrap-books that would have undoubtedly caused my family great conflict as to whether to keep them, or pitch them out after my demise.

It was a stiff challenge to Bill's untried skill in the highly competitive field of play production to have been able to weather the adversities that both preceded and followed our opening. On the third night, scarcely more than a few minutes before curtain time, two men appeared on the set, and began to take measurements. Bill was talking to me in the wings and recognized one of the men to be Michael Todd.

"What the hell do you think you're doing, Todd. Get off this stage and fast, or I'll throw you off!"

"Your play is a flop, so I'm the one who's going to do the throwing around here!" Mr. Todd shouted back. "I happen to own this theatre and I'm bringing in a musical next week!"

"And I happen to have leased this theatre from you, and you have no right, legal or otherwise, to come on my premises. So pick up that tape measure, and get out. And get out quick! You're upsetting the cast and holding up the curtain!"

Remembering the pigeon episode in Hollywood, I haven't the slightest doubt that Bill would have lifted Mr. Todd by the scruff of the neck and ejected him bodily, but the policeman on the block, who had stopped by to pay his respects, saved him the trouble. The policeman liked people who liked his horse and he wasted no time with people he didn't like. He ambled across to Mr. Todd, twirling his stick with leisurely deliberation. "Come on, Buster, out you go, the two of you, and see that you don't come back or I'll turn you in for disturbing the peace."

I went weak with relief. Living with Bill was living under the constant trepidation of his black Irish temper getting him into fist fights. Sam Zolotow, genial ferret of Broadway, and guiding spirit of the *Times* theatrical column, reported the incident the next morning in a mellow mood:

> "With best wishes, Michael Todd is permitting *Outrageous Fortune* to remain at his Forty-Eighth Street Theatre so long as business holds up. One can't ask a paying tenant to clear out just like that. Consequently Mr. Todd will not bring his *"Star and Garter"* there on November 22nd as he intended.

It is not in idle reciprocation to say that we looked on Sam Zolotow as one of our friendlier friends in "show business," but unwittingly he betrayed us with *When Doctors Disagree*, and he couldn't have been more contrite when he realized it.

It was probably because *Outrageous Fortune* finally established itself as a controversial success, that the rumour began to get around of my having written another play. There appeared to be so much interest in it that Bill decided that now might be the auspicious time to produce it, and thereby defray the overheads of an expensive office set-up. We had far from recouped our investment in *Outrageous Fortune*, yet it was surprisingly easy to obtain outside financing for *When Doctors Disagree*. We found ourselves with a waiting line of eager backers, including Gilbert —with whom we remained on the most amicable terms—but Bill wisely chose the impersonal relationship of one of those new pre-production picture deals. Ironically, Harry Cohn, who had been thwarted in buying *Claudia* for Columbia, turned out to be our most importunate bidder—which strengthened my long-standing theory that it was impossible to insult Hollywood.

From start to finish, *When Doctors Disagree* presented no problems whatsoever, actors and script included. After the first smooth reading of the play with an untemperamental but entirely competent cast, I was in full agreement with Bill's suggestion to dispense with the added cost and delay of an out-of-town try-out. By so doing, we were able to book an advantageous theatre on Forty-fifth Street, and also enjoy the upswing of business between Christmas and the New Year.

Three preview performances with carefully diversified audiences justified our daring to "open cold." The separate reactions on each succeeding night were unanimously enthusiastic. I remember Alfred DeLiagre, the producer of *Voice of the Turtle* rushing up to Bill and pumping his hand. "This is what I call a good evening in the theatre, exciting and adult, and it's going to be great having another hit next door to us!"

We were asking for trouble to have believed him, but we both honestly felt that truth was stronger than superstition. This time everything was in our favour. The actors were happy and congenial, the performances as polished and meshed as they were ever likely to be, and the values of the play emerged with validity. Hospitals and doctors had not yet become a fictional drug on the entertainment market, and the story I was telling was rooted legitimately in the drama of medicine, but nevertheless avoided the pitfall of becoming a case history.

Relaxed and unjittery, we lingered over breakfast on the morning of the opening, and leisurely leafed through the papers to check on and admire the good-looking format of Bill's announcement of the première. Then, very suddenly, he said, "Oh, God," and looked stricken.

"What's the matter?"

He handed the *Times* to me across the table. "Read Sam Zolotow's column."

I read it. "Oh, God," I echoed.

Sam had given us generous space, as always, but failing the stormy publicity that had preceded *Outrageous Fortune*, he had gone to great pains to dig up anything he could find out about *When Doctors Disagree*, to stimulate interest in the opening. With no malice whatsoever, he chattily revealed that Bill and I had originally written the play as a serial for the *Ladies' Home Journal*, and he had it on good authority that it was the most successful serial they had ever published. In 1941, he went on, Farrar and Rinehart brought it out as a novel, under one of our magazine pseudonyms, and now, at long last, it was to reach the Broadway stage. (This, of course, is not a word-for-word transcription, but it is certainly the substance of his kindly efforts on our behalf.)

I raced to the telephone—I don't know why, because there was nothing we could do about it. "Sam, what have you done to us!" I wailed, and clarified my lament by informing him that he had his facts backside front. I had written *When Doctors Disagree* as a play before I'd ever met Bill, and we'd merely borrowed bits and pieces of its medical background for *Woman in White*.

Sam was confused. "But the novel that I got out of the library was called *When Doctors Disagree*, and there was a note in the front of the book that it had been serialized in the *Ladies' Home Journal*, otherwise I wouldn't have known about it!"

"John Farrar didn't like the magazine title," I explained hoarsely, "so we substituted the title I'd used for the play, which he did like, because it's from Shakespeare."

Sam couldn't have been sorrier for his mistaken endeavour to help us. "I suppose it doesn't do much good to say I didn't mean to hurt you, and I'll retract everything I said in tomorrow's column," he promised.

"Thanks for offering, Sam, but tomorrow will be too late," I told him bleakly.

I was so certain of it, and Bill too, that he didn't say anything when he saw me lay out an old evening cape for the opening. No rabbit on earth could revive a goose that was already cooked.

And never had there been a goose so thoroughly roasted and basted. There was scarcely a review that did not belabour my material ambition to have two plays "from my pen" running on Broadway simultaneously and I had, moreover, accomplished this unworthy goal by turning out a soap opera, hastily adapted from a slick magazine story. Since I did not expect to escape the onus of *Claudia* completely, I was affronted though not surprised when one of the afternoon papers further decried my greed by calling attention to the fact that I was already rich enough to own a mansion in Washington Square and a two hundred acre estate in Connecticut, while another periodical of the same ilk made an overt allusion to furs and jewels doubtlessly purchased out of my ill-gotten *Claudia* spoils.

All of which did not lie within the decent province of literary criticism. For the first time Bill permitted himself the luxury of damning the souls of all pusillanimous reviewers, and closed both plays in February. "Gather your chinchillas round you," he said, "and let's go back to our Connecticut estate."

I couldn't have been happier to do just that.

Mr. Balmer was among a fair majority of the public who had "loved every minute" of *When Doctors Disagree*. He had seen it twice during its brief run, but he didn't mention whether he'd seen *Outrageous Fortune* even once. He was a gentle man, easily shocked.

In any event, he sent me a note soon after we returned to Lyme to say that although our withdrawal from the theatre was a great disappointment to everyone, he was selfishly pleased that I would, he hoped, be able to resume work on the Claudia stories, and he would be very happy if he could schedule a new one for the Easter issue, with more to follow, and the sooner the better.

"I'll sit right down and write him the one for April," I told

Bill vindictively, "but he'll never publish it, and I can guarantee you that he'll never ask me for another story."

I was beginning to know how Dorothy Maguire felt when she'd recently informed Twentieth Century that *Claudia* was destroying her career, and therefore she did not want to commit herself to the second picture. It meant, of course, the end of the film series, inasmuch as she had become too identified with the character by this time to attempt to substitute another actress, but in my present mood, I was in sympathy with Dorothy rather than the studio. The first picture had already been released at the Radio City Music Hall (or Roxy's, I forget which), and until I saw it I had forgotten how Hollywood could mess up a story if they really set their minds to it. Obedient to the mesmerism of success, however, audiences and critics alike swallowed the nauseating mixture of whimsy and sentiment, and according to the newspapers *Claudia* broke all records at the box office and was held over for an extra week. Which didn't help my reputation any more than it helped Miss Maguire's. No one, least of all my devoted *Redbook* readers, seemed to register the fact that in the three existing novels, the teen-age bride had long since passed the age of childish innocence, and I could only conclude that I had erred on the side of subtlety.

A February thaw fooled the forsythia into mistaking a stretch of balmy days for spring, but I resolutely turned my back on some baby lambs that had likewise pressed the season, and closed my nostrils to the heady whiff of manure that wafted through the open windows. "Here," I said to Bill, as I gave him a sheaf of freshly typed pages. "It's a shame to do it to Mr. Balmer, but his honeymoon with *Claudia* is over."

Bill read my final opus with a broad grin. "This is certainly going to fix her wagon but I don't know how you have the nerve to send it in."

It wasn't a question of nerve, it was a showdown as to which one of us was going to survive, and if I didn't take drastic steps to cut the umbilical cord between us, I knew that I would never be able to pull free of her delicate stranglehold on everything I might write in the future.

Less penitent than defiant, I awaited Mr. Balmer's reaction to her highly sophisticated swan-song, which, incidentally, I rather enjoyed writing. It was his gracious custom to send me a note of appreciation with every story I submitted, but this time he telephoned me. "You must realize," he began apologetically, "that Claudia is loved by men, women and children across this whole country, and we must be very careful never to print anything that might be in the least offensive."

"I know," I broke in eagerly, "and I also realize that this is a very offensive story, so I can quite understand your having to reject it."

He was horrified. "Reject it? Whatever gave you such an idea! I just want to ask your permission to take out the 'didies', and use handkerchiefs instead."

"Yes. Certainly. Of course. That's all right. Go ahead," I replied, with a kind of repetitive paralysis. "But is that all you object to?"

"The rest of the story is delightful, and so witty that I took it home to read aloud to my wife."

"And she liked it?"

"She loved it. She thought it was the best yet."

Bill eyed me apprehensively when he came in from the barn for lunch. "You look sunk, what's wrong?"

" 'Didies'," I said bitterly.

I thought of writing another play as an excuse to evade Mr. Balmer's insistent request for more stories, but I didn't feel like it. A play was either ready to write itself or else it wasn't ready to be written (according to my peculiar way of writing plays), and I had had enough of the theatre for the time being. I wasn't conscious of continuing to smart under a sense of defeat, but equally, I was not possessed by a burning passion to justify myself as a playwright, any more than Bill was consumed with any great desire to prove his worth as a producer. He had his novel to finish, and as always, in spring, there was plenty of ploughing and harrowing and seeding to be done. "Why don't you just sit, for a change, and enjoy the farm," he suggested, "and if it makes you any happier, you can worry about me and the boys."

"It sounds inviting," I said. Not that I ever really stopped thinking about Paul, and waiting for his letters.

One night, quite late, the telephone rang, and my heart did its usual leap into my throat as I reached for the receiver.

"I'm sorry to call at this hour, it's Eleanor."

Eleanor. I felt disgruntled. I knew a number of Eleanors. "Eleanor who?"

"Eleanor Roosevelt."

"Oh, hello! I'm terribly sorry, I should have recognized your voice——"

"I'm afraid I wakened you," she said, "but it's quite urgent, I have a friend who's leaving for Australia very shortly, and she'd be glad to take along a small package of gifts for Paul. She's hoping to get up into New Guinea, but if she doesn't she'll see that they reach him, anyway."

My first thought was that Eleanor was being her naïve self in assuming that a perfect stranger would welcome the idea of lugging stuff clear across the Pacific Ocean to deliver to some unknown soldier. "It's wonderful of you to think of it," I thanked her, "but I wouldn't dream of placing you in the position of asking a favour like that, it's an imposition."

"Please don't argue," she returned with an asperity that sat strangely upon her. "Can you have the package delivered to my apartment in Washington Square by tomorrow afternoon?"

I said slowly, "You're your friend, aren't you?"

"It mustn't leak out," she answered obliquely. "We have to observe the utmost secrecy about the trip. For security reasons."

"I know," I said. "I know."

I didn't tell her how I knew. For a long while after I put the receiver back on the hook, I lay staring into the dark.

"Regrets?" Bill asked softly.

"I'd have more regrets," I said, "if it were anyone else who was going in my place."

We took an early train into town the next morning, and bought the wrist-watch and the cigarette lighter that Bill had wanted to get for Paul months and months ago. Eleanor was at her apartment when we arrived, and she insisted on giving us tea. It wasn't a stylish apartment, and the tea was served in substantial white cups, with large round cookies from the neighbourhood bakery.

It was close to five o'clock before we left, and the trains were already crowded with commuters. There weren't any parlour cars. We moved through coach after coach, disappointed because we could not find two seats together. It was a long ride back to Lyme, and I was fussy about whom I sat next to. "This is for you," Bill signalled, as we came up to a small, grey-haired woman with no bundles, wearing a service pin in the lapel of her tidy serge coat, and reading *Redbook.* "I'll find a seat in the smoking car," he said.

The woman was hardly aware of my sitting down beside her. She drew a little further towards the window, without bothering to look up from the magazine. Sneakily, I peered over her shoulder and recognized the illustration. I wouldn't have been human if I hadn't felt tempted to ask her if she was enjoying the story, but I restrained the impulse. I was more interested in her service pin. Did she have a husband or a son in the war? I wondered. I had met a number of female patriots who sported handsome gold insignias even for nephews, but this was a very modest little pin, and the woman's face was sad in spite of the faint amusement that twitched at her lips as she scanned the pages. We had passed Bridgeport before she finally looked up. As if conscious for the first time of sharing her seat, she turned to me with a smile. "I bought the magazine at the station because there was a Claudia story advertised on the cover. I never miss one if I can help it. Do you ever read them?"

I almost said, "No, I write them," but I thought better of it. It would start much too much talk, and besides, I had, more than ever, the feeling that I was less the author of *Claudia,* than the unwitting instrument for putting words about her down on paper. "Yes," I said merely, and then it was my turn to smile. "My service pin is in my purse. The clasp is faulty, and I was afraid of losing it."

Her eyes, ringed with little half-moons of wrinkles, appraised me warmly. "Have you noticed how those pins seem to bring women together? Is it your son in the war?"

"Yes."

"I have two in it. The youngest is still in training over here, I'm thankful to say, but Joey's been in the South Pacific now nearly two years.—Has your son gone overseas yet?"

"His regiment was the first to sail. He's in the South Pacific, too."

She sighed. "It's awful, isn't it, to think of them in those dreadful jungles? But maybe it isn't as bad as we imagine. Joey wrote that they were having ice cream on Sundays. I couldn't believe it, in all that heat, I think he was trying to cheer me up so that I wouldn't think he was living on cans of beans and K ration."

"He's in the 208th regiment in New Guinea, isn't he?"

She stared at me. "How did you know? I'm sure I didn't mention it, did I? My husband says it's better not to talk about where they are. . . ."

"No. You didn't mention it."

The train jerked to a stop. "Oh, dear, oh, dear," she exclaimed, gathering her magazine and gloves and purse in a flurry. "This is where I get off, and there's no time to ask you however in this world you guessed where Joey was when he could just as easily have been a marine at Guadalcanal or the Solomons for all you could tell. It's the most uncanny thing that's ever happened to me, but I suppose when two mothers meet like this, they just know things out of the air."

I wondered, had she not had to hurry off at her station, whether I would have had the heart to disillusion her with a very down-to-earth explanation of this apparently mystical experience. Simply, it had come to my knowledge through Captain Griswold's wife, who lived in Hartford, that Paul had used a portion of the Australian play royalties assigned to his personal account, to fly down to Melbourne just long enough to buy an ice-cream freezer, a toilet-that-flushed, a ping-pong table, and as many other luxuries of civilization for his men as an Army plane could carry back to the base at Moresby.

I moved over to the window and waved back to the little grey-haired woman who stood looking up at me from the platform. There was a glow on her face, and all the sadness had gone out of it. I could thank *Claudia* for that glow, and I vowed, with humility and gratefulness, that I would never again try to walk out on her, or give her less than the best that was in me to give.

"You should have landed me a good kick in the pants for acting like such a rotten snob," I said to Bill as we climbed into the station wagon that we had left parked at Saybrook. "I'd damn well better see to it from now on that I don't ruin Claudia's reputation, instead of the other way around."

"I was hoping," Bill replied mildly, "that sooner or later you'd come to your senses all by yourself."

"Funny how that little thing on the train could do it."

Bill said, "I think it was a pretty big thing."

I telephoned Mr. Balmer the next morning, and asked him if he could schedule three instalments of a Claudia novelette, instead of three separate stories. "It will help me in reassembling a lot of the material for the fourth novel," I explained.

He accepted the proposition with alacrity. "I couldn't be happier," he said. "Frankly, I've been afraid lately you were going to want to stop the series entirely."

"Frankly," I confessed, "I did want to."

I had always received a good deal of fan mail, but suddenly a fairish number of letters seemed to bear no relation to anything I had written, but alluded, obliquely, to incidents or experiences in which I had presumably participated. They bore no return address, and were rarely signed beyond scrawled initials.

"You're bound to get a few crank letters of one kind or another," Bill dismissed them casually. "Pay no attention to them."

It was around that time, too, I recall, that various rumours about me began to appear in the gossip columns, but I didn't pay any attention to those, either.

I was used to that sort of thing from Hollywood, where I had become convinced that columnists put a lot of names in a hat and withdrew a few at random to make news about. In any event, the world of night clubs and parties was far removed from the farm. We had plenty to keep us busy and occupy our minds without worrying about idle gossip.

Bill finished his book, while I completed the three new instalments for Mr. Balmer, and edited and combined the last ten stories into the fourth novel of the series for Farrar and Rinehart. It was a big and tedious dose of *Claudia*, and for the sheer relaxation of turning out three acts of undiluted dialogue, I wrote another play, and we returned to New York.

Soldier's Wife lingers in my memory for many reasons, apart from a reasonably long and successful run. For one thing, it took this third play to solidly establish Bill's position in the theatre. He moved to larger offices, and reassembled his production staff on a more permanent basis. They were a wonderful group to work with, and I wish I could acknowledge each one of them individually, but the list would be lengthy, and I am afraid that the names would mean little to anyone who was not active on Broadway during those years.

I think, however, that Lee Shubert still remains in the public image as the ruthless czar of the biggest string of theatres in the country. But until Bill and I went into production with *Soldier's Wife*, we knew him only to nod to when we occasionally met him as he emerged, like an omnivorous spider, from his nest of offices over the Shubert Theatre. A small, leathery man, scrupulously neat, with sparse, black patent-leather hair, he smiled rarely and forbiddingly, and strictly from hearsay, Bill did not look forward to his first financial negotiations with him.

It was a revealing experience. Bill sat in a straight chair beside Mr. Shubert's desk, and Mr. Shubert handed him a contract on the Golden Theatre, a few doors down the street from "Sardi's." Bill uncapped his pen and was about to sign the contract, when Mr. Shubert stopped him with a sharp reproof. "Are you in the habit, Mr. Meloney, of putting your name to an agreement that you have not read, much less carefully studied?"

Bill said, "No, Mr. Shubert, I am not. But I am fully aware that any advantageous theatre at the height of the season is at a premium, and I can only assume that you are giving me the fairest terms that you see fit to offer under the circumstances."

Without a word, Mr. Shubert reached for the contract, uncapped his own pen, crossed out an entire paragraph, several additional lines on another page, and jotted down some revised percentages in the margin. Then he returned the document to Bill for his signature.

Our company manager was waiting in a nearby bar, drowning his trepidation in martinis. He greeted Bill dourly. "Okay. Let's see what the old skinflint's done to us."

He knew his way around a contract and his eyes darted to the salient points. "I don't believe it. How in hell did you manage to wangle terms like these out of that penny-pinching bastard?"

It would have been futile to try to explain that there hadn't been any need for wangling. Simply, Lee Shubert wanted to be trusted, and to those who were forever trying to outwit him he was merciless.

Nor do I base this statement on having caught him, for once, in a mellow mood. I remember the night we closed *The Hallams* some years later. Bill and I saw a light burning in the Shubert office, and although it was well on towards the early hours of the morning, we took a chance that Mr. Lee might still be working at his desk. He was. And he was alone. The evening box-office receipts from his theatres had been duly checked and recorded, and everyone had long since gone home. Startled, he looked up as we entered. "We shouldn't have disturbed you at this hour," Bill apologized.

"You haven't. I'm just going over some figures. I won't be but a few moments. Sit down."

Eventually, he put his papers aside. He said, "What can I do for you?"

"We've come to thank you for all the things you've already done for us," Bill said.

Mr. Lee seemed puzzled and a little embarrassed. "That's all right. But what can I do for you now? What it is you want?"

"We don't want anything," I said. "I wanted to thank you too, because Bill told me about your offering this afternoon to let us stay on at the 'Booth'——"

"*The Hallams* is a fine play," he interrupted briskly. "Best you've written, in my opinion. Had to be," he added, with almost a smile, "or John Golden wouldn't have put money into

Another Language: *Left to right*: HERBERT DUFFY, WYRLEY BIRCH, MARGARET WYCHERLY, MAUDE ALLEN, GLENN ANDERS, DOROTHY STICKNEY, MARGARET HAMILTON

Claudia: Curtain scene with DOROTHY MAGUIRE, DONALD COOK
and FRANCES STARR

it.—Did you see what Richard Watts said in the paper today?"

"Yes," Bill said. "He excoriated me good and proper for my lack of foresight in not keeping the play running——"

"And that's changed your mind about closing it?" Mr. Lee broke in, as if he'd uncovered the purpose of our visit.

"On the contrary. I think it's time that the critics began to educate themselves on the facts and figures of production costs. We're up against the same situation as *Outrageous Fortune*. It isn't enough for a handful of reviewers to go all out for us——"

"What about your public?" Mr. Lee interrupted again. "You had the most important social benefit of the year tonight. They don't come any better. A hundred dollars a ticket. You were fair about it, you gave them a chance to cancel as soon as you'd decided to close, but they didn't do it. They wanted to see this particular show. I looked in before the final curtain, and I saw something I've never seen before in the theatre—a standing ovation from the audience, and a move to raise the money privately to keep the play running."

"I know," I murmured. "I'll never forget it."

"You shouldn't," he said severely. "And your husband shouldn't either. Unless he's got no faith in the play."

"I have faith in it," Bill said. "I agree with you that it's the best she's written."

"Then what's your objection to letting me help you to keep it on until it makes the grade financially?"

Bill said, "Because it isn't up to me to teach the critics, or to fight them."

"Very laudable," Mr. Lee said drily. He turned towards me. "What are your thoughts on the subject, Miss Franken?"

"I think Bill's right. We've talked it over. In fact I think he's so right that I've decided that I'll never write another play."

"You're not the first playwright to say that. You'll feel differently about it later on."

"No, Mr. Lee, I won't, and it's not because of pique or retaliation. It's just that I know the theatre is not for me."

He must have sensed that I meant what I said. He got to his feet in his earnestness. "But that's just what I don't want to happen, the theatre needs the kind of plays you write!"

"You'll be surprised how it won't miss me," I returned cheerfully. "I might miss the theatre a little, but it won't miss me. My big trouble is that I've gone out of fashion. I like the tight old-fashioned technique of writing a play in three acts and preferably one set, and I lean towards sentiment because I loved my mother and I'm happily married. All of which is getting to be taboo on Broadway."

Mr. Lee dropped into his chair again. "I can't argue about that," he said a little wearily. He rubbed his hand across his forehead, and we could see that he was tired. We rose to go.

"Wait a minute," he said abruptly. "You didn't come up here expressly to thank me?"

"I can't think of a better reason," Bill told him.

Mr. Lee shook his head as if he couldn't quite conceive it. "This is the first time," he said slowly, "that anyone has ever come to my office without wanting to ask me for a favour."

It is a sad commentary on "show business" that this should have been true. When Lee Shubert died, Bill and I were among the few who mourned him with affection and respect.

Actors, as a breed, are also generally maligned, partly because of what makes them actors, and partly because, in the hazardous world of shifting footlights, they can rarely if ever allow themselves the luxury of quixotic gestures. There are exceptions, of course, and we ran into no less than three of those exceptions in *Soldier's Wife*.

We weathered the tail-end of a sweltering Indian summer by rehearsing at the farm. The result was that everybody had a good time and nobody's nerves were frazzled when we arrived in New Haven to play a split week before continuing on to Philadelphia. New Haven is near enough New York, unfortunately, to attract everyone from a bit player to an important producer—which Leland Heyward had by this time become—and I was dismayed to run into him in the hotel corridor on the morning of the opening. "Couldn't you have waited? Did you have to rush up here to catch us on our first rough performance?"

"Stop being modest," he adjured me. "Even your dress rehearsals aren't rough. How do you do it?"

The farm was largely responsible for our painless openings, but I didn't say so, because John Golden used to warn me that it was against the rules of Equity to sneak in all those extra hours of work in the sunshine drinking fresh milk and eating home-made cookies. "I guess we're in pretty good shape," I admitted to Leland. "It's an easy play to do. I hope you like it."

"I won't," he said. "I intend to hate every minute of it and put a jinx on it besides. Look, I'm joking. I don't blame you, you have a run-of-the-play contract with Tito, so why should you release him? You'd never find another character actor half as good. And neither will I."

"Leland. I don't understand one single word you're talking about."

He could see that I was at a loss so he explained that he had urged Tito Vuolo to leave the play during the five-day option period, when, normally, he would have been free to do so. It was an entirely justifiable thing to do, because Tito had a small rôle of a temperamental photographer in *Soldier's Wife*, and Leland was offering him a very important rôle in *A Bell for Adano*, for a great deal more money. But Tito had said that he couldn't accept the part and Leland had assumed that I was holding him to a contractual obligation.

"The damn fool has a wife and a raft of children," I fumed, "and he never even asked me to release him. I always give a run-of-the-play contract as soon as I engage an actor, but it's a contract that only works one way. If an actor is unhappy, he's not going to be any good, whether he's bound or not. And I can tell you one thing, Tito is leaving just as soon as I can find someone to replace him. You can have him."

Leland shook his head regretfully. "It's too late. Tito is a foreign actor and once he walks on that stage tonight, he can't take another job for six months."

"Then he won't walk on that stage tonight for the simple reason that I'll write him out of the play."

It wasn't difficult to do since Tito appeared only in the second act. Nevertheless, it was the first time I had ever had to subject actors to any rewriting at all, and it was with great contrition that I distributed several pages of revised script at the two o'clock run-through that afternoon.

My apologies were unnecessary. The whole cast was a step ahead of me. Myron McCormick—high on the list of actors who give one no pain—reluctantly revealed Tito's carefully guarded secret. "We all knew about his big chance," Myron said, "but he made us promise not to tell you because he didn't want to leave the play and he knew you wouldn't stand in his way."

Tito nodded abjectly, his plump face beneath his balding hair melancholy as a chastised puppy. "You shouldn't have tried to double-cross me," I reprimanded him severely. "I'm bouncing you here and now, whether you like it or not."

"You may as well know that you've got another double-crosser in this cast," Glenn Anders remarked. "Your friend, Lili here, was offered the star rôle in *Trio* a couple of weeks ago."

Lili Darvas, like Tito, came under the same foreign ruling, and I was glad she hadn't told me about that star part because I would have been hard put to let her go even though it would have been of immense advantage to her to have had her name in lights on the marquee and Lili knew it. She was one of the few real ladies of tradition in the theatre, and I want to add that Glenn Anders is pretty much one himself, because six or eight months after we'd opened in New York, he turned his back on all sorts of blandishments to appear in a new Philip Barry production. I don't want to give the impression that Bill and I think all actors are nice people, and bright, but by and large, we were pretty fortunate in being able to like and respect almost every one who worked for us, and we certainly had more than our share of luck in the case of *Soldier's Wife*.

I had every intention of writing back the part of the photographer again, and finding an adequate substitute for Tito before we opened in New York, but circumstances conspired against me. We had no sooner arrived in Philadelphia, than the second big hurricane of the decade unleashed its fury along the Jersey shore and all means of communication was cut off, which meant, also, that there was no possible way of getting through to the farm. I am not of that patrician school that feels that "the show must go on" at any cost, and if there had been any means of transportation, nothing would have kept me from getting back to Lyme, because the boys and my aunt were stranded there, and I had full significance of the devastation that a hurricane could leave in its wake.

I neglected to mention that for a long while past my Aunt Jane had made her home with us in the old schoolhouse on the property that we had restored for her especial use. It is a sad fate to live to be the last remaining member of a large devoted family, and to my great joy, it was Bill who suggested that she lived with us. It wasn't always easy either for us or for her (I love my children but I pray that I need never have to move in with any of them), and often as the years took their slow toll of her physical vitality and mental vigour it was as if she were another child to look after and protect. Sometimes I envy those robust souls who have the moral strength to shut themselves off from the material and spiritual needs of another human being, for surely they can travel faster, and further, unhampered by the yoke of sentiment. And yet, blessed in both my marriages, I wonder whether the capacity for compassion and understanding is not the true measure of a man's maturity.

To get back to Philadelphia and the hurricane, it was almost curtain time when Bill came hurrying towards me with a beaming smile on his face. "Hurry up to the telephone!"

I raced to the cubby-hole behind the ticket office where we'd been trying for hours to reach the farm. The receiver was dangling off the hook and I thought, perhaps he had finally got through to the farm.

"It's Helen. Helen Reid."

"Oh." I tried to hide my disappointment, and then I realized that he must have managed to get in touch with the *Tribune*, and who could better give us first-hand information on the hurricane than the publisher and owner of the newspaper? Helen, who showed her devotion to Missy in her kindness to us, had contacted her reporter in the area. "I just heard from him," she told me,

[357]

"you have nothing to worry about, there are only two casualties. An old lady and a little boy have been drowned."

The floor moved beneath me. All I could think of was the pond that we had dredged when we had rebuilt the schoolhouse, and Peter struggling through its swollen waters to save his pet ducks and geese, and my aunt struggling to save Peter.

"I'm so terribly sorry," Helen said unhappily. "I was so hoping to relieve your mind and now I've only added to your agony."

"But how could you have possibly known about my aunt and Peter——"

"Try not to worry," she begged me. "I'll find out as much as I can, and call you back right away."

Bill and I stood at the rear of the theatre, watching the play unseeingly. Helen wasn't able to get through to us again that night, and by the time she reached us in the morning, the papers had the story. We didn't even recognize the names of the old lady and the little boy.

I also have a faint recollection that the papers carried favourable reviews of *Soldier's Wife*, but it didn't seem very important whether the critics liked the play or not. The only important thing was that the telephone lines were working again "No damage," Vernon assured us in his laconic Yankee way. "Leastways nothing that we can't fix up, except that we lost a couple of trees."

"No livestock lost?"

"Couple of geese, maybe."

We counted the days until we could get back to the farm to see for ourselves what had happened. We'd lost a little more than a couple of trees and a couple of geese, but we couldn't complain. We'd come off very well compared with the last hurricane.

We came off so well with *Soldier's Wife*, compared with *When Doctors Disagree*, that Bill insisted it was high time for me to replenish my wardrobe. "Those poor little rabbits are dead on their tails," he said. "Give them a rest and buy yourself a mink coat."

"Mink is for football," I objected, quoting the expensive

couturière who was very much in vogue in those days. Actresses felt cheated if they couldn't boast her label. MISS SO-AND-SO'S GOWNS BY MADAME SO-AND-SO.

In a moment of madness, I went to Madame So-and-So myself, and ordered a street ensemble to go under the mink coat that I finally bought in another moment of madness, plus a mink hat, for which I mistook the federal luxury tax to be the purchase price, which shows how expensive it was. Largely, I was influenced, I think, by the fact that my chinchillas really were beginning to look a little bedraggled after their labour of love for *Soldier's Wife*. They had earned a long rest, and I had them gently glazed, and laid them away between layers of pink tissue spangled with camphor flakes. Then I waited for the weather to turn cool enough to wear my mink, but it was one of those stubborn autumns that refuse to let go of summer, so I wore the new dress without the coat as a concession to autumn fashion.

There could have been any number of reasons why I didn't feel easy in it. Not only had it cost more than twice as much as any dress I had ever bought before, but it didn't fit. It hiked, and constrained me uncomfortably around the middle. Indignant, I returned the garment for a proper alteration, and was stiffly informed that I had increased a full inch and a half round the waist-line since my measurements had first been taken. It gave me a jolt. Could it be that calories had finally caught up with me in all those table d'hôte lunches and dinners on the try-out? Or was it more likely to be mental? People had been known to blow up in various places purely from emotional strain, and I had been under enough tension, what with the opening and the hurricane, to account for my shift in bulk. Still, it was pretty risky to dismiss an inch and a half on psychosomatic grounds, so I made an appointment with my obstetrician. I hadn't set foot inside his office since Peter was born, but he knew me inside out from the old days, and he could at least tell me that there wasn't a shadow of a doubt that the shadow of a doubt that suddenly assailed me was even remotely possible.

"It isn't possible, is it?" I whistled in the dark from across his desk.

"I wouldn't say that it wasn't," he answered cautiously.

Afterwards, facing him again across the desk, I said with suspicion, "I don't like the way you look."

"I don't like what I've found. Can you take it straight or shall I beat about the bush?"

"Don't be ridiculous," I protested hotly, as if it were his fault. "Paul's twenty-four years old."

"You're not pregnant."

"Then why didn't you say so!" Distrust quickly followed on the heels of relief. "You're going to tell me that it's just plain middle-aged spread, and I should begin wearing a girdle," I anticipated him glumly.

He shook his head. "I wish it were that easy. I hope I'm wrong, but I don't think so. You need to have an operation, and without delay."

I stared at him as if he'd taken leave of his senses. "Me? I've never been sick a day in my life and I'd sooner be dead than operated on."

"You will, if you're not," he said, and suddenly I saw that he was really letting me have it straight, and I could not mistake the message.

"Cancer?"

"I don't know." He lifted the telephone. "You're not calling Bill!" I stopped him swiftly.

"I'm calling deWitt Stetten. After you've seen deWitt, we'll tell Bill."

"We're not telling him at all," I said firmly. "He went through this with my sister and I'm not going to put him through it again until we find out if it is or isn't. And if it needs an operation to find out, then whatever it is—or isn't—will have to take its chances and wait."

"It will be taking too big a chance. If you go into the hospital tonight, it's not too soon."

"I can't. I have to wait at least a few weeks."

"*Soldier's Wife* can run very well without you for the time being."

"It's not the play." I hesitated, disciplined to Army security. Eleanor Roosevelt had showed me a communication from the War

Department during a week-end at Hyde Park, to the effect that all men who had been overseas for a period exceeding three years, were due for a thirty-day leave to the States, provided they were not engaged in active combat. That was early in July. Paul's last letter implied that he had returned from the northern area of Lae and Salumaua to the base at Moresby, which meant one thing: he might be on his way home now, for all we knew. It was unthinkable that I should welcome him from a hospital bed, but at the same time it availed nothing to postpone the operation if he wasn't on his way home. In that case, better to get it over and finished with.

"I'll see deWitt," I compromised.

DeWitt examined me. "You mustn't wait," he said.

"This is just a case of knowing too many doctors too well," I thought disgustedly as I hailed a taxi down to Washington Square. I was in a hurry to get to a telephone before Bill showed up from the matinée. I had no scruples in calling Eleanor to ask her please to try her best to find out Paul's whereabouts, but I was in for a disappointment. "She's down at the Springs with the President until Sunday," Malvina Thompson told me. "Is there anything I can do for you?"

"I don't think so, Tommy. Thanks just the same."

There was only one person who could conceivably help me. Bill Donovan. General Donovan, now. "I'll get busy on it right away," he promised.

He called me the following evening to say that he hadn't been able to find out anything at all about Paul. "But don't ask me to keep this from your husband because I won't," he said sternly. "He has a right to know."

"He does know. He picked up the receiver downstairs this morning when deWitt telephoned that he'd taken matters into his own hands and engaged a room and nurses for tomorrow."

"Ask Bill to keep me posted."

"I'll be calling you myself," I promised jauntily.

I had no conception of what an operation was like. The weather was still warm, but I walked into the hospital swathed in mink, bound to get at least one wearing out of that coat and hat. The nurse said I was very brave, but I wasn't. I was coward enough to be thankful that it wasn't Bill or one of the boys who was headed for that operating room. It would have been awful for me if it had been Bill or the boys.

Afterwards, Bill told me how deWitt came racing down the corridor with his white coat flapping open. "It's all right!" he shouted at the top of his voice. "It's not malignant!"

That was the time, if you remember back so far, that I almost died anyway, and got a free obituary. An embolism feels like a heavy glass inkwell smashing into your lungs suddenly, without any warning, spattering blackness and splinters around your heart, so that it's foolish to even try to breathe against the pain of it. It happened in the middle of the night, but somehow deWitt was there, for I remember him as a white blur, bending over the bed, and I remember dimly that his voice was low and that it was trembling.

"Listen to me. You have to get well. You must get well. Paul is home."

5

FULL CIRCLE

DeWitt said that he knew from the old days that I was strong as a horse. And indeed my recovery was spectacular, with the elastic bandages round my legs the only badge of my bout with death. But they were a nuisance, so I soon discarded them.

Paul talked very little about the war. Just wandering in and out of the barns and kennels seemed to be all that he wanted, and I was grateful that, except for Missy and Pat, we had been able to keep his world intact for him to come back to. I was grateful, too, that he appeared to have safely weathered those grim jungle years, for the copper tinge of atabrin that lurked beneath the burn of sun and wind lent him a deceiving semblance of health. Until suddenly the malaria, held so long under control, flared into a ghastly siege of chills and fever.

Finally, his leave ended in an army hospital in Atlantic City, and on the pretext that the ocean was a good place for me to recuperate, we visited him over the Thanksgiving holidays. It was a disturbing experience to walk into a big hotel which I had known as a child to find it converted into wards filled with haggard, shivering men in the various stages of convalescence. There was small chance that any of them, including Paul, would be returned to active service in the South Pacific. And if it was wrong to give thanks for this strange beneficence, then I was wrong.

On the Sunday afternoon before our return to New York, Paul told me that his Army doctor had asked if he could join us for cocktails. "Damned if I know why, though, he steers clear of parents like the plague," Paul added.

We weren't long in finding out why. "Three Martinis," Bill ordered in a secluded corner of the lounge, and waited for me to decide between my usual orange juice and tomato juice.

"Lemonade," I surprised him. "With a cherry."

The doctor's smile reached across the table to me. "Oh, come now," he said smoothly. "No need to punish yourself, have a Martini."

"I don't like the taste of alcohol," I said.

The lift of the doctor's brows was ironic. "You don't really expect me to believe that, do you?"

"My mother doesn't drink or smoke," Paul put in, rather shortly.

The doctor turned to Bill. "Is this actually true?"

I could tell by the tone of Bill's reply that he, too, was nettled by the innuendo. "I see no reason for you to doubt Paul's word. Or did you have something more in mind than a casual social afternoon?"

"You're very astute, Mr. Meloney. Frankly, I do have another purpose in being here, and perhaps I ought to stop beating about the bush." He sounded like my obstetrician, only it seemed that this time I wasn't threatened by a deadly malady, I was engraved in the Army records of a recent court-martial. "That's why I was curious to find out for myself what sort of woman you really are," he admitted, "particularly because I have come to have the highest regard for your son."

"But how did I get into a court-martial, what did I do?" I asked, rather pleased at this singular honour.

He hesitated. "It isn't a pretty story, but according to the sworn testimony of the officer in question, who, incidentally, was AWOL for the better part of a week, it appears that he had spent several of those obviously gay and inebriated nights in the company of Rose Franken, but—and this is all down in the record —he states that he wasn't so drunk that he agreed to marry her."

I burst out laughing. "That's the funniest thing I ever heard. There must be two of us with the same name, but just to confuse you, I think I will have a Martini after all. With an olive."

From the way Bill and Paul glared at me, they didn't think

I was as witty as I thought I was. In fact, I forgot all about what I considered to be a ridiculous coincidence until a week or so later one of Leland Hayward's associates telephoned to ask me if I had had a nice time the previous evening.

"Very. I was in bed at nine o'clock."

"You might have been in bed at nine o'clock," he told me, "but somewhere around midnight, my dear girl, you were up and drowning yourself in champagne at the 'Copacabana'."

Since I had never set foot in the "Copacabana," it suddenly occurred to me that my supposed presence might shed some light on the doctor's story. "What makes you think I was there?" I inquired cautiously.

"Because I happened to have been talking business to the owner of the club when your secretary phoned to make your reservation. As befits a celebrity, the red carpet was rolled out for you with champagne on the house, and baby, from the way I heard it this morning, you guzzled the stuff."

I was quite upset by this new development. "I don't like having the reputation for accepting free champagne," I said to Bill. "Do you think I'm the same woman who got drunk and slept with the Army officer?"

"I also think you're the same woman who got those anonymous letters a while back. Let's have another look at them."

"I threw them out."

"That wasn't very smart."

"But you told me not to pay any attention to them."

He had no comeback for that. "Better start your clipping service again so that we can keep a check on the columns."

That made sense, but it wasn't necessary, because the next incident, a few days later, brought matters to a head. Peter was, by this time, enrolled in Columbia University, very much in advance of his age group, and Bill, having taught at Columbia, thought it wouldn't hurt to renew an old friendship with one of Peter's professors. "I'll call him up and tell him that you'll get in touch with his wife to arrange an evening for dinner."

"If you think it's all right."

"Why shouldn't it be all right?"

"I don't want it to look as if we're angling for Peter to be a teacher's pet."

Bill telephoned and grimly reported the gist of the conversation with his former colleague. "He says 'thank you, no'—he'd rather not. But Peter's not the reason. You are. It appears that you and he have met before."

"We have? When? I don't remember."

"Don't lie. You shared a taxi from the station on a rainy night in Westport last summer, and I gather you were in your usual state of amorous inebriation. His wife noticed lipstick on his collar when he got home. So she knows exactly who and what you are."

"This isn't funny any more," I said. "I don't like people feeling sorry for the boys for having a mother like me."

"Nor do I particularly like having a wife like you. I'm going to call in a private detective and put an end to this business."

I still didn't think it was important enough to take such drastic measures, but I changed my mind when the detective brought in his first conclusive evidence. Using a faint brogue that strengthened an immediate affiliation with Bill for being a Meloney. "It's a pity what I'm about to tell you, sir, I'm the last one to do anything to break up a marriage, and things like this usually do, in my experience," he began apologetically.

"What have you discovered?" I interrupted from my corner of the office where we happened to be working at the moment.

He eyed me with ill-concealed distaste. "I traced the gentleman you were out with and showed him the photograph of you that your husband gave me. There's no doubt in his mind at all that you're one and the same."

"That's a little premature," Bill said. "Photographs are apt not to be too accurate."

"I'm sorry to say it isn't the photograph alone, sir. His whole story tallies, even to a letter from the son in New Guinea, and your barns burning down on the farm. If you'd care to have a word with the witness yourself, he's outside in the waiting-room."

"Bring him in," I grinned. "I'd love to meet him."

The detective looked at me as if to say, "Okay, you're asking for it." He gave Bill a commiserating shake of his head. "A thing like this is enough to take the heart out of a man."

"It's just as well to bring the whole miserable business out in the open," Bill responded with appropriate melancholy.

I was gratified to note that the witness was quite attractive in spite of his acute discomfiture when he saw me. "This is very unpleasant for all of us," he said, lowering his gaze in tacit acknowledgement of our combined guilt. "Perhaps if you were to step a little closer, you might find dissimilarities," Bill suggested.

"Such as, for example, did she have a broken nose?" I added, and was conscious of another withering look from the detective, branding me a drunken hussy determined to brazen through my shameful indiscretions. I must say, however, that it required a degree of composure to submit to a thorough inspection of my face, feature by feature, until a carefully reconsidered verdict exonerated me from adultery. "I confess that I didn't pay very much attention to her nose, but with her make-up removed"—the gentleman blushed discreetly—"I couldn't help noticing her complexion."

I froze. "Am I to gather that she had a bad complexion?"

He was nothing if not chivalrous to his erstwhile amour. "A skin condition," he temporized. "Acne, for want of a better word."

That I should be impersonated by a woman with pimples was the supreme indignity. "Get the entire police force on this case if you have to," I commanded the detective furiously, "and stop this creature from saying that she's me!"

We never did discover the true identity of my double, although it was rumoured that she was the sister of a world-famous writer, which added up to some sort of rather sad, psychological sense. But whoever she was, I am in her debt for allowing me to take the credit for all the gay doings that accrued to my colourful reputation while I was leading a life of exemplary virtue, and very little social distinction. It was certainly a case of having the name without the bother and I actually missed being in the limelight as she gradually tapered off my activities. Her complete withdrawal from the scene was due not so much to the intervention of the police as the fact that I guess I began to cramp her style when I started to circulate a letter for myself after we sold the farm.

After we sold the farm. How simply, and with what finality, those few words mark the end of more than a decade of very nearly complete happiness and fulfilment.

It is not easy to recognize, and accept, the rightful end of any phase of living, but with the war over, Bill and I realized that Lyme had served its purpose. Paul, like thousands of other veterans, began to adjust himself to piecing together his disordered youth. Four years too late, and still combating recurrent onslaughts of malaria, he started his law career, while John, also four years out of step, finished his sophomore year at college, and then left, floundering for a while until he found himself. Only Peter's young life remained undisrupted. He streaked ahead, delving into the mysteries of the space age, and when last heard from was bouncing light-beams off the moon from his laboratory in Michigan.

Directly after the peace was won in Japan, all our activities suddenly centred in New York, so that it became increasingly impracticable to drive three hours for an occasional hurried week-end and, reluctantly, we decided that no good could come of trying to run a productive farm on an absentee basis. We had built a small world which we had loved and cared for, and there was something immoral about allowing it to become burdensome, and less than cherished.

I remembered the effortlessness with which I had disposed of the apartment at the Kenilworth when the time came for me to relinquish it. It happened much the same way with the farm. A newly married couple—not young, but newly married to each other—fell in love with it and wanted to make it their home, and keep all the livestock, and the dogs, and the cats, as well as Vernon and Al to stay on to look after everything just as if we were there. We couldn't have asked for a more perfect arrangement, and so, with sorrow, but no misgiving, we took our leave of Lyme, and lived in a fool's paradise in New York for two

The Hallams: JOHN MCKEE, ETHEL GRIFFITHS, KATHERINE BARD, MILDRED DUNNOCK, DEAN NORTON, MATT BRIGGS and FRANK THOMAS

In Riverdale, our livestock supply finally dwindles to MASCARA

months, during which time we kept in touch with Vernon at regular intervals. "Everything's going fine," he invariably assured us with his monosyllabic reticence, until one evening, he sounded as if he were holding back some bad news. "What's wrong, has anything happened to one of the Danes?" I prodded anxiously.

The question sent Bill running to one extension and Paul to another, and by dint of concerted pressure, we finally persuaded Vernon to unburden his Yankee soul. He said that he'd taken his day off as usual last Thursday, and had come back to find the kennels empty. He feared that all the dogs had been sold to a dealer, because he'd noticed a couple of odd characters hanging around lately, and it wouldn't surprise him if the livestock was the next to go.

We were stunned. "Do everything you can to find out the name of the dealer," Bill instructed him, "phone as soon as possible."

Army language, strong and searing, poured out of Paul's lips, but I saved my ammunition until I was put through to the main house, where I reached the wife of the gentleman who had purchased the farm and she now had the audacity to inform me that she never so much as laid eyes on the Danes. "Please listen to me. I've only been here a couple of days," she finally managed to stem my apopletic accusation. "You're confusing me with the former Mrs. Manville."

Not the first or the second or the third Mrs. Manville, I registered dazedly, but the "former Mrs. Manville." "Divorced already," I said grimly, as I hung up the receiver. "What do we do now?"

"Nail the dealer and—" Paul reverted to battlefield authority. "We'll trace every Dane he's sold."

It took us weeks to do it, but we did it. The dealer had asked high prices for long pedigrees, so fortunately they had all found good homes and affluent larders, with the exception of Black Knight, who was too mammoth, too ferocious-looking, and a sissy. He had broken his leg when a puppy, and we had coddled and pampered him until he fancied himself a lap dog. His present owners did not so fancy him, having purchased him on the

z   [369]

reasonable assumption that he was a hundred and forty pounds of protection, and not vice versa. They sold him back to us with alacrity.

By that time we had moved from Washington Square, which we had only rented, to a house on Sutton Place, which we bought. We were flanked with a small, select coterie of neighbours, and Black Knight's first unheralded romp in our communal garden caused great consternation and alarm. We had no alternative but to give him to friends who owned a large house off Fifth Avenue where the run of Central Park was none too big for him. They adored him, and privately we thought they spoiled him horribly, and we couldn't have been more pleased about it.

When we could bring ourselves to do it, we drove up to Lyme. We passed and repassed the farm at the pace of a funeral car. We hardly recognized it. It sprouted elaborate additions and an oblong swimming pool; the school-house had been sold as separate acreage, and the barns were empty. We never returned for another look. You can't hold on to places, even in your mind. You have to let go of them, the same as people.

That might have been one of the reasons that we didn't encourage ourselves to become too attached to our new house. We liked it, we admired it, but we never really loved it, although it had great charm, with marble floors and eighteenth-century boisseries. We bought it on the theory—my theory—that it would kill two birds with one stone, and do double duty for city and country because of the stretch of green that ran down to the river, and a terrace that overlooked the bridge, but we soon found out that these were poor substitutes for hills and meadows. However, the house itself did serve a dual purpose in providing a convenient base for all of us—including my aunt—and a gratifying outlet for the frustrated architect in me. On the farm, like every good farm, the barns had taken precedence over our own living quarters, but now I could go back to the days of the Kenilworth and give full vent to my addiction to tearing down walls, and making over bathrooms and buying furniture only this time with no restrictions as to budget, thanks to all sorts of royalties that kept pouring in. At least I thought there was no monetary limit to my expenditures until one day, in search of a tall mahogany ladder for the library, I happened to pass the palatial but restrained exterior of French & Co. on Fifty-seventh Street. The massive oak doors opened to my touch as if by invisible hands, but a substantial young man, sitting guard in the cathedral-like foyer, immediately blocked my entry. Did I have an appointment?—No I did not have an appointment—Then perhaps he could arrange for me to return the following day if I would be good enough to leave my name and telephone number?

This was verging on the ridiculous. Was it necessary to go through a third degree in order to make the simple purchase of a library ladder? The young man assured me that such was the customary procedure for prospective clients, and held a silver pencil poised above a leather-encased pad. It was all too apparent that I should have worn my chinchillas, but, thrifty me, I hadn't even worn my mink to go antique-hunting in my favourite haunts tucked away in cellars and up flights of rickety stairs.

"Meloney," I grudgingly revealed, conscious that the name might have curried favour with a detective, but obviously did not further my present cause. The young man stifled a yawn. "And the initials?"

"W!" I snapped. "Short for 'William.' "

"Mrs. William Maloney." He savoured the sound on his lips, with his nose in the air.

"Mrs. William *Brown* Meloney. Spelled with an 'e'." I watched him write it down and study it. "The Fifth," I added nastily.

As he affixed the numeral, the gloom lightened from his countenance. The combination of the Brown and the Fifth did it every time.

"And your address?" he murmured diffidently.

I was tempted to dash his rising hopes by giving him the address of the forty-dollar flat on Morningside Drive that popped, unbidden, into my mind. But I loved that little place, it remained like a small shrine in my heart and I'd be damned if I'd demean it.

"Two Sutton Square," I admitted, and realized how time can

[371]

change the course of one's life, but not the essentials of one's being.

"Why, that's the house on the corner of Sutton Place!" the young man exclaimed, as if he'd struck gold. "It's my favourite house in all New York!"

"It's very pleasant," I agreed, not meaning to sound as if I were used to better, but I suppose I did sound that way, because I felt that way. Nothing could ever again be as wonderful to me as my first home—those four sunny little rooms on Morningside Drive.

I was vaguely aware, out of the nostalgia of the past, that I was being led to a needlepoint love-seat, in front of which there was a low square table supplied with ashtrays and the latest editions of two dollar magazines. "Someone will be with you immediately," the young man said.

"Thank you."

From where I sat, I could see a vista of restrained magnificence that stretched out endlessly beyond the main hall. If it hadn't been for an unobtrusive little tag peeping out from a leg of the table, I would have felt that I was in a great museum rather than an antique shop. Surreptitiously, I stole a glance at the description on one side of the tag and the price mark on the other. I didn't need glasses at that time, but surely my eyes deceived me? it wasn't possible for a table to cost that much, short of being made of solid gold. I spied a similar tag dangling from the arm of the love-seat. The figure was astronomical.

I'd barely regained my composure when a pleasant middle-aged man stepped from the lift, greeted me with the effortless courtesy of addressing me by name, and told me that French & Co. was regrettably lacking in library ladders. I noticed that he made no attempt to interest me in any other purchases, which I liked, particularly since I wasn't interested in anything else after the shock of those price tags. I couldn't get out of the place fast enough, but I didn't quite make it to the door. Another gentleman, somewhat older and heavier, came stomping up the short stone steps that led to the vista of rooms beyond—he didn't actually stomp, he wore a brace round one leg, and used a cane. His years became him, and even before he spoke, there was something in his bearing that made me know at once that here indeed was Mr. French, himself. "We have library ladders, Robert," he said in a tone that would have carried a reprimand, had his voice been deeper. "My brother does not know all the things I have hidden away," he confided to me with a smile, which I'd call boyish, or even impish, if I weren't scared of words like that. "Come, my dear, we will go upstairs and I will show them to you."

That was my first tour of French & Co.—not with Mr. French who was but a name carried on through the years—but with Mr. Samuels—or "Mr. Mitchell" as he was called by the many great collectors who knew and loved him.

I glimpsed, through the slow-mounting cage of the old-fashioned lift, floor after floor of treasures that I was one day to know as intimately as the floors of my own home. "Third, Mr. Mitchell?" the attendant inquired.

"No. The fourth. And find Jimmy and send him to me in the Chopin Room."

The Chopin Room. "Is it really?" I asked in awe.

"It's actually the room from George Sand's house where Chopin played for her." He withdrew a chain of keys from his pocket as Jimmy appeared. "You'll find two library ladders in the vault beyond the tapestries," he instructed. "Bring them to me."

"Yes, sir."

They were specimens of art the like of which I had never seen, or dreamed of, for at first glance they appeared to be only slim eighteenth-century mahogany bed posts, until a finger-touch opened up skilfully concealed rungs to ladder-width.

"Are they very expensive?" I asked, feeling gauche about such a mundane question.

Mr. Mitchell glanced at the tags, and deftly snapped them off and put them in his pocket. "No, my dear, not at all expensive," he assured me.

I swallowed the impulse to pursue our relative ideas of costliness, and murmured a reasonable conjecture that the smaller of the two ladders was probably the cheaper. "It is. Considerably," Mr. Mitchell said, and quoted a price that staggered me, because it was less than the usual clumsy contraptions in the merest junk shop.

"It's exactly what I want!" I exulted. "I only hope it'll fit in a taxi."

"That won't be necessary, my dear. We will deliver it."

"But when I buy something, I have to have it right away," I demurred.

"You have the spirit of the true collector," he smiled. "You shall have the ladder this afternoon."

"But it's after five already," I reminded him.

"No matter. It will be there."

I'd been disappointed in deliveries before, and I fully expected to be disappointed in this one, but scarcely an hour later, an immense plum-coloured van, with the elegant gold letters of French & Co. inscribed unobtrusively in the lower right hand corner, drew to a velvet stop before our door. "It's here!" I shouted to Bill, who was pouring himself a cocktail. "Go down quickly and bring it up, it's not heavy!"

Before he could get to the stairs, a brace of stalwart men had reached the library door. "Is this where you want it, Mrs. Meloney?"

"Yes, thank you."

Would they allow Bill to place the ladder against the shelves? By no means. They opened it, anchored it firmly, and held it while he negotiated the rungs. "Not high enough," the one called Earl decreed.

"We'll go back and get the big one," said Jack. Or was it the other way round? For the next dozen years, they were as familiar to us as our family, but I always had difficulty in telling them apart.

"Go back and get the big one?" I echoed incredulously. "Now?"

"Why not? Mr. Mitchell had them both cleaned and waxed. Just in case."

"What a piece of cabinet work," Bill marvelled after they'd toted it off.

"The other one they're bringing is even more beautiful," I said. "But of course it's much more expensive."

"How much more?"

"I didn't ask."

Weeks passed, without our knowing what the taller ladder cost. I notified the accounting department that they had neglected to send the bill, and then more weeks passed, and we finally did get a bill, but it was for the ladder we had sent back. I telephoned Mr. Mitchell to refresh his memory that we had decided on the more expensive one, and if he would be good enough to tell me the amount we would forward the cheque without further delay. There was a silence so brief as to be imperceptible. Then he said, "My dear, your bill is correct as it is. I wanted you to have the better ladder at the same price."

During the close years of our friendship with Mitchell, I could never cajole him into confessing whether he'd quickly covered up a bookkeeping error, or whether he'd been wonderfully gracious, or whether he'd just been plain wily.

"We ought to buy some little ormanent, or something, to make up for his being so generous to us," I told Bill. "Besides, I want you to see the Chopin Room. You'll lose your head over a pair of Louis Quinze Bergères."

Bill lost his, sure enough, but I kept mine and caught Mitchell red-handed as he quickly snipped off the little white tag on one of the chairs. "You can put it back," I said sternly. "We can't afford them, I saw the price the last time I was here."

"Nonsense, my dear, that was a telephone number," he replied blandly.

No wonder people got the impression that we were rolling in wealth, and I realize, of course, that it is as tasteless to brag about not having money as the other way round. Still, having exploded the legend of my chinchillas and my pearls, my conscience is now completely clear in revealing how we could afford to possess some of the choicest treasures from what was then the most prohibitively expensive establishment in the world.

We know a lot of people who really are millionaires—and some of them are our friends—but we're not in that class, and we never will be, because we spend what we earn and enjoy it like mad. On the other hand, we don't owe a penny to anyone, and we pay our bills with plebeian promptness, which is conclusive proof that we're not rich—from having money, that is.

I realize also, that living at Two Sutton Square didn't exactly negate a pervading aura of success, but it wasn't as if we had aspired either to that particular location or any sort of social status. The property simply happened to come on the market when we were looking for a place in town, and being back in New York began the vicious cycle of being back in so-called civilization, part of which meant giving endless dinner parties in return for endless dinner parties. "Do you really like this social rat-race?" I put it to Bill at the end of an especially full week of accomplishing nothing whatsoever.

"I thought you liked it. Let's buy a boat and get away from it all."

It was the last thing I had in mind, but I'd long suspected that he'd had a boat in his blood ever since Catalina, so I resigned myself to learning all about teak decks and galleys and heads, and pretended to revel in long—but very long—week-ends of salt air and baked beans. In between we kept busy with a lot of hard work on Claudia for by this time it was irritatingly apparent that whenever she was translated into a new medium, she would either drag me along in it, or fall flat on her rear. So it was that Twentieth Century Fox recognized that the second screenplay, which Dorothy Maguire had finally consented to appear in, bore very little resemblance to the content and intent of the original stories when Mr. Perlberg sent me the script and asked me to read it and make any suggestions that might better it. I had only one suggestion—to throw it into the wastepaper basket.

"But we can't," he telephoned me in a high state of agitation. "I have to start production within a couple of weeks."

I felt like asking him why he'd waited until the last minute, but I knew the answer without asking. Hollywood. And I also knew that this was no time to desert Claudia. Coca-Cola, the most desirable and dignified of sponsors, had just contracted for a new radio series, and the fifth novel was about to be published. "If Bill is willing to help me," I calmed Mr. Perlberg's nerves, "we'll write a new script for you and you'll have it in time but with one provision."

"Name your price, money's no object."

"Money's not the provision. I have to be sure that you won't mess up what we write with some pixie director who's going to think it's cute for Claudia to skip and flounce like a wide-eyed idiot."

"We've learned our lesson," he assured me earnestly. "We've got Walter Lang, and if you can't come to Hollywood, we'll send him on to New York so that he can learn what makes Claudia tick."

Had the studio been in a position to continue the series with Dorothy, I couldn't have asked for a more sensitive and perceptive director than Walter Lang. However, it was just as well that Claudia's motion picture career terminated with the second film, because no sooner had we finished the screenplay, than we had to sit down and write the initial radio scripts in order to set the story-line and the mood of the Coca-Cola programme. "I've had enough of Claudia," I rebelled. "I'll finish the novel when we come back."

Bill pricked up his ears. "Come back from where?" he asked hopefully.

"Europe."

"Well, why didn't you say so?"

"I thought you knew."

There was really nothing to prevent our going. We had trust-worthy servants to look after the boys and my aunt, and with travelling restrictions lifted, we encountered no delay in getting new passports—a procedure slightly complicated by the forgotten problem of our mixed-up birth dates.

Bill had lived abroad for years before our marriage, so all I had to do was tag along without a worry about tickets or Customs or anything else. Our first stop was London. I hadn't been there since the days of *Another Language*, and it was shocking to see the destruction and the ravages that the bombings had left in their wake. It was also somewhat of a shock, though of less emotional impact, to discover that Claudia had arrived and had been making herself at home in Britain for quite some time thanks to the promotion of the books by an excellent English publisher (Mark Goulden of W. H. Allen) combined with a long, successful run of the play starring Pamela Brown. When we reached our hotel, I simply couldn't believe that the line of people in the corridor outside our door had gathered for the express purpose of greeting me with words of welcome and mementoes of appreciation, I was much moved by this unexpected demonstration, but I didn't bargain for an invasion of reporters and photographers. Half unpacked, I submitted restlessly to hours of interviewing, only to discover capsuled paragraphs in the morning and evening papers flanked by unnecessarily candid shots of me wincing and squinting against a barrage of flashbulbs.

On the day before we were to leave London to fly to Holland at the behest of my Dutch publisher, Lord Strabolgi, an old friend, and one of our frequent guests on his visits to America, gave a large, formal luncheon at the House of Lords. "In honour of Claudia," he affectionately put it, and I thought resentfully how much more important that wayward brainchild of mine was than I could ever be.

Towards the end of the luncheon, my host whispered to me that it would be fitting for me to mingle with the guests at the farther end of the long table. I still had an occasional kick-back from the embolisms, and as he started to pull out my chair, I was aware that having sat in one position for so long my legs had gone completely numb, and down I went with my mink hat sliding rakishly over my eyes from the abrupt impact of the floor against the lower regions of my anatomy. A wave of restrained contempt from the notable assemblage blanketed all conversation into a thick silence. My face burned. A tipsy American.

Later, Bill grudgingly admitted that my handling of this delicate, almost international situation, was nothing short of sheer inspiration. It must have been, because the only thing I could think of was that King George had been in the papers recently with a similar leg ailment, so instead of attempting an awkward scramble to my feet, making matters even worse than they appeared to be, I simply waited until sensation finally returned to my limbs. "You

must forgive me," I said apologetically as I straightened my hat
and reclaimed the spilled contents of my handbag. "I am suffering
from your Monarch's disease."

Immediately, the frigid pall of disapproval melted into a
murmur of warm sympathy, and when Lord Strabolgi finally
did escort me to the other end of the table, I was conscious of the
understated overtones of British respect and admiration. I had
put on a "good show," and I was not above feeling pleased and a
little spiteful about it. Even if I had had to fall on my bottom to do
it, I had stolen the scene from Claudia.

My Dutch publisher was excessively efficient in presenting me
immediately upon my arrival with a typewritten sheet of the daily
activities expected of a visiting author in a foreign land, the most
important of which was a series of lectures I was to deliver
throughout the major cities of this small, lovely country. I had
never made a speech in my life, even in English, and the prospect
filled me with dismay until I discovered that I was practically
Siamese twins with an interpreter, and the burden of properly
transmitting anything I said, or didn't say, lay entirely upon his
shoulders. I promptly tested his linguistic acrobatics by announcing
that Claudia had been a pain in the neck to me since the day she
was born. He apparently did very well by me on that one, because
the audience beamed and applauded, whereupon I set out in cold
blood to further win their favour by extolling the magnificence of
their cuisine, but in the next breath, deplored the fact that their
hotels and restaurants were too stylish to serve Limburger cheese
to go with their wonderful Heineken's beer. Frankly, a little beer
went a long way with me, and I wouldn't have ordered the
Limburger cheese anyway, but I couldn't understand why the
Dutch felt that they were putting their best foot forward with
Edam. Of course I diplomatically witheld this observation, and
the lecture tour ended in an unsullied blaze of glory. My publisher
was overjoyed at the rise in sales, I autographed mountains of
Claudia books, and received innumerable gifts from "unknown
admirers," consisting largely of hand-embroidered linens which I
could tuck into odd corners of my suitcase, and Delft figurines which

had to be declared at the air terminal before we took off for Paris.

I don't know whether the Dutch Customs are as meticulous now as they used to be, but I recall having to stand around interminably while Bill submitted to a rigmarole of rigorous rummaging. I passed the time watching a couple of other inspectors have the audacity even to go through a passenger's cigarettes, breaking each one open so that they could sift the tobacco through their fingers—"As if they were looking for diamonds," I snorted to Bill.

"They were."

"Really? Did they do that to yours too?"

"They weren't interested in my cigarettes."

"Then what exactly were they interested in that they took for ever with you?"

"Currency," he replied tersely. "And our flight's been delayed an hour."

"My non-sequiturs seem to be contagious."

"That was no non-sequitur."

"Well, anyway, you can relax now."

"I can? Thanks."

I sought to enliven the long wait by making pleasant conversation. "The man with the cigarettes seemed to be in trouble about the guilders he was taking out of the country, too," I remarked chattily. "It was his own money, but an officer had the nerve to come and cart him off to headquarters or somewhere."

"I could do with a cup of coffee," Bill interrupted.

I greeted the suggestion with alacrity. I always love any sort of refreshments when travelling, and I was in the middle of a sandwich when a loudspeaker suddenly blasted out a sound that sounded like my name. "Did you hear what I heard?" I asked Bill, but he had already put his cup down with a noisy clatter, and was clamping his hand on my shoulder. "You stay here and be quiet," he ordered, and before I could protest about his bossiness, he had disappeared.

He returned shortly with a heavy square box which he ungraciously plunked down on the table in front of me. "You and your damn presents," he muttered.

I read the attached card. "It's from another unknown admirer, somebody must have heard me say I love Dutch chocolates," I gloated. "But I wonder it wasn't sent to the hotel."

"We'd already left. A uniformed chauffeur chased after us to the airport," he said tersely.

"Oh," I said, eyeing him as he gulped a second cup of coffee, black and hot. Evidently, the loudspeaker and the uniform had given him a rough few minutes, and something suddenly told me that although we'd bought presents galore in Amsterdam, maybe we hadn't been able to spend all the back royalties that we'd collected and were taking the remaining guilders along with us. But something also told me to shut up about it until we'd boarded the plane.

"In case we are," I mentioned obliquely, the minute we were in our seats, "and they found out about it, they couldn't have kept us from leaving."

"Oh, couldn't they?"

I was appalled at the risk we had taken. "But there's a limit to the things you can buy in Holland," I argued. "It isn't like France or England."

"Read," he said, handing me a magazine in which I was serialized.

"I can't. It's in Dutch."

"Then look at the pictures, and stop talking, we haven't left the ground yet."

I gathered that it was still within the realm of possibility that they could take us apart like the cigarettes, so I waited until we were safely in the air before I spoke again. I said, "It's getting awfully stuffy in this plane. Open the blower, will you?"

He leaned across me to twist the knob above my seat. "The word 'stuffy', my love, is a polite understatement."

"Oh. Then you smell a sort of little smell too?'"

"Since you've brought it up, yes."

"I resent your implication," I bridled. "I think the blower is making it worse. Better turn it off."

He turned it off.

Most smells wear themselves out in time, but this one didn't. It gained strength and momentum as the cabin grew increasingly warmer with the mingling of cigarette smoke and human bodies. Uncomfortably, I noticed that the passengers were beginning to cast overt glances in our general direction. I opened the Dutch magazine and hid behind the pages. "What'll we do?" I whispered to Bill. "Can't we dump it?"

"You do not dump on a non-stop flight to Paris," he replied icily.

"But this is awful, I'm going to tell the stewardess to tell the pasengers what it is," I whimpered. "It might make them feel better about it."

"The situation is one that a lady does not try to explain away. I hope this teaches you a lesson."

I was too distraught to ask him what kind of a lesson, I only know I suffered the indignity of being linked with that Limburger cheese for as long as I could stand it. Then I reached up and lifted the lovely, square, heavy box from the rack, and stealthily hurried down the aisle with it, praying that one of the two neat little lavatories would be vacant.

Bill gave me a frosty look when I returned to my seat empty handed. "That was a dastardly, cowardly thing to do."

"Messy too," I admitted. "But can you think of a better place for it?"

He couldn't.

We had a lovely time in Paris turning guilders into francs, and when we returned to America, there were cases and cases of Heineken's beer awaiting us. With the compliments of the Dutch Government.

There was no use crying over spilled milk, but I wished I'd had the sense to have raved about their tulips.

In the following years we toured the restless, seething continents of Europe, Asia and Africa, and yet another incident that happened on our second visit to the peaceful little kingdom of Holland, stands out in my memory. We'd brought our own car over with us this time instead of hiring one abroad. Bill didn't like American cars, but when power-steering and power-brakes and power-seats and power-windows came in, he finally succumbed to the sellingpower of the domestic market and bought a station-wagon that did everything but the laundry at the push of a button—and what could be more effortless and luxurious to travel in?

We drove from London to Harwich to take a boat to the Hook of Holland. We'd been on the road only an hour or so when we were suddenly blanketed in a thick fog. Bill had been fighting off a cold for a day or two, and inching along mile after mile in a drenching mist did him no good. I worried about him all night in our draughty little state-room and in the morning I worried about him some more because we landed at dawn in a freezing rain and he got sopping wet watching the station-wagon being hauled down off the boat on to the dock.

After we both brooded over an infinitesimal dent in the fender, he filled the tank with petrol, and we climbed into a clammy front seat to await the pleasure of the representative from the automobile club. There is always a disgusting amount of red tape to go through at any foreign border, but it's a lot redder if you're bringing in or taking out a car on account of having to have something called a carnet, which is twice the nuisance of a human passport. There were a number of vehicles on the boat that morning, and the process of clearance was interminable. Bill had run out of handkerchiefs and I was running out of tissues for him. He doesn't get colds often, but when he does, it's nothing short of catastrophic with that long, skinny patrician nose of his, since a cold has to spread out somewhere. He was starting to cough a little and I was afraid that this one was making for his chest, which was why I didn't say what was on the tip of my tongue when a uniformed arm finally thrust itself through the car window, and a hand handed over a batch of documents which Bill immediately stuck into his briefcase. I was going to say, "Hadn't you better check if they're ours, the way you always do?" but I was glad he didn't bother for once, especially since government officials, like banks, were never known to make mistakes. With a tortured sneeze he turned on the ignition and said, "*Gott-sei-Dank*, we're on our way."

He spoke a fluent French, but no German, so when he de-livered himself of that "*Gott-sei-Dank*," it was pretty eloquent that he felt pretty awful. I wondered how I was going to persuade him to go to bed once we arrived at our hotel in Amsterdam, and I was upset when I found out that I had little difficulty in doing so. He took a steaming bath and scrambled straight into his pyjamas, which was enough to send me to the extension in the sitting-room to ask the clerk at the desk to call a doctor. In the meantime, I got a hot bath behind me myself, and didn't hear the bellboy knock on the door to deliver a bouquet of flowers from the management and some mail. "On the bureau," Bill croaked from beneath a feather quilt, where he was huddled like an overgrown embryo.

"Nothing from home," I volunteered, "but there's a couple of fan letters and a very elegant invitation to a reception at The Hague from the Baroness ——; it's the longest name I ever saw, I can't make it out. Anyway, it must have been waiting here for us almost a week, because we're expected Sunday the eighth, and that's today. At six o'clock. I'm glad I called a doctor," I sneaked it in neatly.

"If you did," he threatened, "I'll throw him out!"

"Don't be stubborn. Let him examine you and if it's only a cold in the head we can go to the reception."

"Oh, jolly," he said.

It was just as well to let him think that I was joking until after the doctor had looked him over. But I wasn't joking. For some inexplicable reason I was suddenly hell-bent to go to a strange party in a foreign language given by a completely unknown hostess, even though it meant practically driving back to where we'd just come from. Moreover, it was raining harder than ever, and the canal looked bleak and grey beneath our windows. "I must be absolutely insane," I decided, and put the idea out of my mind.

I thought it had stayed out until the doctor folded his stethoscope and pronounced Bill's lungs to be free of any alarming sounds.

"Then do you think he can go to a reception at The Hague?" I heard myself ask.

"That depends on when."

"This afternoon," I admitted faintly.

"Your husband's throat is considerably inflamed, and if you

wish him to court pneumonia," the doctor informed me with an air of washing his hands of the whole kit and kaboodle of selfish and party-mad American wives, "by all means go to your reception." He picked up his black bag. "If I can be of any further service to you," he addressed himself conspicuously to Bill, "please feel free to call upon me."

"What was the point?" Bill asked curiously after the doctor had stalked off.

"What point?" I evaded.

"That nonsense about the reception."

"It's not nonsense. I want to go."

He sat bolt upright. "I don't believe it," he said flatly. "Nothing can drag you to a party in New York, even when your friends give them."

"Maybe I'm a social climber in Dutch."

"By God, I think you mean it!"

"Please don't get excited, it's the worst thing for your throat."

"The worst thing for my throat is to drive fifty miles in the rain after having just driven fifty miles in the rain!" he shouted.

"I know. I'm sorry," I admitted abjectly. "Don't ask me why I want to go, I don't know why. I just want to go, that's all. And we ought to be starting very soon."

He extended one long leg out of bed. "Very well, I'll take you," he said in a tone that filled me with misery and no triumph.

I had forgotten that my publisher was due to arrive at three o'clock. I hastily donned the one cocktail dress I had brought along, and hurried into the sitting-room to make my apologies for having to curtail his visit so unceremoniously. I showed him the invitation in the hope that he could decipher the signature. "It is from the Baroness Van Tuyll van Serovskerken!" he exclaimed.

"That's what I thought it looked like," I said.

"It will be a most important affair, I assure you. The Baroness is Lady-in-Waiting to the Queen, and she lives in one of those very beautiful mansions next to the Hotel des Indes that I pointed out to you on your previous trip."

"How nice," I said, dutifully impressed.

"It would be most ungracious for you and your husband not to attend," he impressed upon me earnestly. "And I might add that your presence will greatly benefit the sale of your books."

Maybe that's the reason you want to go, I thought, for I was still wondering at the unexplainable compulsion that possessed me.

"I have brought the contract for the new novel, and a royalty statement to date," my publisher was digressing. "It will take only a few moments for you to sign them, and then I will not detain you."

I never signed anything until Bill put a pen in my hand, and said, "Write your name on the line I'm pointing to, and put your initials where I've marked a cross." I was about to suggest that all business details be postponed until the following day, when we were startled by a sudden anguished cry, and with one accord we fled to the bedroom whence it came.

Bill was standing by the bureau, his face stripped of colour, and his brief-case open in front of him. "We've got the wrong carnet!" he said hoarsely. "It's for a Jaguar!"

"And for that you scare the wits out of me!"

"But this is terrible!" my publisher gasped. "How do you do, Mr. Meloney," he remembered his manners.

"How do you do," Bill returned vacantly. "I could kill myself for not checking it on the dock this morning."

"Nonsense. What's so awful about it?"

"Tell her." Bill gestured weakly to my publisher, who seemed to have equal difficulty in moving his lips. He said, "Your husband realizes, as you do not, that you cannot leave Holland until your carnet has been found and returned."

"That's ridiculous. We'll use the one that was handed us by mistake."

"Impossible! Absolutely impossible."

"We'd land in gaol," Bill added bloodlessly.

"But we're not planning to stay in Holland more than a couple of days! How long will it take to get our own carnet back?"

"It could take months!" my publisher bleated in agitation, leaping to the telephone.

I had a vague impression, as I heard him pleading with the police to try to trace every car on the dock that morning, that he did not welcome our continued presence in Holland, but of course I may have imagined it, for surely he wasn't guilty of any monkey-business in his royalty accountings.

"*Months?*" I echoed in horror.

"Years," Bill amended.

My publisher replaced the receiver on the hook. "The police are not optimistic," he reported, looking almost as stricken as Bill. "The cars by this time could well be on the way to Germany or France or even Italy. It is a most unhappy state of affairs."

"But what'll we do!" I wailed. "We're supposed to be in Madrid in three weeks!"

My publisher brightened. "Then by all means you must go," he almost smiled.

"No!" Bill said loudly and firmly.

I turned on him. "What do you mean 'No!' "

"I mean 'No, we will not leave the station-wagon in Holland.' "

I was aghast at the mere idea of such a thing. A car that cost six thousand dollars with the extras? And was supposed to pack all my boxes and stuff on the rear seat in suitcases.

"Failing that alternative, which I admit I was about to suggest," my publisher continued unhappily, "you will simply have to remain in Holland until the police trace your carnet."

"Is that true?" I appealed to Bill.

"Why do you think I want to kill myself."

"You phoned. But not until after the reception."

"Oh, God," he said.

"Don't 'oh, God' me." I wanted to remind him that he was in no position to thwart me at this point, but I think he got the general idea.

"There is certainly nothing to be gained by sitting in the hotel," my publisher upheld me with an eye to business. "The baroness is well known and I have arranged for the police to contact you at her home if there is any news."

So we went. It was a grisly ride, and it was almost dark when we parked in front of the Hotel des Indes, and walked the short distance to the great lighted mansion next door. Almost immediately Bill disappeared, and I was worried to death about him until I found him at the bar like a dead man with a glass in his hand. "I just discovered that the Baroness is an old Claudia fan. We're guests of honour," I informed him briskly. "So you can't keep on standing here with that glaze in your eyes."

"I'll take my eyes out, if you'd like."

"Oh, stop it! We've had things happen to us that were a lot worse than this."

"That's what you think."

Prying him away from that bar was like dragging a heavy sack of potatoes round with me, and finally I felt called upon to make some sort of excuse for his abnormal behaviour. "My husband is a little upset because we lost our carnet," I remarked lightly to a distinguished gentleman of portly proportion with medals all over the front of him.

"Lost your carnet! My word, I should think he would be upset!"

"Well, not lost it, exactly. We got someone else's by mistake."

Well. I might just as well have thrown a hand grenade in the middle of that festive gathering. The word spread like wildfire and pretty soon every man in the room and a few of the women were crowding round Bill expressing the greatest consternation and placing their contacts and their influence at his disposal. At the height of the hubbub, a butler announced that an officer of the police wished to speak to Mr. Meloney on the telephone. "If you will follow me, sir"—Bill followed the butler at a run and everyone followed Bill at a run, in the hope that the carnet had been traced. But no, the police merely wished to verify the name and the licence number of the carnet that Bill held in his possession. "The name is J. H. Cassalibra," Bill read from the document in his hand, "and the licence number is T T 99009." The numeral was intelligible, but evidently the officer had difficulty in understanding Bill's pronunciation of the T.T.

"Tee-Tee," Bill spelled it out. And then he tried Tay-Tay, and back again to Tee-Tee.

An elderly dowager, leaning on the arm of a slim young man, was arrested by Bill's difficulty in making himself clear. "That is very odd," she observed.

"What is odd, Mama?"

"It is odd that I should have noticed that very same licence number on a car parked in front of the Hotel des Indes when we arrived a little while ago."

"Oh, come now, Mama," the young man said. "I didn't see it. And besides, licence numbers all look alike."

"Not this one. I noticed this one especially, because it was on a Jaguar, and I do so love Jaguars."

Bill wheeled about from the telephone. "Madam, did I hear you say *Jaguar*?"

"Yes," she said, "it was a bright red, so I couldn't help but notice it."

It was likely to have been the most disrupted party that the poor Baroness had ever given, or was likely ever to give again, for a good chunk of her guests trooped over to the Hotel des Indes and palpitated in the lobby while Bill verified with the desk-clerk an overnight reservation for one Mr. Cassalibra, the indisputable owner of the Jaguar.

"I have your carnet," Bill bluntly announced over the room telephone.

Apparently Mr. Cassalibra replied that the hell Bill did (or words to that effect), for his carnet, my dear sir, happened to be locked safely in the glove compartment of his car.

"Your carnet, my dear sir, happens to be in my hand," Bill enlightened him, in response to which information we could hear the reverberation of stark panic sizzling out of the receiver. "He's in the bath," Bill relayed. "He'll be right down."

Within minutes, a wild-eyed man who could be none other than Mr. Cassalibra, rushed blindly past us, and out through the doors that led to the parking space. The gentleman with the medals turned to Bill. "Of course you realize that there is only one possibility in six that it is your carnet that he has in his possession —I believe you mentioned that there were six cars on the dock this morning?"

Bill nodded.

"Therefore, under no circumstances should you surrender the carnet that you now hold."

"But it belongs to him!"

"My dear fellow, do not be quixotic. I have been born and bred in the diplomatic service of my country, and I beg you to view the situation quite cold-bloodedly. If two people are frantically searching for your carnet—as this Mr. Cassalibra will undoubtedly join you in doing—it is logical that this will double your chances of recovering it."

It would have been a tough decision whether to adopt this heartless procedure or face a likely eternity of breakfasts served with Edam cheese sliced thin like bacon. But by some incredible miracle, coincidence, or demonstration—whichever sits more comfortably on the tongue—we were spared temptation. Mr. Cassalibra came staggering back into the lobby, his face ashen. "Good God, it isn't mine!" he gasped. "It was dark on the dock and I couldn't see——"

"Whose is it?" everyone asked at once.

I noticed that Mr. Cassalibra's hand was shaking as he held the document to the light to decipher the signature. He said, "This carnet belongs to some poor bastard by the name of Meloney."

"Give it over," Bill said mopping his brow like a badly directed actor. "I'll swap with you."

He didn't once allude to the strange unfolding of events until we were on our way back to Amsterdam. "Goddam it, you're too normal to be psychic!" he suddenly burst out.

"I thank you," I said, and meant it.

"Then what the hell are you, I'd like to know! You pulled the same damn stunt when you dragged me up to Quincy in the middle of a blizzard to see Paul."

I didn't add to his intellectual conflict by telling him that Paul might never have been born if I hadn't wakened one morning to the certain knowledge that I must marry his father before the day was over. . . .

"Go on. Explain it," he insisted accusingly.

I couldn't explain it. I didn't want to, or feel the need to explain it. "I'm obedient," I told him. "I always have been."

He might have said any number of things in reply if he hadn't had to sneeze several times in quick succession.

"Gesundheit," I murmured, hoping devoutly that the doctor's dour prophecy wasn't going to come true. It was a consoling thought that, if I were really psychic, I'd have known whether or not he was coming down with pneumonia. Fortunately, he didn't have so much as a sniffle in the morning, and we started off after lunch, a day ahead of schedule. We never kept to any previously planned itinerary, and on that particular trip we ended up in Casablanca.

When we got back to America, we told a couple of friends the story of the Baroness' party and the carnet, but they looked so sceptical that we invented a lurid tale of how we narrowly escaped being shot in the uprising of Rabat, which they believed like fools. As a matter of fact, this is the first time in years that I've thought about that rather weird episode in Holland, and now that I've mentioned it, I realize how often, in the various crises of my life—far more numerous than I have here recounted—I managed by the very skin of my teeth to abstain from using the supernatural as a crutch. I realize, too, how frequently I have resorted to trivia in this chronicle as a cover for much that I have chosen, consciously and unconsciously, to withhold, lest I invade the privacy of those whose lives have impinged upon my own. Heartache is a universal by-product of this business of living and giving life, but it becomes an indecency of the soul when paraded into the particularized.

I have known few writers who can indulge in orgies of revelation and yet achieve the honest dignity of art. I am not one of them, and I admit that my recourse to the oblique is an inherent limitation in what presumes to be an autobiography. I am also aware that a preoccupation with the importance of the unimportant has induced a leisurely approach resulting in many more pages than I intended to write. Now, however, the past is beginning to merge more quickly into the present, and memories, unharnessed, would only tend to repetition, for I think that we do not ever really change, we merely become more of what we were. Or should I not retract a dangerous generalization by saying that for me, at least, the years that followed the first half century of my life were like so much icing on a cake already risen. Nor do I mean to imply that a cake cannot be the better or the worse for its icing.

Buying the house in New Canaan was, in itself, a reversion to an old pattern. "Why don't we face up to the fact that we're not city people," I said to Bill on a day when April was busy opening buds and stirring up the soil.

"I've faced it," he said.

So we got in touch with rural real-estate agents, and told them exactly what we wanted—an old house, a brook, plenty of land, easy commuting, but not suburban. They didn't tell us in so many words that we were asking the impossible, but mostly we didn't even bother to get out of the car to look at what they showed us.

We were leaving for the office one morning when the head of a large New York agency telephoned. We knew him quite well but, more important, he knew what we liked and didn't like in the way of houses. "I've just got a new listing. I haven't seen it myself but it sounds like your cup of tea," he said.

"Where is it?"

"New Canaan."

"Too inconvenient," I objected. "You have to change trains at Stamford."

"That's what keeps it from being like the places you don't have to change trains to get to."

He had a point, but I told him I didn't think we'd like New Canaan anyway, it was full of artists.

"And bankers," he added, as a balancing inducement. "Why not take a drive up and look at it? I understand it's a fine old house with columns and a river running straight through thirty odd acres of land."

We had been on too many wild-goose chases. "It doesn't sound very old, the columns sound like mid-nineteenth-century Greek Revival, and besides, old houses sit close to the road," I carped.

"This one was moved down from Vermont. It was originally the Governor's Mansion in Windsor, which evidently accounts for its unusual and circular stairway."

I had managed to resist the lure of the river—which was as apt as not to be a muddy stream—but I was a softie for circular stairways and I guess Bill was too, because a couple of hours later we were turning into a long tree-shaded entrance that led to a magnificent yet grave façade.

The house and grounds were truly beautiful, but they were vastly more beautiful after we finished doing all the things that we ached to do the moment we laid eyes on the place. "We ought to widen the river, and build a bridge across to the other bank, and we'll need a library, and of course we have to tear down the wall that hides the palladium window from the front door."

"You've just spent a fortune," Bill reminded me mildly. "What'll we use for money?"

I hadn't the vaguest idea of the state of our finances, having reverted to the period in my life that preceded the responsibility of raising, planning for, and supporting three children. It was quite a while since I had balanced a cheque book or cautiously weighed income against outgo, for I felt that in so far as I knew how to do it, and didn't have to, it was better not to. I've seen money, too much of it as well as too little of it, become too important in too many marriages. We know a lot of people who are millionaires—and some of them are our friends but we don't aspire to ape them, because we'd rather spend what we have and enjoy it like crazy, provided we pay our bills and put aside sufficient funds to take care of rainy days and old age.

"I thought you said we were earning enough to buy a place in the country," I now challenged Bill's query.

"Not enough for you to begin tearing down walls again and making love to a bulldozer."

"Then let's let Claudia go to work on television. By the way," I commended him somewhat tardily, "you were mighty smart to insist on keeping those rights. Who'd have ever thought they'd turn out to be so valuable?"

Even today, few people suspect that Bill has such a good business head on his impeccably tailored shoulders, and they are invariably surprised to discover that he is a partner in a leading brokerage firm. I was especially pleased at the affiliation, in view of the fact that he had eventually to take over both the radio and television programmes to save them from a deadly mediocrity, and I would have been obsessed by an increasing guilt had Claudia's omnivorous activities continued to occupy him to the exclusion of his own apparently inexhaustible capacities.

Indeed, the more I think of it, the more I realize how easily she might have become the other woman in our marriage.

The ten years that we spent in New Canaan were, on the whole, extremely happy, except for the normal sorrows and disappointments that come to all of us if we live long enough. Wounds heal with time and a healthy application of philosophy, but happiness is rarely lost in memory, and one of my highlights of remembrance is Max Perkins coming back into my life. I recalled vaguely that he lived somewhere in the vicinity, but I didn't expect to meet him on the station platform at the end of our first week-end in New Canaan. It was Monday morning, and I was dropping John at the station on my way to the village for provisions. Peter and Paul had early classes and had driven into town the night before, and Bill and I were staying on to await the van from French & Co., along with the brawny help of Jack and Earl. ("Don't buy anything in a hurry," Mitchell told us. "We'll lend you what you need until you get settled.")

I couldn't be sure that it was Max until I caught sight of him full-faced, and then it was as if we had seen each other only yesterday. "This is John," I said, shattering the illusion.

Max hesitated, in that diffident way of his, before he acknowledged the introduction. "John," he repeated. "Yes, it was John.—I remember when you were born, young man. It must be twenty years ago."

"It's longer than that, sir," John said.

Max shook his head unbelievingly. He turned to me. "You look the same as the first day you walked into my office."

"How blind can we be?" I said. "You look the same to me, too."

Ours was the gentle recall of an old association, but for all too short a time. He was shy, as he always was, yet he sought us out as if he wanted to be with us, and I believe he did, for he felt an immediate kinship with Bill. "They are very much alike," Max told me elliptically, "even though they appear to be very different."

"I know," I said.

"I'm glad you found happiness again. I was afraid you mightn't. Your ideals were very high."

Sitting on the lawn beside the river, we talked often of the past, and there was in Max, during those last days of his life, a strange impatience and anger. "*The Hallams* was a good play, it shouldn't have closed, but I'm glad it did. You're a novelist, I always told you that. You must write another book. Soon."

"You think *Claudia*'s been a waste——" I anticipated him.

"No. I don't. I've read all five books and I wish you had brought them to me to publish."

"But I never dreamed Scribner's would take light fiction!"

"It isn't light fiction," he reproved me. "Don't ever belittle writing that doesn't strain for profundity, but achieves it through simplicity."

I will never forget Max's words, and I will never forget that he asked me for the sixth book which I had just completed. "You mentioned that you might be changing publishers, now that John Farrar is resigning from Rinehart," he blurted out. "I wish you'd come back to us."

I felt that this was the crowning glory of my whole writing career, but I told Max that I was sure that Scribner's would not be willing to accept what I planned to be the final novel of the series.

"You will write more," he said. "And we will publish them. When can I have the manuscript?"

"As soon as it comes back from the typist."

I waited for his verdict in an agony of suspense that I hadn't experienced since the earliest days of my first short stories. "Whatever he says," I unloaded my nervousness on Bill, "I'll at least benefit by some expert criticism."

"That you will," Bill acknowledged.

I was due for a let-down. Max said, "I have no changes or suggestions to make except one."

"I'll make it," I agreed promptly. "What is it?"

"I was disappointed that you hadn't put in more about the cat. Shakespeare plays a big role in the story and I wanted to hear more about him."

"One of the great editors of all time," I again unburdened to Bill, "and all he wants is more of the cat."

The contract for the book was being drawn up when Max telephoned from his office on a June afternoon, and asked if he could have dinner with us that evening. I knew that Louise, his wife, was away for a few days but, even so, Max's almost painful reticence had made him into something of a hermit.

"You and Bill are alone," he added, less as a question than a statement.

"Except for my aunt, but she hasn't been feeling well enough the last week or so to leave her room."

"That's too bad," he said, but he seemed relieved that we were to dine by ourselves.

It was a strange evening, at once eerie and lovely. I see again the shadows haunting the grass as we lingered over cocktails on the lawn, and the way twilight descended softly to meet the mist rising from the river. Max's mood was not one of depression; he appeared, rather, to be in the grip of competing emotions welling up out of the past. He talked of our first luncheon together. "That dreadful salad. And no Martinis," he said ruefully.

But when Bill poured him a brandy after dinner, he waved it away, and that, too, was strange, because normally he could out-drink Bill without half trying.

"Look here," he burst out suddenly, "I don't want you to feel tied."

I swallowed the bitter taste of disappointment. "If you're trying to tell me that you've changed your mind about publishing the book, Max, please don't be upset because you think I'll be upset. I can understand the reasons against it."

"No, you don't understand," he said harshly. "Of course I want to publish the book. But I want you to feel free. We've known each other too long, and too well, to be bound by words and promises.—Bill, I think I'll have that brandy after all, and then I'll go home."

Max didn't drive. We left him at his door. I said, "I wish he weren't alone tonight."

"I do too," Bill said.

I slept restlessly. In the morning I telephoned his office. I felt that I must speak to him, I must assure him that it was all right about Scribner's not taking me back on their list. I might even tell him that Cass Canfield at Harper's had offered to publish *Claudia* when he'd heard I was leaving Rinehart's. It would make Max feel better about it.

"Who is calling?" his secretary wanted to know.

I gave my name.

"Mr. Perkins isn't in."

How odd. Max was rarely away from his office during hours. I could see him, standing up in front of that high lectern that he used as a desk, always with his hat on. . . .

"Will you tell him I called?"

I waited all day to hear from him, and that evening I telephoned him at home. There wasn't any answer.

"Would you like to drive over?" Bill asked

I nodded. "If there's a light, we'll go in."

The house looked empty. We rang the bell several times. There was no answer.

At dawn the next morning, the telephone rang. It was Bertha, the eldest of Max's five daughters, married to John Frothingham, one of the town's leading physicians.

"We took Father to the hospital the morning after he had dinner with you. He died a little while ago."

I could only say, "I think he was ready to go. Be thankful he didn't suffer long."

It was ironic that I should at last meet Mr. Charles Scribner, at Max's funeral. "It's time we met," he said, holding my hand in both of his. "I was away, I remember, when you brought *Pattern* to us, so many years ago. I want you to know how happy we are to have you back with us. Max would want us to carry on for him."

I shook my head. He wouldn't have wanted it, he wanted me

[397]

to be free, knowing that Scribner's would never be the same to me if he weren't there. I hoped that Mr. Scribner understood the way I felt when I gave the book to Harper's.

I wrote two other novels other than *Claudia* within the next several years, which I think Max would have liked. And I'm certain that he would have been pleased that *Intimate Story* was as good as chosen as a "Book-of-the-Month." At the last moment, however, in spite of the gratifying endorsement of such discerning critics as Clifton Fadiman, one of the judges cast his vote against the selection on the grounds that it was too much of a woman's novel.

Whether the objection was valid, or whether *Claudia* still remained a thorn in my literary side, or even whether the award might have broken the jinx of my being pigeon-holed as a writer for female consumption, was secondary to the amazing discovery that I felt neither argumentative nor indignant about the decision. In the healthy process of growing older, and possibly wiser, I had, unknown to myself, stopped fighting my limitations, but more important, they had stopped fighting me. Born a woman, predominantly feminine, I was at last resigned to the fact that it was my natural destiny and incontestable privilege to write like a woman, and function like a woman. Oddly enough, I've run across a number of men who, on the whole, aren't as much what they are, as I am what I am, and yet it's a puzzling thing how it can work the opposite way in literary circles—femininity often inflates rather than diminishes the stature of a male novelist or dramatist. "Oh, well, that's the way the balls bounce." I salved the initial sting of rejection, and hoped that this philosophical attitude predicated a coming-of-age rather than a retrogression into mental inertia. The truth is, it appears to have wrought no conspicuous change in either direction, since I continue to be griped by all the slender little volumes, purposively monosyllabic, that have to be eked out to a saleable number of pages by means of large print or line drawings, and damn me if they don't sit on the bestseller list, shoulder to shoulder with volumes that are too ponderous with the mere weight of words to read comfortably in bed.

Still, it would be a case of very sour grapes if I didn't admit that, in this age of extremes, I could wish that I, who have always been so far from moderate in my general conduct, had not clung to an undistinguished norm in the mature and telling years of my creative output. I wonder, though, whether I would have been willing to pay the price for prestige and join the ranks of all the successful people who can't afford enough time off from themselves really to enjoy themselves beyond pampering their ulcers and allergies. Whereas Bill and I developed hobbies instead of ailments.

Among the less spectacular of them, we passed through the usual phases of "collecting"—not things like stamps or paperweights—we went head over heels on soft-paste porcelain and French prints, and then Paul took over with Bill on first editions, which were a little beyond my depth. I shudder to think of the afternoon when I wandered into the Parke-Bernet Galleries to look at an exhibition of ceramics, and on the way out poked my head in at a book auction that was going on, and lingered just long enough to bid for a Shakespeare Folio. It was my blind luck that it happened to be an exceptionally good specimen, with contemporary binding and uncut margins, or I'd have never heard the end of it. As it turned out, Bill and Paul have never heard the end of it. It sits in a place of honour on our library shelves, and I use it as a weapon against the smugness of their male superiority.

There is nothing like a congenial hobby to refresh a relationship, whether marital or filial, but over and above being salutary, hobbies are like passports to alien worlds in which no two kinds of people are alike. In our time we've rubbed shoulders with dairy and poultry people, dog-show people, boat people, porcelain people, art people, book people, and antique furniture people, and we found each group to be different, and newly stimulating. But zoo people were the most fascinating of all.

The zoo was more than a hobby with us—in fact, I suspect that the citizenry of New Canaan considered it little less than a borderline case of insanity. In defence, however, let me explain that it was not our premeditated intention to become the owners of a private menagerie. For a year or two we were content to make do with a boxer, a standard poodle on whom Paul, in disdain of his fancy French hair-cut, bestowed the lasting name of Schultz, a pair of peacocks, and a variety of swans and ducks and geese. They were not tidy in their habits, and the lawn was apt to be a little sloppy and slippery under foot, but nevertheless, it was a lovely thing to paddle our canoe along the river, followed by an inquisitive and trusting escort of water-fowl. If we hadn't had to fly to the coast for a series of conferences, and then taken a couple of weeks' holiday in the desert, we would never have embarked on what proved to be the most rewarding folly of our lives.

Yucca Loma had long since passed into oblivion, but La Quinta had not yet come into its hey-day with a golf course and the added popularity of President Eisenhower playing on it. It was quiet and remote enough to shake Hollywood out of our heads, but we didn't intend to shake anything else in, until we happened to meet Dr. Charles Mayo and his wife, who also preferred La Quinta to the gayer resort hotels of Palm Springs.

The words "Mayo Clinic" were as familiar to my ears as "Niagara Falls," or the "Statue of Liberty," but Dr. Mayo was not at all as I pictured him to be. What really important person is?

One morning, as he drew his chair towards mine at the pool, we became mutually intrigued in watching a brace of plump females dedicating themselves to the ritual of sunbathing.

"You seem to prefer animals to people," Dr. Mayo observed after a companionable silence.

"Most animals, and some people," I qualified.

"You'd like my Japanese deer."

"Deer?" I sat up, agog. "Where are they?"

"Well, I haven't any with me at the moment," he smiled, "but I raise them back home. They're not easy to come by in this country. Why don't you let me send you a pair?"

"*Let* you?"

"Don't be too hasty," he warned. "They're very small, but they need high fencing, a shed for protection, plenty of space to run in, and access to water."

"We have acres to spare, a river running right through the property, and fencing is no problem." I promptly sealed up any possible loopholes in his offer.

"Good," he said. "As soon as I return to Minnesota, you shall have them."

How that poor man must have regretted his impulsiveness. For the whole of the following month I nagged him unmercifully, but his patience never faltered. "It takes a little time to round them up and crate them," he explained the delay. "Have you got the fencing ready?"

"Truckloads of it, ten feet high. And housing that I wouldn't mind living in myself."

"It sounds as if you've gone a bit overboard," he said doubtfully.

"I'm afraid we've gone quite a lot overboard for two tiny little deer," I admitted to Bill.

"You, not me," he set me straight on the facts. "You've spent enough to accommodate a full-fledged zoo."

"Exactly." I agreed with complacency. "If we had more animals to use the fencing and the shed, we could reduce our initial cost per head to very little."

He said, "There goes your stingy streak again."

All at once, New Canaan became as exciting as the farm, if not more so in a very special way. By the time the little deer arrived, we were practically saving money on our expenditures. Of course we had to put up another shed for the llama, but once it was shared by the ostriches and the emus and the audads and the kangaroo, the overhead for each animal was greatly defrayed. We soon discovered, however, that the audads, having originated from the Atlas Mountains in Africa, preferred high places to housing, and it presented something of an undertaking to move in a couple of huge rocks so that they could enjoy themselves leaping from one to the other. So, apart from attaching additional metal mesh to the fence at right angles to keep the cranes from flying out, we had no further problems. That is, apart from care and feeding.

Unhappily, the little deer showed the effects of having had to be shipped in crates, and for a while they were skittish and timid. Therefore, we toured the country from dealer to dealer and zoo to zoo, and brought each new acquisition home with us in the station-wagon. The llama came from nearby, however. I drove over to the Prospect Park Zoo all by myself one snowy day and picked him out from a seething pen of baby llamas as a surprise to Bill on his birthday, which was four months off in May. We called him Igmfu, which made him sound as if he came straight from Peru.

We are indebted to Raymond and Dorothy Massey for the name. They lived in the adjoining town of Wilton and one afternoon when they drove over to see us, we noticed an emblem on their car above the licence plate. IGMFU. "What does that stand for?" Bill asked.

"It's a private club," Dorothy said, "and blow me down if you two don't qualify for membership."

Dorothy liked to talk tough to hide a heart of mush, but we were as fond of her as of Ray, and had no reservations in joining a club of which they were charter members.

"Us and Ty Power," she modified their priority, and proceeded to enliven us with a spirited account of how they had been marooned in a blizzard in the midwest while Ray was touring with *John Brown's Body*, and Ty had said, "Let's get off the train and try to find a place where we can get some hot coffee while we can."

"Sold," Dorothy agreed. "I'll wake the others."

"Oh, Igmfu," said Ty. "We haven't time to wait for them to get dressed."

But Dorothy's conscience continued to bother her as they climbed up on high stools at a lunch counter down the road.

"I still think I ought to go back for the others," she said

"Igmfu," said Ty.

"You said that before," Ray remarked. "What does it mean?"

"It's a club I belong to," Ty explained laconically. "I've got mine fuddle you."

Igmfu. We couldn't have hit on anything more Peruvian for a llama born in Brooklyn, and all our proper neighbours in the neighbourhood thought it was a delightful name. And it fitted his character as perfectly as the short neat tail that he wore discreetly clamped down over his graceful high-waisted rear. He was the only one who wheedled his way into the library, and his behaviour was irreproachable. He never broke a thing, stepping as delicately round chairs and tables as a Siamese cat. Celebrities rarely sought us out, but Igmfu's impressive parade of callers could have filled a guest book.

One Sunday morning I had gone on ahead of Bill to a birthday party that Armina Marshall was giving for her husband, Lawrence Langner—they lived in Wilton, too—and Bill, who was off fishing, said, "If I'm not home by one o'clock, don't wait for me, I'll meet you there." I waited until one-thirty and then went on without him. I had no talent whatsoever for giving big parties, but I was always impressed by the ease with which Armina tossed them off in the middle of managing the Theatre Guild.

John was sitting on the lawn with his future bride when Bill came home.

"Mother just left."

"How could she? She's still in her bathing suit showing Igmfu off."

"That's not Mother."

Bill shaded his eyes against the sun. "So it isn't. Who is it?"

"Marilyn Monroe," John said.

"Don't be funny. I'm in a hurry. Who is it?"

John shrugged. "Marilyn Monroe."

"And darned if it wasn't," Bill reported to me when he arrived at the Langners'. "Cheryl Crawforned brought her over for a swim, but chiefly to see Igmfu."

"And John just sat there?"

"He didn't care for her complexion."

"And what did you think of her?" I inquired with a silky smile.

"I didn't care for her figure," Bill said.

Maybe he was tongue-in-cheek, or pulling my leg, but I didn't push my luck.

We always named our dairy stock because of pedigree requirements for our breeding programme, but the zoo, being more like people than the other way around, named themselves. The little deer of course had to be Chuck and Alice, after Dr. Mayo and his wife, and one of the emus, with its perky black pompadoured head atop its long neck, was obviously Audrey, and the female audad, who leapt from rock to rock like a middle-aged housewife dashing from sales-counter to sales-counter, was, without alternative, "Charge-and-Send", while her prospective mate, whom, on professional advice, we bought at the age of four weeks from the Central Park Zoo, we called "L'Enfant Mandelbaum"—a name straight off the passenger list coming home from our last trip to Paris. Later, after he grew out of his long, sad little face and tiny legs, we shortened it to Mandelbaum—which our neighbours didn't approve as unqualifiedly as Igmfu.

We soon found out that animals have psychological problems, the same as humans. Kangaroos, for example, are supposed to shun the water, but ours virtually lived in the river, and got pneumonia. On the other extreme, we had a rare tropical bird who should have dunked himself like an otter, but he wouldn't so much as wet his feet. We had to bathe him in a bucket, because although his plumage was brilliantly impressive, he was filthy underneath. Him, we called Dirty Herbie.

And then, one day, our Garden of Eden became a roaring death-trap when all of us, including the zoo, nearly lost our lives in the big flood of '55 that inundated large areas of Connecticut. We had weathered an earthquake and a mud-storm in California, and a fire and two hurricanes on the farm, but of all the elements, the unleashed fury of water is the most terrifying and savage. Our beautiful river turned on us. It raged over the lawn and rushed through the house, and cornered us on the attic stairs as it slowly and inexorably climbed upwards towards the bedrooms. But that was the least of the nightmare. We stood outside the fence of the zoo, training our flashlights into the swirling blackness, and Bill held my hand while we watched the water mount until we could watch no longer, or we would have drowned. "Only the peacocks can possibly survive," I sobbed, as we returned to the sodden ruins of our once lovely house.

"Yes, they're safe," Bill said. "I caught sight of them on the top branch of the big maple."

Thankful to be kept busy, we worked until dawn, lugging furniture and rugs to the floor above. And we were thankful that we were alone—the boys were in town that week-end, and the help had gone for the day. We were not unaware of the danger of our plight, but we had no way of knowing then how many drowned in that flood, or how staggering was the devastation all around us. A stone bridge beyond our entrance collapsed like a matchstick, sweeping a car with two people in it to their deaths, and roads within miles of us were gutted as if by an avalanche. But it wasn't courage that kept us free of panic that night, it was the thought of all those helpless animals whom we had undertaken to care for and protect.

When the river receded towards daylight, we made our way in our bathing suits across the lake that had once been our lawn, and prepared to face the carnage that had once been our joyous zoo. We could scarcely credit our eyes, for, on first glance, they seemed all to be alive. Igmfu and the emus and the ostriches were standing with their heads above the water, and Charge-and-Send shared her high rock with the deer. The cranes, only partially pinioned, were clinging to the heavy mesh of the fencing, and Dirty Herbie and the kangaroo were shivering, but safe, on the roof of the shed. But the poor little baby oudad was still swimming for his life, his tiny legs thrashing, his strength almost exhausted. Bill leaped over the fence to rescue him, and we brought him back to the house to dry and warm him. "We lost our peacocks," Bill broke the news to me on the way. "Oh no, not the peacocks!"

"How could it happen, they were in the tree?"

"It looks as if they chose to stay on the ground with the others. And they didn't stand a chance with the heavy spread of their tails dragging them down. God, what a wonderful gesture—they're all wonderful, every one of them!" he said, and it was as if, drenched and bareheaded, with L'Enfant Mandelbaum in his arms, he paused for a moment to remove his hat in homage.

Our beautiful house was not destroyed, but it took much time and hard labour to restore the whole place to the loveliness that we had worked so long and arduously to achieve. "We've gone through this too often for there not to be a lesson in it somewhere," I told Bill wearily, "but I'm too tired to try to find it."

I was affronted that I should be tired, having always taken for granted a quick replenishment of my energies no matter how freely I expended them. But this time the nag of depletion did not vanish quite as fast or as completely as I expected. "Every minute it's Friday," I complained aloud one March afternoon, as we crawled through sleety blocks of city traffic to reach the highway.

"We could have stayed in town this week-end," Bill said, "but I thought we ought to check on the zoo and the pipes. We're in for a freeze according to the weather report."

"I know," I said.

"You know what?"

"I don't know."

"Come out with it. What's on your mind?"

"I hate to admit it, but all of a sudden it's a chore for me to run two stoves, two refrigerators and two sets of cleaning women."

"I don't think you'd like commuting from New Canaan every day," he remarked tentatively.

"I'd loathe it, and so would you."

"I'll divorce you if you tell me you want to come back to New York for good."

"I'll divorce you for even suggesting it."

"That's a relief." He kept his eyes on the road. "Any other ideas?"

"No. It's just that we're not able to enjoy either place as much as we should. We're always racing from one to the other."

"We could pick up stakes and work in Paris, London, Switzerland—anywhere you want."

"You're not serious, are you?"

"Why not? Some of our best friends are ex-patriots—no taxes," he enticed me.

"I'd rather pay them, and I never thought I'd live to hear myself say it."

[406]

We fell silent until we passed the toll bridge. "Is it ten or eleven years ago next month?" I asked.

"Ten."

"Lots of people live in the same place for twenty and thirty years."

"We live twice as much in half the time as most people. And lots of people don't realize when a place has served its purpose," he added soberly.

"Are you trying to say that New Canaan has served its purpose?"

"I thought that that's what you were trying to say. And finding it hard. So I'll say it for you. We don't need thirty-five acres and a big house any longer. We haven't got Aunt Jane to look after, and the boys have homes of their own. We've both come to the age when it's time to begin to think about simplifying our lives."

He was right. But I didn't want to begin thinking about it quite yet; I wasn't ready to let go of the need of being needed. The last ten years had been full and rich, but looking back over them, memory slows and quickens, like a metronome slows and quickens, marking time to the will that guides its rhythm. I suppose there are things that happened in that period that I would rather not remember—one of them, a telephone call in the night from a brain surgeon in Palo Alto, where Peter was holding his first professorial post at Stanford University. On that endless plane trip across the country, Bill sat beside me as he had during the Coral Sea Battle, powerless once again to offer a single word of hope. I had become disciplined to the special grief of mothers so akin to the spiritual labour of birth, but it was not given to me to know until long afterwards, when Peter lost his own child, that the heartbreak hardest to bear is when your heart breaks, not for yourself, but for those you love. I experienced that anguish many times and in many ways during those ten years, but sorrow, allowed to heal, lingers less in the memory than happiness.

And there was plenty of happiness packed into New Canaan. Particularly am I grateful for a late windfall of new friends, for it is not often that one forms close friendships after the first half-century of one's life. Fairfield County abounded in people from the theatre and the magazine world whom we had known for a long while, but it was during that same lucky holiday in La Quinta that we met Perc and Tamara Brown. They lived in San Francisco, yet distance didn't lessen the feeling that we knew each other always. There are few women with whom I can unlimber completely, even on the telephone, and giggle myself into a state of hiccups. My sister was one of those women, Tamara is another and Jane Goulden, the wife of my English publisher, still another. It is one of those small, rare dividends of human relationship.

It was in New Canaan, too, that we first encountered the Fitzgeralds. Like thousands of others, we listened, intermittently, to their early morning broadcasts, and although we were not addicted to "breakfast couples"—of which Ed and Pegeen were the original and most successful—we reluctantly admired their superior contempt towards the foibles of mankind, as opposed to their inordinate respect for, and love of, animals. However, a transient sharing of interests does not always lead to anything beyond a pleasant acquaintanceship, but with the Fitzgeralds, it was the springboard to an attunement between the four of us that has steadily strengthened throughout the years. I don't know what Ed and Bill find endlessly to talk about—beyond comparing the relative merits of pipe tobacco—but Pegeen and I never discuss anything that has to do with our allied professions. From the start, we preferred swapping recipes and clothes, a transaction in which I always came off a lot better than she did. I still flaunt, but less often than I used to, a glamorous pair of purple lounging pyjamas spangled with sequins from which she disrobed in the middle of her living-room one day, in exchange for the skirt and sweater I was wearing.

Such shenanigans may seem inconsistent with the fact that I neither seek, nor gracefully tolerate, the society of my sex. I can count the times when I have taken time off to suffer through one of those chatty lunches where women convene after a morning of shopping, or before a matinée—or just convene. I prefer, on the increasingly rare occasions when I find myself in New York, the solitary enjoyment of an ice-cream soda and a sandwich at a drug store, provided I can choose a seat where I can't see the sketchy dishwashing that goes on behind the counter.

I remember, though, a day when Faith Baldwin and I sat together in the very proper dining-room of the Carlyle Hotel, where she was staying during the ordeal of her husband's illness. We scarcely touched the food that was placed before us, and we scarcely spoke. There was little that we could say, and less that needed to be said. We hadn't known each other long, but we knew each other well. For months after we'd bought the house in New Canaan, I didn't lay eyes on Faith, "Come over some time, I never call on people," she announced briskly, when I telephoned to thank her for a basket of home-grown blueberries she had sent over to me—not so much out of a neighbourly impulse to a fellow novelist, I suspected, but because her bushes were so laden she couldn't get rid of them fast enough. "Sorry, but I don't call on people either," I returned with amiable finality, and to this day I'm not sure which one of us unbent first, or whether we just happened to bump into each other in the village. . . .

Recently, I passed the Carlyle Hotel on my way from the dentist, and I think I might have been tempted to forgo the soda fountain on the corner, if the pavement in front of the entrance hadn't been jammed with policemen and crowds of on-lookers. This was not the opportune time to recapture the memory of that quiet luncheon, with President Kennedy due to arrive at the hotel at any moment. But the past caught up with me anyway, and I recalled (with something of the same chagrin of having tossed Jonas Salk's influenza serum into the garbage pail) an evening, several years ago, when Bill and I were invited to a small dinner party, because "a friend of mine," our hostess explained, "wants to meet you, he's a fan of Claudia's."

"One of those again," Bill grunted.

I shared his aversion; male fans embarrassed me even more than female fans, but it happened to be the cook's day off, and I'd long since passed through the phase of liking to potter around the kitchen. "We'll go late, eat fast and leave early," I cajoled him into accepting a ready-made meal.

He was somewhat mollified by the excellent dinner, combined

with the discovery that he knew Mr. Bouvier from his college days, and I was equally pleased to discover that my admirer turned out to be a very solid-looking gentleman, so deeply bronzed that he reminded me of the way Paul had looked when he'd returned from New Guinea, full of atabrine. I was so impressed with the sheer weight of his masculinity that, when we dropped him at his apartment on our way home, I was curious to find out whether his professed delight in Claudia had been a mere social gambit. "I don't believe you've ever read a line of the books," I told him flatly.

"You're wrong," he said. "Men like them as well as women."

"That's because Claudia either reminds them of their wives, or the way they'd like their wives to be, and some of them remind themselves of David. But I can't fit you into either category."

"That's because I don't belong in either category," he smiled. "You see, I have two daughters."

"Eight and ten," I hazarded tersely. To very young teenagers, Claudia was like Elsie Dinsmore (with spice).

"On the contrary," Mr. Bouvier assuaged my ego, "both my daughters are married. In fact, Lee just married the son of your publisher, and you probably know Jacqueline's husband, too —John Kennedy."

"No, I don't," I said, but added cosily, " Lee and Jacqueline are very pretty names, though."

"They're very pretty girls." He turned to Bill. "You must know young Kennedy?"

"I seem to recall that he was in Harvard with Paul. . . ."

"Beyond that recommendation"—Mr. Bouvier had a pleasant sense of humour—"all signs point to the fact that he's headed for a spectacularly brilliant political career."

"It's quite a start to have made the Senate at such an early age," Bill conceded obliquely.

"You must be awfully happy about your daughters," I covered my ignorance. "And do tell them," I added, as gracious as all hell, "that I'm very glad that they're the reason for your liking Claudia."

"And that, young lady," I silently and rather cattily addressed my literary offspring as I indulged in the caloric indecency of a chicken salad sandwich, "is the nearest *you'll* ever get to the White House again."

It was true. Neither Bill nor I had ever gone back after President Roosevelt's death, and it was not in the realm of likelihood that we would ever have occasion to step inside those doors again. A few weeks ago, however, we'd walked along the wide corridors, and wandered through the once-familiar rooms—on television. There had been many changes.

The world had changed, too, but I wondered whether it had changed as much as we prided ourselves that it had. Only that morning five thousand of our troops had landed in Thailand. My mind was not geared to comprehend the deadly interplay of nations, but my heart was educated to the pain of five thousand wives and mothers and sweethearts. Could it be—I wondered—that with every forward leap into space, we were slowly walking backwards?

We didn't rush into giving up New Canaan, because we weren't taking any chances that our menagerie would meet with the same fate as our Danes. We decided, finally, to send the audads, and the ostriches and three buck deer, to the Bridgeport Zoo, which was, in any event, expedient, for they had all got too wild and too big for their breeches, expecially Mandelbaum. And then a young couple, long in love with Igmfu, and already committed to horses and children, begged to have all the others, including the cranes and water-fowl, and this time we knew for a certainty that they would be in safe hands.

The wrench of letting them go was harder than we'd thought it was going to be. Phantoms reproached us from behind the fences, and the river looked empty and mournful.

"It's not the same any more," I told Bill. "I'm ready to say goodbye to the place if you are."

We had no difficulty in disposing of what had suddenly become a gentleman's estate, imposing and static. A neighbour came in to say good-bye a few days before our departure. "It does seem a shame to leave that beautiful crane here all by himself," she remarked.

We set her right on it by telling her that she must have seen a blue heron that sometimes flew in for a quick look at us.

"This is a black crane with a red top-knot," she insisted. "Come on, I'll show you where he is."

I could have blubbered like a fool, for waiting patiently, sadly, outside the fence, was indeed one of our beautiful Crown cranes, but when we came close to him, he skimmed off across the meadow and into the woods, and we couldn't catch up with him.

We were comforted to learn that the young couple had already missed him and had set up a widespread search for him, but that he could have found his way, over a distance of miles and miles, to come back to his old home was as incredible to them as to us. We asked the new owners of the house to keep a watch out for him, but no one ever saw him again.

"I guess he thought we let him down pretty badly," I brooded.

"I guess he must have a pretty poor opinion of human beings," Bill wryly agreed.

We took the first step in the simplification of our lives by combining all our living under one roof. We bought a house in New York—not in the fifties, like Sutton Square—but two hundred blocks farther up, in Riverdale, with an acre of ground that ran straight down to the edge of the teeming traffic of the parkway instead of to the banks of a lovely river. I can't recall a single friend of ours who wasn't horrified at our choice, including the entire staff of French & Co. "Don't do it," Mitchell implored us. "This isn't for you and Bill. The house and grounds are a shambles, it will cost you a fortune to fix it up."

"New Canaan cost a fortune," Bill reminded him, "and we never regretted it."

"But you had something that was fundamentally beautiful and distinguished to work with."

"So if we tried to duplicate what we had, we'd end up with a shabby imitation," I argued. "We want something entirely different that won't remind us of New Canaan. Or of the zoo."

"Then, my dear, you've succeeded in finding it," Mitchell conceded in his driest, highest voice.

"And what do you want to bet we succeed in making it into a little corner of Paris?" I retorted. "We have the basic façade of faded brick to start with, and an elevation that will lend itself to terracing down to a lower garden. And a rumpus room, excuse the expression, in a completely separate building, that we could turn into a marvellous library—provided of course," I amended with a calculated wistfulness, "that Robert could draw us some of his wonderful sketches."

Bill and I evaded each other's eyes as we watched Mitchell's reservations slowly melt in the fire of enthusiasm. "It has possibilities," he admitted thoughtfully, and then clutched at prudence. "You'll never overcome the parkway problem and the feeling that you're in the middle of New York," he maintained.

"That's the challenge of it," Bill told him. "We'll drown out the noise with fountains and high brick walls, and thick plantings of trees and evergreens."

"And the traffic will sound like the distant murmur of the surf," I took it from there.

At moments like this, when Mitchell blazed into action, it was difficult to realize that he had passed his seventy-fifth birthday. "When do we begin?" he demanded impatiently.

It is one of my dearest memories that he so loved the place that, for the remaining years of his life, he scarcely missed a Sunday with us, and often, during the week, he would drive up for dinner with a curator from some museum, or a knowledgeable client, for we had assembled, by this time, one of the finest collections of soft-paste porcelain in the world, as well as a notable collection of furniture and books. "This place is even more beautiful than Sutton Square or New Canaan, because it's unique," Mitchell acknowledged generously, which was praise indeed from the greatest connoisseur of them all. "You missed your vocation as an architect and a decorator," he added half in jest. "Just say the word, and you can have a job with French & Co."

"I'd rather do that than write," I said. "If I were younger you wouldn't have to ask me twice."

He thought, of course, that I was not half, but wholly, in jest, but I wasn't. Miraculously, my energies had come flooding back with the first rubble of demolition piling up around me, and the music of a blow torch in my ears. The days weren't long enough. I was like a dope addict when it came to doing over houses. But this time the end result left me strangely remote from what we had achieved. "Do you remember, after the flood," I asked Bill, "that I said there was a lesson in all the destruction we'd been through, but I was too tired to look for it? Well, I've found it. If we had another hurricane tomorrow, and it blew down the big cherry tree on the terrace——"

"I'll thank you not to mention it," Bill interrupted. "It would wreck the drawing-room."

"But the point I'm trying to make is that it wouldn't wreck me," I said. "I've dispossessed myself of everything I own, because it's the only way to possess anything."

"You're not planning to die, are you?"

"I'm planning to live," I assured him. "I hadn't learned that lesson on the farm. Or with the zoo."

I didn't confess to it, but I still hadn't learned it with Mascara, a miniature poodle we had bought on a recent short-as-possible trip to the coast—not because we liked small breeds, but because the woman who had brought her up needed the money for a brain operation.

Mascara will be six this summer, and she gives the lie to all our lofty pretence to emancipation. She was, we thought, safely past her puppy stage, when we decided to spend Christmas with Peter and his family in Oxford, where Peter was a visiting professor. She was beautifully behaved when travelling, but the English laws prevented us from taking her with us, and we had to leave her at home. We had been in London only a short while, when I telephoned Paul late one night, after we were in bed, to make sure that she wasn't missing us too much.

"I told you I'd check on her every day."

"Is that why you phoned?"

It seemed a proper enough answer, so I evaded the admission. "You'll be even more disgusted with us when I tell you that we bought a six-week-old Pekinese this morning."

He amazed me by saying, "That's good." Mascara had won

him over, but he'd always drawn the line at Pekes, as we had, too, until the moment this one waved to us from a pet shop window in Lansdowne Road. "I expected you to crucify us," I said.

He hesitated before he answered. "Look, Mother, I didn't want to tell you, but I'm glad you've got the little Peke. Mascara came down with distemper a few days ago, apparently from the booster shot. The vet's doing everything he can to save her. I was just leaving to drive up to see her when you called."

I was aware of Bill edging towards me. "What's wrong. Let me talk to him."

"Keep us posted, Paul," I managed somehow to form the words and hung up before Bill could wrest the receiver from me.

"What's wrong?" he demanded.

"Nothing."

"Your face turned white."

"You imagined it."

"What should Paul keep us posted about?"

"About everything, naturally. I'm going to sleep, it's after midnight." I reached up and turned off the bedlights. He turned them on again, and leaned on his elbow to glare down at me. "You not only look like death, but you're trying your damnedest not to cry.—It's Mascara, isn't it?"

From the very start, she had given her heart and soul to Bill. She lavished great affection upon me, but she was Bill's shadow. How could I bear to tell him that we had left her to die alone? I'd have to tell him in the morning, but there wasn't anything either of us could do about it tonight, except suffer. Yet I could see that he wasn't to be put off. "All right, something did happen, we had a fire in the house," I invented desperately.

"You wouldn't look like that if it was only a fire. It's Mascara," he insisted. "Tell me."

I cried, then, and he knew. We called Paul back, but there wasn't any answer. "He must have left already, he was going up to see her."

"Then we'll telephone the veterinarian," Bill said.

"But I don't know which one," I faltered. "I didn't dare ask

[415]

Paul anything that would make you suspicious, but I left the names and numbers of the three best animal hospitals in the neighbourhood, to be on the safe side. She's been so healthy, we've never had to take her to any of them. Except for her inoculations. We'll have to try one after another until we find the one she's at."

I was abjectly grateful to the overseas operator for complying to this extraordinary demand upon the time and patience involved in tracing the whereabouts of one small beloved pet across the vast expanse of an ocean. "An American operator would tell you straight away she couldn't help without more definite information than a dog's name, but the English are diplomatic," Bill prepared me for disappointment.

"This wasn't a woman," I offered for what it was worth.

Within fifteen minutes, the telephone rang. I leapt to answer it. "We've found Mascara, madam. It wasn't too difficult. We had a bit of luck, it was the second hospital we called. The doctor will be on the line in a moment."

I was cowardly enough to let Bill take over from there—I couldn't bear to hear that she was dead. But no—she was still alive, that much I gathered from the one-sided conversation. "She's been free of convulsions for eight hours," Bill summed up for me briefly when he'd hung up. "If she holds off for another twelve hours, there's a ray of hope that she'll pull through. Paul authorized a cable to Spain for a new drug. There's no use in our flying home until we know if it's effective."

"Reserve our flight accommodations anyway."

"I will. Try to get some sleep."

The telephone rang as we climbed into bed again—one bed. There are times when one bed helps. I recognized the pleasant voice of the overseas operator, who was doubtless notifying us of the charges. He made no mention of them, however. He said, apologetically, "I want to confess that we monitored your call, Mrs. Meloney, we were all very concerned about Mascara and we're profoundly touched that an American lady and gentleman should be ready to fly all the way back to the States to care for a sick puppy. It rather cements our international relationship, in a manner of speaking."

"It does with us, too," I said unsteadily.

The same operator handled our call to the doctor the following day. After Bill finished talking, I asked to be re-connected with "overseas." "Mascara hasn't had another convulsion since last night," I said, as to an old friend.

"And you're going home," he finished for me. "We listened in again and took another calculated risk that we might lose our job."

"And they could have," Bill told me, deeply moved.

We were used to moving quickly and changing our plans at the last minute. We explained to Peter why we wouldn't be spending Christmas with him, and dropped a note to the proprietor of the inn at Broadway, Oxford, that we would not be needing the accommodations he had so kindly reserved for us over a crowded holiday. *"Serious illness in the family has called us back to America,"* Bill wrote, but the letter crossed with one that had already been mailed out to us in which the proprietor said that having read the sad news about Mascara in one of the London papers, he thought it very possible that we would not be spending Christmas in England as we had planned, and he would be praying for the little dog's recovery.

It would seem, from this heart-warming experience, that our days of suspense should have culminated in a quick and happy ending, but heavy fogs grounded all planes out of London Airport, and the landing conditions at Idlewild were equally unpredictable. "Advise fast boat. Mascara holding her own," Paul cabled.

Even the boat was six hours late, but Paul was waiting for us on the dock. He looked so tired and strained that his first words nearly shattered us with relief. "The vet says you can call for Mascara in the morning and bring her home, you can do more for her now than he can."—He peered into a miniscule carrying case. "So this is the Peke. Shame on you."

"Shame on us, nothing," Bill told him. "These aren't dogs, they're lions."

"In fact we call him Lygon," I explained. "After The Lygon Arms, the inn where we didn't spend Christmas. You're not lying to us about Mascara?"

"No."

"Then why do you look so tense?"

"I suppose I was more attached to that little monkey than I've been willing to admit," he said. "She gave me a rough time."

It wasn't the real reason. He drove home with us, although it wasn't necessary, and waited around until after I'd called John, and then I started to call Mitchell, as I always did when we returned from a trip.

"Don't do it, Mother," Paul said quietly, and took the receiver from my hand and laid it back in its cradle. He didn't have to tell me.

It was just as well that the boat was so late that we were not in time for the funeral, which had been held that morning. We didn't believe in funerals, and we didn't need any services for Mitchell. But I still miss him when the big cherry tree comes into blossom. He loved that tree, and it was the way he would want to be missed.

Labour conditions were good for labour, but they'd become an abomination to everybody else. Rebuilding New Canaan had been bad enough, but what with six-hour days and five-day weeks and coffee every minute, it had seemed to take for ever before the last old cobble was laid in the courtyard, and the last old brick set into the walls round the swimming pool. I remember that the painters were just moving in with their spattered cloths and buckets and smell—when I fell, walking over to the library, and broke my knee—the same one I'd broken during the rehearsal of *Another Language*. But this time I couldn't scrabble to my feet again, the whole kneecap looked like a mess of red jelly decorated with splinters of blanched almonds, and I suffered the indignity of being carted into an ambulance on a stretcher. I gnashed my teeth in frustration. "You'll just have to stand over them while they mix the paint," I exhorted Bill, who accompanied me on this luxurious ride to the hospital. "Don't let them use more than a few drops of ochre, pretend it's vermouth, off-white is the most subtle and difficult of all colours to get right."

"Shut up and tend to your knitting," he punned grimly. "Now

look, I'm warning you, if you don't learn to walk instead of run, and watch where you're going, you'll break your neck one of these days."

"But for once I wasn't running, and I didn't trip," I defended myself. "It was just as if I took a step that wasn't there, or vice versa. It was the funniest thing . . ."

It really wasn't as funny as I tried to make believe. Bone surgery is a nasty business, and the after-pain is excruciating, but I must have still been as strong as a horse, because I didn't even finish out a week's rental on a wheelchair after I got home, and never gave another thought to my knee until the following spring, when I had to take it out of mothballs, like my chinchilla coat, when I went to Pittsburgh to make a speech at the University.

How far away that literary convention seems now. How far away, in fact, it actually is. I am startled—and it is a word I choose with accuracy—that I have taken so long to write this book, and have slaved over it as I have never slaved over anything else that I have written. I wonder, in retrospect, why I felt inspired to go on with it, instead of dropping it at any one of a dozen points that irked and discomforted me. I honestly do not believe that I became enamoured of the mistaken idea that it was important for the world to hear what I had to say, but I'm beginning to think that maybe it was important to myself to say it.

This is a pointed admission, but now that I am reaching the end, I can no longer evade the hidden machinations of my psyche. All that I have thus far written—and I have written far too much—has been little more than the prelude to a closing chord of self-knowledge, which is the ultimate distillation of any lifetime of living.

With this freshly objective approach, I wish I could omit sections of the opening chapter, but unfortunately my publishers got tired of my promises and sought to hurry me along by getting the completed portions of the manuscript into galley-proof. Also the blocks for the Genthe photograph have already been made, otherwise I wouldn't have the nerve, at this stage, to use it. I am nagged by an annoying feeling that I was pretty arrogant about a lot of things in that first chapter. For one thing, I glibly announced that I enjoyed the benefits of growing older, and experienced but a passing discomfiture when I inadvertently caught my reflection in a triple mirror, and if I recall correctly, I was concerned, even amused, by the fact that I didn't look anywhere near as youthful as I felt. Now the word "youthful" has become what I would like to pass off as a typographical error. Some friendly acquaintance asked me, the other day, if Paul was the youngest of my sons. "No," I snapped back at her, "he's my oldest," and enjoyed the doubtful satisfaction of watching her try to figure that one out. In the days of visiting him at Quincy, I used to be taken for his sister. He was forty-three last April, and is he my youngest?

That's not my main concern, though. I not only don't look as young as I feel any more, but I'm slowly getting not to feel as young as I look. Awareness is creeping up on me. It's a small thing, but noteworthy, that I no longer wear Pegeen's purple-spangled lounging pyjamas. "I think I look silly in anything as gay as these." I gave Bill plenty of leeway for denial the last time I put them on.

"I was never as smitten with them as you were," he evaded the issue tactfully. "Why don't you trade them back to her for something else?"

It was pleasant to reflect that the enduring strength of our friendship would have supported this double swap with Pegeen, but the implication of Bill's suggestion did not escape me. "At least the pants still fit me round the waist," I retorted, with my claws showing. But I was tasting sour grapes of the sourest variety, so vastly has age become him. His hair, especially. It is as soft and thick as it was when I first met him, and I could easily hate him for the way it has quietly turned into an even, silvery white, while mine remains stubbornly spiked with grey. I even envy him the bifocals that he wears with such a distinguished, professorial air. I can't wear bifocals. They wouldn't do me any good. Not even ordinary glasses do me much good. I discovered that fact a short while after I came back from the trip to Pittsburgh.

My eyes had never given me any trouble. I didn't need glasses to look at people, movies, or television, and I could read everything but the telephone directory without them. That's why I couldn't think why the big print on the reference cards I'd prepared for the speech swam into a blur before my vision. Nothing but nerves, I decided. However, when I got back home I wasn't nervous, and I found that I had to begin to wear my glasses more and more. *I'd better get a new pair*, I decided, *Mascara must have scratched these.* She'd taken a fancy to batting them around, but I was so happy that she felt like playing after her dreadful illness, that I wouldn't have stopped her for anything.

"They're too badly damaged to grind them down," the optometrist told me, and fitted me a new pair. "So," he said, "that should be better." He placed a card in front of me. "Read the bottom line."

"I can't. The print's too small. Maybe I need a stronger prescription."

"I've given you stronger lenses. I advise you to go to your doctor and get a thorough examination."

My eyes were one thing I wasn't going to neglect, and luckily I was able to kill two birds with one stone as long as I was in town, and I got an appointment with the oculist who had originally advised me to wear glasses when reading galley-proofs.

He completed his examination in silence, and motioned me to sit beside his desk.

"Who is your physician?"

The past claimed me fleetingly as it had a way of doing, recently. DeWitt was gone, Menas Gregory had died shortly after Missy died—there was no one left of the old school. "Dr. Williams," I answered. "Byard Williams." Byard had been a classmate of Bill's at college, and he had become our family doctor as well. It was he who had ordered the ambulance for my knee, and he wasn't taking any back-talk from me, either. We always argued a little over one thing or another; he said I knew too much for my own good. "Medicine has made great strides since you were in general practice," he informed me dryly, when I was worried about one of the boys having red palms. "And anyway, why do you insist on everyone else having regular check-ups, if you won't?"

"Because I'm fine, I don't need one."

But it appeared that I needed one now. The eye-doctor telephoned Byard's nurse for an appointment. "Yes, it's urgent," I heard him say. "Today, if possible."

"Why does it have to be today?" I grumbled. "What's this all about?"

Byard told me what it was all about after he had checked me over pretty thoroughly, cardiogram included.

"The haemorrhaging behind your left eye is a danger signal that you have no right to ignore," he told me.

"I have a medical background," I retorted, although the word haemorrhage made me wince, "you don't have to mince matters with me. Do I have to have an operation on it?"

"No."

That was a relief, I couldn't bear so much as having my lid rolled up to take out a cinder. "If I follow your orders, when do I get my sight back in that eye?"

"You won't."

"But I can't see," I protested. "I mean, I can't see the way I used to. Maybe that's why I broke my knee, I seem to take steps that aren't there, and yesterday I thought I'd parked the car close up against the kerb, until I got out and discovered that it was sticking about six feet out in the street."

"That's what happens," he said, "when you've lost your depth perception."

"And is that why I put a glass of water down on the table and it goes in my lap?" I asked meekly.

"I'm afraid so."

"Then this business is going to be a bloody nuisance. What do we do about it?"

"That's up to you. You have to slow down. You're getting on in years, like all of us. But in your case, your blood-vessels aren't as strong as they used to be."

"You mean they bust."

"Fortunately they busted, as you so delicately put it, behind your eye."

"And if they bust in the other eye, I'll go completely blind."

"The chances are good that your other eye won't be affected."

"You mean they can bust somewhere else." I didn't bother to wait for his answer. "Well, if they do," I shrugged," the worst that can happen to me is that I'll drop dead."

"That's the best that can happen to you," he said—for him—quite gently.

"My mother had a stroke, if that's what you're trying to warn me about."

"That's part of it.—Take these pills I'm going to give you," he reverted to briskness, "and don't move furniture, or dig up trees, and come back and see me in a week."

"You want to make an invalid out of me," I accused him.

"I want to keep you from being an invalid. I want you to begin to take it easy. It's high time."

"Well, I can't begin until I've finished this damned autobiography, and I don't seem to be able to work at it without getting tired. Could my silly blood-vessels be one of the reasons it's been so hard for me to concentrate? And type?"

"I shouldn't be surprised," he said.

It occurred to me, driving home—and it was one of the last times I drove by myself—that I'd never been much of a typist anyway. And I also recalled, as I threaded my way cautiously through city traffic, a certain sunny afternoon when we had docked our boat at Martha's Vineyard for a visit to Emily Post. She had taken us gaily through her garden in bright red pumps, and I had thought, *Who but Emily Post could sprint around in bright red pumps with such propriety?* And then I remembered an evening some years later, when she invited us for dinner at her apartment in New York, and I noticed how slowly she walked through the hall to the dining-room, and afterwards I remarked on it to Bill.

"Emily's sight is failing," he told me, "but she never talks about it."

"She certainly minds her manners," I said, and now I hoped that I could do the same. I had one thing in my favour—anything that was going on, was going on behind, and not in front. My blind eye looked perfectly normal, as if butter wouldn't melt in its mouth.

There isn't any happy marriage that is completely free of

deception—small, protective deceptions. My first marriage was full of them, and I was for ever thankful for the blessed and forgivable deviousness of love.

I have yet to know whether Bill wanted to buy the log cabin on Preston Mountain for his benefit, or mine. For years he belonged to a fishing club in Canada, and I went with him when I couldn't get out of it. Actually, I didn't mind the long portages to the outlying lakes, with our guides muttering their strange French patois from beneath the canoes that they carried on their heads, but that was about all that I didn't mind, so I wasn't sorry when he announced that he had decided to give up the "Masti-gouche" and join a club in the Berkshires instead. "At least you can drive there, instead of having to take a plane to Montreal, and a train to San Gabriel, and then top it off with a thirty-mile perpendicular ride in a bumpy jeep," I finally unburdened my grievances against Canada.

He was impervious to my barbs. "The Preston Mountain Club has another advantage; it's open in the hunting season, too. But no women allowed except once in a while on Wednesdays during July," he tried to temper the blow.

"Oh, dear, that's a great disappointment," I said. He was dim-witted as well as thick-skinned not to have guessed how little I would miss sitting in a wet boat hour after hour in hot sun or cold drizzle, sticking pins in a poor fish without benefit of even the most basic conveniences. Of course when he mentioned "hunting" in the new club, I didn't like the idea of guns, either, but you couldn't have everything, it was enough not to have to go along with him.

He took Mascara instead. They went trout fishing in the spring, bass fishing in the summer, and duck and pheasant shooting in the autumn. And I had to buy an extra freezer, and wished I had more neighbours to give the trout, the bass, the pheasants and the ducks to.

"Don't be so generous," Bill suddenly turned sensitive, "we're not getting them for nothing, you know."

I didn't know. I was under the impression that all the produce was included in the dues. "We have to pay for all this mess you bring home? How much?" I demanded indignantly.

[424]

"Roughly it comes to about three dollars a trout, two dollars a bass, six dollars a duck and eight dollars a pheasant."

I was speechless as I contemplated the number of lobsters and capons I could have bought for the same money. But it was cheap at the price, anyway. He had a wonderful time at his new club, and I had a wonderful time staying at home.

It was too good to last. He came back one evening, smelling fishy and looking sheepish. "Come upstairs with me while I wash, I want to tell you something," he said.

I followed him, without the faintest premonition of disaster, and sat companionably on the bath while he peeled off his red shirt and khaki pants. "These can go in the laundry," he said. "Catch."

I caught. "What did you want to tell me?"

"Well, about thirty-five years ago, before the club was founded," he began, dressing it up like a fairy story, "three of the present members built three log cabins on the mountain——"

"For the mother bear, the father bear and the baby bear."

"Do you want to be funny or do you want me to tell you?"

"Both."

"Do you remember the Gilbert Meccano sets the boys used to play with when they were young?"

"Vividly. Are you buying me one to play with?"

He ignored the interjection. "J. C. Gilbert, the man who invented them—he's over eighty now, but still one of the great sportsmen of all time——"

"Really?"

"Owns the cabin next to ours," he finished doggedly.

Flippancy died within me. "Say that again, please?"

"Well, it isn't ours yet," he hedged, fidgeting a little, "but the man who built it died years ago, and the member of the club who bought it hasn't been able to use it, and it's up for sale to any other member of the club who wants to buy it.—You'll love it, it has a wonderful waterfall, a beautiful pond and a magnificent hemlock grove."

"In case you've forgotten, we already have a wonderful fountain, a beautiful swimming pool, and a magnificent cherry tree. And allow me also to remind you that we're simplifying, not complicating our lives."

"But you don't understand. This would be the ultimate simplification when the time comes for us to retire. We don't need any servants up there, the place doesn't need any upkeep, and the taxes are practically nothing."

"You make it sound fascinating, but isn't it a little too soon to think of retiring?"

"It's never too soon to plan for the future, especially when something as perfect as this falls in your lap. How about driving up in the morning to take a look at it?"

I bit my lips. Maria Jeritza, whom I hadn't seen since she got married again and moved to New Jersey, had asked us for dinner last week. But would he go? Oh, no. It was too much for him to drive fifteen miles. . . .

"What's the matter?"

"Nothing, nothing."

"I can't abide thin-lipped women."

"I thought your precious club couldn't abide women at all."

"Nobody will even know you're there."

"And since when do I go anywhere on sufferance?"

"This is different, you'd be in your own cabin and the cabin just happens to be on the club grounds."

"I bet you bought it already."

"You know I wouldn't do a thing like that."

"I should hope you wouldn't," I retracted grudgingly.

"You didn't have anything special on for tomorrow, did you?"

"Yes. I have an important engagement."

"Can't you postpone it?"

"No. It's urgent. I've got a date with a damn fool to look at a damn-fool cabin. And, for heaven's sake, take that boyish grin off your face, it doesn't become you, you look silly."

It was more of a drive than I'd expected it to be. We passed the little road in Pawling where we used to turn off to visit Missy, but I didn't call attention to it because I was loath to cast a shadow on Bill's happiness. "This is much too far for the boys to come very often," I said instead. "Is it shorter by train?"

"I'm afraid it's longer," he admitted.

"Well, maybe that's the way it ought to be now," I said, with my thoughts still on Missy. "The hills are beautiful, in the distance."

"Wait until we get there, you'll think we're in Canada."

I thought it was lovelier than Canada, what with the waterfall and the hemlock grove, and the way the little cabin nestled sweetly in the wild and picturesque terrain. "And it's actually made of logs!"

"What did you think a log cabin was made of?"

"I was surprised when I saw the leaning Tower of Pisa really leaning," I explained. "Where's the pond?"

"You're looking at it."

"That's a mud-hole."

"It won't be when we build a dam.—And you know what that means," he added with a winning smile. "A bulldozer."

I was aware that he was watching my face intently, so I didn't disillusion him by saying that I suddenly seemed to have lost my passion for bulldozers.

"Did I exaggerate the beauty of this place?" he persisted anxiously.

"Let's look at the inside," I held off prudently.

He knew exactly where to find the key, hidden in some chink or other. "The door sticks a little," he prepared me. "We'll probably need to replace it."

"You will if you don't want a hernia," I amended silently.

He finally got it open, and I followed him into a dim, evil-smelling area which I barely recognized to be the room he had so glowingly described as being twice as large as our library, with a vast vaulted ceiling and a huge stone fireplace. The fireplace was there, but the ceiling was spoiled by a network of cross-beams, and if my one eye didn't deceive me, the room was about half as big as his heart had measured it. If we bought the place (and I wasn't sure at this point that I was going to be insane enough to do it), we could do away with the low-hanging beams, and rebuild the rickety porch and throw it into the living-room to make it the size he thought it was. However, I withheld my immediate comment. "Show me the bedroom," I said instead.

[427]

He waved towards four divans lined up against the peeling logs of the walls. "Didn't I tell you? Those hooks on the beams are for curtains in case you want privacy."

I schooled my voice to an excessive gentleness. "No, dear, you neglected to tell me that there were no separate sleeping quarters. You also neglected to mention that there are more caterpillars indoors than out. And you know, dear, that I have a real thing about caterpillars. I might at any moment go into convulsions."

"Hold on to yourself. Those aren't caterpillars, they're only inch-worms. They crawl in where the screens are torn. Anyway, they'll be gone in another couple of weeks."

"And may I ask what they turn into after they're gone?"

"I think this kind has already been whatever they turn into. It's the carpenter ants we have to do something about. See how they've eaten into the logs?"

"Yes, dear, I saw. Where's the bathroom, I think I'm going to need it."

"It's a sort of shower arrangement off the kitchen."

"Well, I've always liked shower arrangements, so let's start with first things first.—Where is the kitchen hiding?"

"You went through it coming in." He looked grieved. "Didn't you see all the nails with pots and pans, and the stove and refrigerator?"

If I did, they mercifully hadn't sunk in. I retraced my steps and turned on a faucet in the ancient sink. The pipes groaned and shuddered and spat out a trickle of rust-coloured fluid.

"Don't worry about that," he read the blazing of my thoughts, "there'll be plenty of water when we put in new pipes and a pressure tank." He lifted a trap-door hinged into the rough floor-boards. "Look down here, we can make this into a good wine cellar."

I averted my gaze from a small, dank cavern yawning beneath a steep flight of broken steps. "A wine cellar is not our major problem," I remarked coldly.

"If you're wondering where to put suitcases and things," he offered smugly, "you've got a completely rat-proof storage space off the wood shed."

Rats. "No mice?" I inquired with a lift of my brows.

"Oh, sure," he said, "but we won't be bothered with them once we live here. And when we cut in more doors and windows for light and air, and clean out the dead trees and heavy brush, there won't be that damp smell either."

"Why, dear, I didn't know you'd noticed," I murmured.

He bridled slightly. "Well, what do you expect a log cabin to smell like after it's been closed up for months?"

Frankly, I wasn't expecting at all, at this advanced stage of my life. Having a house together is as near to having a baby together as a married couple can get, short of the actuality, but this was one baby I didn't want. Nevertheless, I knew from the familiar gleam in his eyes that I was going to have it, so I decided then and there that I might as well learn to love it. I also decided to take the benzedrine tablets that a television producer had thoughtfully given to me on the same trip to Hollywood when we'd bought Mascara. I'd never even opened the bottle, but now I had a strong feeling that I was going to need all the energy I could muster to meet this final challenge to our architectural pretensions.

I was right. It was by far the hardest job we'd ever tackled in the way of reconstruction, simply because we started with a log cabin and we wanted to end with a log cabin, with no outward violation of its simple charm. "But I'm not young enough any more to enjoy roughing it," I stipulated firmly. "I want comfort and convenience and all the modern appliances, including electrically heated towel-bars in the bathrooms, and nobody has to know about it, because they'll be hidden under the towels."

"I'll use mine to dry my socks and underwear," Bill retreated in cowardice.

"You intend to do your own laundry?"

"I'm certainly not going to ask you to do it."

It was also one of my amazements that he, who had never so much as boiled a pot of water in the whole of his pampered domestic existence, should suddenly blossom out into a talent for broiling steaks and spitting pheasants on the charcoal grill he painstakingly designed to stand next to the oven. Paul gaped, when, on his first visit, he saw him thoughtfully assembling a long row of bottles, spices, oil, garlic and cognac on the stainless steel of the kitchen counter. "Shh, don't disturb him," I whispered, "he's about to make a marinade for the chops."

"Does he make spaghetti, too?" Paul whispered hoarsely.

"Of course not. He wouldn't be found dead boiling or frying on a stove. He just grills and spits on charcoal."

I was happier in the cabin than in our corner of Paris in New York, but I fought against admitting it, fearing acquiescence to the encroaching limitations of my physical being. During the months of rebuilding we had reversed our routine of living, remaining on the mountain during the week in order to plan and supervise the work, and returning home for the week-ends. "Every minute it's Friday," I had gone so far as to complain to Bill.

"I hate to leave too," he said. "Why don't we get smart and stay up here? We've nothing to go back for except to play nurse-maid to a houseful of possessions."

Was he saying it for my sake?

"I'm not ready to retire quite yet," I resisted with asperity, "and you're a long way from it."

"All right, but what's to prevent our bringing up our type-writers? I've got another novel in me, I can keep in touch with the office by phone, and you can finish your autobiography without being interrupted every minute by this and that."

"You know perfectly well I can't work if I'm not interrupted by this and that. And what's more, I should never have begun it," I harped back gloomily. "Now that I see my life stretched out in front of me on paper, I'm not very satisfied with what I've been, or with what I've accomplished."

"Oh, I wouldn't say that exactly. You've raised a family, almost won the book-of-the-month, travelled all over the world, and had your fling getting drunk in night clubs and carrying on wild affairs with strange men. What more do you want?"

"Importance. I still never sat at the Round Table at the Algonquin, or played croquet with Alexander Woolcott."

"Well, it's too late for that now," he rejoined briskly, "so you might as well make the most of your unimportance, and enjoy it."

There was a lot of truth beneath his banter. I didn't know how much, or how little time was yet to be portioned out to either of us, nor was it given to anyone on earth to count beyond the moment. I only knew that, whatever was left of my life, whether it was weeks or months or years, suddenly assumed a vast importance, for each new dawn brought new vision, and each twilight filled me with a feeling that I had lived that day more fully than I had ever lived before.

Slowly, and ever less reluctantly, I began to absorb the peace and serenity of the little New England village that went its quiet way a few miles from our mountain. No one cared who we were or what we'd done. And yet they cared that we were there.

We always waken very early at the cabin, and even in the middle of winter, we stand on the porch in our bathrobes watching that Mascara and Lygon don't wander too far chasing a chipmunk, or getting into trouble with a porcupine. Only when we see that the waterfall is encased like a shimmering ribbon of silver moire within a sheet of ice, do we realize how cold it is, and then Bill can't resist checking the thermometer with the same foolish pride that I remembered when the thermometer dropped to ten or twenty below at Trudeau. . . .

Sometimes, if we stand there long enough, and still enough, we glimpse a deer, picking his dainty way through the hemlock grove to peer at us across the pond, and almost always we find footprints on the porch to tell us that a raccoon or a fox had visited us in the night.

We own a vast zoo up on our mountain—otters, beavers, partridge, woodchucks and, once in a while, a pair of wild geese pass on their way to one of the lakes. They all belong to us, but we possess not one of them.